INTRODUCTION
TO
CELESTIAL
MECHANICS

This book is in the

ADDISON-WESLEY SERIES IN
AEROSPACE SCIENCE

Consulting Editors

HOWARD W. EMMONS   JAMES FLETCHER
S. S. PENNER

INTRODUCTION
TO
CELESTIAL
MECHANICS

by

S. W. McCUSKEY

Department of Astronomy
Case Institute of Technology

ADDISON-WESLEY PUBLISHING COMPANY, INC.

READING, MASSACHUSETTS · PALO ALTO · LONDON

PREFACE

The study of celestial mechanics has become increasingly important during the past five years. This is due primarily to the advent of man-made earth satellites, to the possibility of interplanetary travel in the near future, and to the opportunity now available for the scientific exploration of interplanetary space.

As a branch of mathematical astronomy, celestial mechanics was developed early in the history of astronomy. During recent years, however, astrophysical problems have dominated astronomy with the result that the number of astronomers specializing in celestial mechanics has been small. This branch of astronomy is again flourishing. The astronomical literature is overflowing with research contributions in this field. Furthermore, scientists well versed in celestial mechanics are now required in many industrial and governmental laboratories.

In view of this development many students of mathematics and physics, as well as those majoring in astronomy, should have at least an introductory course in celestial mechanics. Such a one-semester course meeting three hours per week is being offered at Case Institute of Technology. It is required of undergraduate astronomy majors in the junior or senior year and is an elective for both undergraduate and graduate students in other departments. The subject matter included in this course forms the content of the present book.

It is clear that one cannot do more than introduce the basic concepts of celestial mechanics in such a short time. Therefore this book is limited in its coverage to the dynamics of motion of bodies which can be treated as mass points. Only in the discussion of perturbations due to the oblateness of the earth does the size and shape of the celestial object enter. Furthermore, the Newtonian dynamical description of motion has been adopted as being most familiar to the student. He is assumed to have had a good course in differential equations and some familiarity with vector notation and operations. It is assumed, also, that he has had an elementary course, or courses, in dynamics. A brief review of dynamical principles, however, is included here in Chapter 1.

One of the basic problems of celestial mechanics is the calculation of orbital elements for a planet or satellite from observations of position in the sky. This aspect has been introduced in Chapter 4. Only the rudiments of orbit calculation are included. This is a large subject in itself and the student who wishes to become proficient in it must turn to a study of the references mentioned. Nevertheless every student should work through the examples and the problems presented in Chapter 4 in order to get a feel for the analysis.

Perturbation theory forms a large segment of the analysis in celestial mechanics. No two bodies in the solar system, for example, are completely isolated. Perturbative forces cause deviations from simple two-body Keplerian motion. The student should gain an understanding of the influence of such forces on the motion of a given celestial body. In this book the variation of parameters technique, introduced by Lagrange, has been adopted as being the method most closely linked with the student's background in differential equations.

A perusal of the literature will show clearly that the mathematical methods devised for studying the motions of celestial objects are legion. The introduction of canonical equations, the Hamilton-Jacobi theory, and other general and elegant methods have been deliberately avoided in this book. These are more appropriately included in a more sophisticated course. The bibliography will indicate references to which the interested student may turn for a more advanced discussion based upon these methods.

To the many students who have contributed their critical reading of earlier versions of the notes from which this book has evolved, a hearty vote of thanks is due. To Dr. Paul Herget and to Dr. G. M. Clemence, I extend my sincere thanks for reading parts of the manuscript and for making valuable suggestions.

East Cleveland, Ohio   S. W. M.
November, 1962

CONTENTS

CHAPTER 1. FUNDAMENTAL DYNAMICS 1

1-1 Introduction 1
1-2 Kinematics of curvilinear motion 2
1-3 Areal velocity 5
1-4 Dynamics of curvilinear motion 6
1-5 Potential due to a sphere 9
1-6 Systems of particles 12

CHAPTER 2. CENTRAL FORCE MOTION 19

2-1 The law of areas 19
2-2 Linear and angular velocities 20
2-3 Integrals of angular momentum and energy 21
2-4 The equation of the orbit 23
2-5 The inverse square force 25
2-6 From orbit to force law 30

CHAPTER 3. THE TWO-BODY PROBLEM 32

3-1 Motion of the center of mass 32
3-2 Relative motion 33
3-3 The integral of areas 35
3-4 Elements of the orbit from initial position and velocity . . . 38
3-5 Properties of the motion 42
3-6 The constant of gravitation 44
3-7 Kepler's equation 45
3-8 Position in the elliptical orbit 51
3-9 Position in a parabolic orbit 54
3-10 Position in a hyperbolic orbit 55
3-11 Position in near-parabolic orbits 57
3-12 Position on the celestial sphere 62

CHAPTER 4. COMPUTATION OF ORBITS 70

4-1 The radius vector is known 70
4-2 Laplace's method 76
4-3 Gauss's method 86

CHAPTER 5. THE THREE- AND n-BODY PROBLEMS 92

5-1 Motion of the center of mass 92
5-2 The angular momentum, or areal velocity, integrals 94

5–3   The integral of energy   97
5–4   Summary of properties: n-body problem   98
5–5   Equations of relative motion   100
5–6   Stationary solutions of the three-body problem   102
5–7   The restricted three-body problem   109
5–8   Stability of motion near the Lagrangian points   118

CHAPTER 6.   THEORY OF PERTURBATIONS   128

6–1   Variation of parameters   128
6–2   Properties of the Lagrange brackets   135
6–3   Evaluation of Lagrange's brackets   137
6–4   Solution of the perturbation equations   142
6–5   Expansion of the perturbation function   149
6–6   The earth-moon system   158
6–7   Potential due to an oblate spheroid   163
6–8   Perturbations due to an oblate planet   167
6–9   Perturbations due to atmospheric drag   175

REFERENCES . . . :   179

INDEX   180

CHAPTER 1

FUNDAMENTAL DYNAMICS

1-1 Introduction. Celestial mechanics embraces the dynamical and mathematical theory describing the motions of the planets around the sun, the satellites around their parent planets, one member of a double star pair around the other, and other similar phenomena. Observational data and mathematical theory together have given a clear picture of the motions of celestial bodies throughout the observable universe. Sir Isaac Newton was perhaps the first to bring powerful dynamical ideas and the necessary mathematics to bear on motion in the solar system. His *Principia*, published in 1686, laid the groundwork for later generations to exploit. Needless to say, Newton built on the scientific contributions of his predecessors, particularly Kepler and Galileo.

In 1609 Johannes Kepler enunciated two of his three laws of planetary motion. The third followed in 1619. These were based upon the observations of Mars made by Tycho Brahe during the latter part of the 16th century. Kepler's laws may be stated as follows:

1. The orbit of each planet is an ellipse with the sun at one focus.
2. The radius vector joining sun to planet sweeps over equal areas in equal intervals of time.
3. The ratio of the squares of the periods of any two planets is equal to the ratio of the cubes of their mean distances from the sun.

As we shall see later, the last of these laws is only approximately true. Its validity in the form stated here depends upon the fact that the masses of the planets are very small compared with the mass of the sun.

The empirical laws enunciated by Kepler led Newton, among others, to the conclusion that the force which keeps a planet in its orbit around the sun varies inversely as the square of the distance from sun to planet. As soon as Newton had proved that the gravitational attraction between two homogeneous spheres could be calculated as if the masses of the spheres were concentrated at their centers, the progress of dynamical astronomy was clear and rapid. The law of universal gravitation, conceived by Newton, states: *If two particles of masses m_1 and m_2 are situated a distance r apart, each particle attracts the other with a force Gm_1m_2/r^2, where G is a universal constant. The forces act along the line joining the particles.* On this fundamental law hinges the entire structure of celestial mechanics.

The *Principia* (1686) contains also the dynamical postulates on which subsequent analysis rests. These "laws" are three in number:

First law. A particle of constant mass remains at rest, or moves with constant speed in a straight line, unless acted upon by some force.

1

Second law. A particle subjected to the action of a force moves in such a way that the time rate of change of the linear momentum equals the force.

Third law. When two particles act upon each other, the force exerted on the second particle by the first is equal in magnitude and opposite in direction to the force exerted by the second on the first.

In succeeding sections we shall formulate these postulates in mathematical form.

1–2 Kinematics of curvilinear motion. Let a point $P(x, y, z)$ in a cartesian 3-dimensional reference system move along a curve C (Fig. 1–1) in such a way that the arc length s increases continuously with the time. The position of P can be specified succinctly by the position vector

$$\mathbf{r} = x(t)\mathbf{i} + y(t)\mathbf{j} + z(t)\mathbf{k}.$$

Then, by definition, the *velocity*

$$\mathbf{v} = \dot{\mathbf{r}} \equiv \frac{d\mathbf{r}}{dt} = \dot{x}(t)\mathbf{i} + \dot{y}(t)\mathbf{j} + \dot{z}(t)\mathbf{k}, \tag{1–1}$$

and the *acceleration*

$$\mathbf{a} = \ddot{x}(t)\mathbf{i} + \ddot{y}(t)\mathbf{j} + \ddot{z}(t)\mathbf{k}. \tag{1–2}$$

In these relations $\mathbf{i}$, $\mathbf{j}$, $\mathbf{k}$ are unit vectors along the three axes, and dots denote differentiation with respect to the time.

Suppose P moves to P' in a time interval Δt. Then $\mathbf{r}$ changes in both magnitude and direction, its increment being $\Delta\mathbf{r}$. At the same time the arc changes by an amount Δs (Fig. 1–1). By definition, then,

$$\mathbf{v} = \dot{\mathbf{r}} = \lim_{\Delta t \to 0}\left(\frac{\Delta\mathbf{r}}{\Delta t}\right), \tag{1–3}$$

and

$$\mathbf{a} = \dot{\mathbf{v}} = \lim_{\Delta t \to 0}\left(\frac{\Delta\mathbf{v}}{\Delta t}\right). \tag{1–4}$$

From Eq. (1–3) we may write

$$\lim_{\Delta t \to 0}\left(\frac{\Delta\mathbf{r}}{\Delta t}\right) = \lim_{\substack{\Delta t \to 0 \\ \Delta s \to 0}}\left(\frac{\Delta\mathbf{r}}{\Delta s}\right)\left(\frac{\Delta s}{\Delta t}\right) = \lim_{\Delta s \to 0}\left(\frac{\Delta\mathbf{r}}{\Delta s}\right)\lim_{\Delta t \to 0}\left(\frac{\Delta s}{\Delta t}\right).$$

But $\lim_{\Delta s \to 0} (\Delta\mathbf{r}/\Delta s)$ is a unit vector tangent to C at P; call it $\mathbf{u}_T$. Also $\lim_{\Delta t \to 0} (\Delta s/\Delta t) = \dot{s} = v$, the speed of the particle at P. Hence $\mathbf{v}$ is a vector tangent to C and of magnitude v; that is,

$$\mathbf{v} = v\mathbf{u}_T. \tag{1–5}$$

The existence of $\mathbf{v}$ implies the differentiability of $\mathbf{r}$ as a function of t.

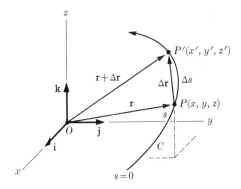

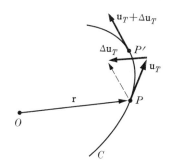

FIG. 1–1. Vector representation of cur-   FIG. 1–2. Change in unit tangent
vilinear motion.   in curvilinear motion.

Again from Eq. (1–5),

$$\dot{\mathbf{v}} = \dot{v}\mathbf{u}_T + v\dot{\mathbf{u}}_T. \tag{1–6}$$

As P moves to P' (Fig. 1–2) along the curve C, $\mathbf{u}_T$ changes by an amount $\Delta\mathbf{u}_T$ and in the limit, as $\Delta t \to 0$, $\Delta\mathbf{u}_T/\Delta t \to \dot{\mathbf{u}}_T$, a vector perpendicular to $\mathbf{u}_T$. Furthermore,

$$\dot{\mathbf{u}}_T = \lim_{\substack{\Delta s \to 0 \\ \Delta t \to 0}} \left(\frac{\Delta\mathbf{u}_T}{\Delta s}\right)\left(\frac{\Delta s}{\Delta t}\right) = v\frac{d\mathbf{u}_T}{ds}.$$

But

$$\left|\frac{d\mathbf{u}_T}{ds}\right|$$

is by definition the magnitude of the curvature of C at P. The reciprocal of the curvature is the radius of curvature ρ. Thus we have

$$\dot{\mathbf{u}}_T = \frac{v}{\rho}\mathbf{u}_N, \tag{1–7}$$

where $\mathbf{u}_N$ is a unit vector normal to the curve and directed toward its concave side.

Finally, from Eq. (1–6) we find

$$\dot{\mathbf{v}} = \dot{v}\mathbf{u}_T + \frac{v^2}{\rho}\mathbf{u}_N. \tag{1–8}$$

Thus the acceleration is resolved into tangential and normal components. It is clear from Eq. (1–8) that a particle moving along a circle with constant speed experiences an acceleration. For if $\dot{v} = 0$, the acceleration is $(v^2/\rho)\mathbf{u}_N$, and is directed along a radius of the circle toward its center.

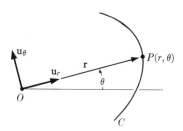

FIG. 1–3. Radial and transverse unit vectors.

For astronomical purposes, a resolution of $\mathbf{v}$ and $\mathbf{a}$ into components along and perpendicular to the radius vector in a plane polar coordinate system is desirable. Let the particle at P (Fig. 1–3) traverse the curve in the direction of increasing θ. Let $\mathbf{u}_r$ and $\mathbf{u}_\theta$ be unit vectors along and perpendicular, respectively, to the position vector $\mathbf{r}$. Then since $\mathbf{r} = r\mathbf{u}_r$, we have

$$\dot{\mathbf{r}} = \dot{r}\mathbf{u}_r + r\dot{\mathbf{u}}_r. \tag{1–9}$$

But $\dot{\mathbf{u}}_r = \dot{\theta}\mathbf{u}_\theta$. Hence

$$\mathbf{v} = \dot{\mathbf{r}} = \dot{r}\mathbf{u}_r + r\dot{\theta}\mathbf{u}_\theta. \tag{1–10}$$

Similarly, by differentiating Eq. (1–10), we find

$$\mathbf{a} = \dot{\mathbf{v}} = \ddot{r}\mathbf{u}_r + \dot{r}\dot{\mathbf{u}}_r + \dot{r}\dot{\theta}\mathbf{u}_\theta + r\ddot{\theta}\mathbf{u}_\theta + r\dot{\theta}\dot{\mathbf{u}}_\theta.$$

Again, since $\dot{\mathbf{u}}_\theta = -\dot{\theta}\mathbf{u}_r$, we may simplify the last expression to obtain

$$\mathbf{a} = (\ddot{r} - r\dot{\theta}^2)\mathbf{u}_r + (2\dot{r}\dot{\theta} + r\ddot{\theta})\mathbf{u}_\theta. \tag{1–11}$$

Equations (1–10) and (1–11) are the required resolutions of $\mathbf{v}$ and $\mathbf{a}$ into radial and transverse components.

PROBLEMS

1. By using the transformation equations $x = r \cos \theta$ and $y = r \sin \theta$, show that Eqs. (1–10) and (1–11) are reducible to Eqs. (1–1) and (1–2).

2. A particle moves along the space curve $\mathbf{r} = (\cos t)\mathbf{i} + (\sin t)\mathbf{j} + t\mathbf{k}$, starting at $t = 0$. Sketch the curve. Find $\mathbf{v}$ and $\mathbf{a}$ at $t = \pi/2$.

3. A particle moves along the curve $r = 1 - \cos \theta$. Exhibit the radial and transverse components of $\mathbf{v}$ and $\mathbf{a}$ at the point for which $\dot{\theta} = 2$.

4. A particle moves along the ellipse $r = p/(1 + e \cos \theta)$ in such a way that $\dot{\theta} = \alpha$ (a constant). Find the radial and transverse components of the velocity and acceleration.

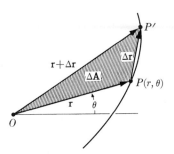

Fɪɢ. 1–4. Increment of area in curvilinear motion.

1–3 Areal velocity. The rate at which the radius vector joining a fixed origin O (Fig. 1–4) to a moving point P sweeps out a surface is called the *areal velocity* relative to the fixed origin. Suppose that P moves in the xy-plane and has polar coordinates (r, θ) at time t. Let $\Delta \mathbf{A}$ represent vectorially the area of the triangle OPP' swept out by the radius vector in time Δt; $\Delta \mathbf{A}$ is taken to be positive in the sense of advance of a right-threaded screw from $\mathbf{r}$ to $(\mathbf{r} + \Delta \mathbf{r})$. Then

$$\Delta \mathbf{A} = \tfrac{1}{2}[\mathbf{r} \times (\mathbf{r} + \Delta \mathbf{r})] = \tfrac{1}{2}\mathbf{r} \times \Delta \mathbf{r}.$$

Hence

$$\frac{\Delta \mathbf{A}}{\Delta t} = \tfrac{1}{2}\mathbf{r} \times \frac{\Delta \mathbf{r}}{\Delta t},$$

and in the limit as $\Delta t \to 0$, we have

$$\frac{d\mathbf{A}}{dt} = \tfrac{1}{2}\mathbf{r} \times \mathbf{v}. \qquad (1\text{--}12)$$

This is the *areal velocity* at P. It is a vector perpendicular to the plane containing $\mathbf{r}$ and $\mathbf{v}$, and pointing toward the reader from the plane of the paper in Fig. 1–4.

To place Eq. (1–12) in the context of polar coordinates, let $\mathbf{r} = r\mathbf{u}_r$ and $\mathbf{v} = \dot{r}\mathbf{u}_r + r\dot{\theta}\mathbf{u}_\theta$. Then

$$\frac{d\mathbf{A}}{dt} = \tfrac{1}{2}(r\mathbf{u}_r) \times (\dot{r}\mathbf{u}_r + r\dot{\theta}\mathbf{u}_\theta) = \tfrac{1}{2}r^2\dot{\theta}\mathbf{u}_A, \qquad (1\text{--}13)$$

where $\mathbf{u}_A$ is a unit vector in the direction of $\mathbf{r} \times \mathbf{v}$. The magnitude of the areal velocity is thus $\tfrac{1}{2}r^2\dot{\theta}$.

If the motion is not in the xy-plane, the projections of the areal velocity upon the three fundamental planes are used. From Eq. (1–12), with $\mathbf{r}$

and **v** in cartesian coordinates, we have

$$\frac{d\mathbf{A}}{dt} = \frac{1}{2} \begin{vmatrix} \mathbf{i} & \mathbf{j} & \mathbf{k} \\ x & y & z \\ \dot{x} & \dot{y} & \dot{z} \end{vmatrix},$$

and the components of this vector are

$$\dot{A}_x = \tfrac{1}{2}\{y\dot{z} - z\dot{y}\},$$
$$\dot{A}_y = \tfrac{1}{2}\{z\dot{x} - x\dot{z}\}, \qquad (1\text{--}14)$$
$$\dot{A}_z = \tfrac{1}{2}\{x\dot{y} - y\dot{x}\}.$$

In many applications in celestial mechanics, the mass moves so that the areal velocity is constant relative to the fixed origin of reference. The particle then is said to obey the law of areas. Such is the case, for example, in the motion of a planet around the sun. In fact, a simple statement of Kepler's second law (Section 1–1) is that "a planet moves around the sun with constant areal velocity." Since in this case $r^2\dot{\theta} = $ constant, it follows from Eq. (1–11) that the acceleration transverse to the radius vector is zero.

Problems

1. A body moves in an ellipse, whose parametric equations are $x = a \cos \phi$, $y = b \sin \phi$. The areal velocity relative to the center of the ellipse is constant. Find the transverse and radial acceleration components.

2. A particle moves in a parabolic path $r = 1/(1 + \cos \theta)$ in such a way that the areal velocity relative to the origin is a constant, α. Show that the acceleration is entirely radial. At what rate is the radius vector changing when $\theta = 0$? What is the velocity of the particle when $\theta = \pi/2$?

1–4 Dynamics of curvilinear motion. We assume that a particle of mass m is caused to move by application of a force **F**. Then the mathematical statement of Newton's second law of motion (Section 1–1) is

$$\frac{d(m\mathbf{v})}{dt} = \mathbf{F}, \qquad (1\text{--}15)$$

where by definition the quantity $m\mathbf{v} = \mathbf{p}$ is the *linear momentum*. It is assumed here that both **v** and **F** are referred to an origin sufficiently fixed in space for Eq. (1–15) to hold. Such a coordinate system will be designated as a *primary inertial system*. A coordinate system fixed to the earth, for example, is not a primary inertial system, because it takes part in the rotational and the orbital motion of the earth. A system which is fixed with respect to the average position of the stars which can be seen by the unaided eye more nearly fulfills the definition.

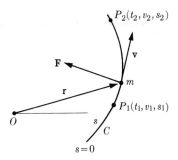

FIG. 1–5. Work done by a force in curvilinear motion.

Suppose that two masses m_1 and m_2 interact with each other. Let the force on m_1 due to m_2 be $\mathbf{F}_{12}$; let the force on m_2 due to m_1 be $\mathbf{F}_{21}$. Then Newton's third law of motion, expressed mathematically, is

$$\mathbf{F}_{12} = -\mathbf{F}_{21}. \qquad (1\text{--}16)$$

In all that follows we shall assume these dynamical concepts to hold.

By definition, the *angular momentum* of a mass m moving in a curved path C is

$$\mathbf{L} = \mathbf{r} \times m\mathbf{v}, \qquad (1\text{--}17)$$

where $\mathbf{r}$ and $\mathbf{v}$ are the position and velocity vectors, respectively, of the particle at time t.

Differentiating Eq. (1–17) with respect to the time and keeping m constant, we find

$$\dot{\mathbf{L}} = \dot{\mathbf{r}} \times m\mathbf{v} + \mathbf{r} \times m\dot{\mathbf{v}} = \mathbf{r} \times \mathbf{F} = \mathbf{N}, \qquad (1\text{--}18)$$

where the last cross product follows from Eq. (1–15). The vector $\mathbf{N}$ is the *torque* or *moment* of $\mathbf{F}$ about the origin O. It is a vector perpendicular to the plane defined by $\mathbf{r}$ and $\mathbf{F}$.

Equation (1–18) expresses Newton's second law for rotational motion, namely, *the time rate of change of the angular momentum equals the torque.*

In general, the force $\mathbf{F}$ may be a function of position, of velocity, of the time, or of all three. In most of our applications, however, it will be independent of velocity and, explicitly, of the time.

Consider now a constant mass m moving under the action of a force $\mathbf{F}$ along a curve C (Fig. 1–5). Then $m\dot{\mathbf{v}} = \mathbf{F}$, and taking the scalar product by $\mathbf{v}$, we find

$$m\mathbf{v} \cdot \dot{\mathbf{v}} = \mathbf{v} \cdot \mathbf{F}.$$

But $d(\mathbf{v} \cdot \mathbf{v})/dt = 2\mathbf{v} \cdot \dot{\mathbf{v}}$. Hence, since $\mathbf{v} \cdot \mathbf{v} = v^2$, we write

$$\frac{d}{dt}\left(\tfrac{1}{2}mv^2\right) = \mathbf{v} \cdot \mathbf{F}. \tag{1-19}$$

The quantity $\tfrac{1}{2}mv^2$ is the *kinetic energy* T. The quantity $\mathbf{v} \cdot \mathbf{F}$ is the rate of working by the force $\mathbf{F}$ on the mass m. If we multiply both sides of Eq. (1–19) by dt and integrate, we obtain

$$\tfrac{1}{2}m(v_2^2 - v_1^2) = \int_{t_1}^{t_2} \mathbf{v} \cdot \mathbf{F}\, dt. \tag{1-20}$$

But $\mathbf{v}\, dt$ is the element of arc $d\mathbf{s}$. Therefore the integral above becomes

$$\int_{s_1}^{s_2} \mathbf{F} \cdot d\mathbf{s}.$$

This is a line integral along C and represents the work done by $\mathbf{F}$ in the motion of m from P_1 to P_2. Thus we note that *the change in kinetic energy in the motion of m from P_1 to P_2 equals the work done by the force in that interval.*

If the $\int_{s_1}^{s_2} \mathbf{F} \cdot d\mathbf{s}$ is independent of the path joining P_1 and P_2, there exists a scalar function of position V defined by

$$\int_{s_1}^{s_2} \mathbf{F} \cdot d\mathbf{s} = V(s_1) - V(s_2). \tag{1-21}$$

This is called the *potential energy* function. The expression $V(s)$ denotes the value of the potential energy at the point whose arc length along C, measured from $s = 0$, is s. Using this value, we may write Eq. (1–20) in the form

$$\tfrac{1}{2}mv_2^2 + V(s_2) = \tfrac{1}{2}mv_1^2 + V(s_1). \tag{1-22}$$

This equation expresses the *conservation of energy* for the moving mass. It says, in words, that *the sum of the kinetic and potential energies of the system remains constant* during the motion.

At this point it is convenient to revert to cartesian coordinates. Let $\mathbf{F} = X\mathbf{i} + Y\mathbf{j} + Z\mathbf{k}$ and let $d\mathbf{s} = dx\mathbf{i} + dy\mathbf{j} + dz\mathbf{k}$. Here X, Y, and Z are functions of x, y, z. Then the integral in Eq. (1–21) becomes

$$\int_{(x_1, y_1, z_1)}^{(x_2, y_2, z_2)} X\, dx + Y\, dy + Z\, dz = V(x_1, y_1, z_1) - V(x_2, y_2, z_2).$$

This relationship implies*

$$X = -\frac{\partial V}{\partial x}, \qquad Y = -\frac{\partial V}{\partial y}, \qquad Z = -\frac{\partial V}{\partial z}.$$

Now the gradient of $V(x, y, z)$ is defined by

$$\nabla V = \frac{\partial V}{\partial x}\mathbf{i} + \frac{\partial V}{\partial y}\mathbf{j} + \frac{\partial V}{\partial z}\mathbf{k}.$$

Hence ∇V can be written

$$\nabla V = -X\mathbf{i} - Y\mathbf{j} - Z\mathbf{k} = -\mathbf{F}. \qquad (1\text{-}23)$$

When this relationship exists between the force $\mathbf{F}$ at all points of a space and the corresponding $V(x, y, z)$, we say that the *force field is conservative.* It can be shown* that a necessary and sufficient condition for the existence of $V(x, y, z)$ is

$$\frac{\partial Z}{\partial y} - \frac{\partial Y}{\partial z} = 0, \qquad \frac{\partial Z}{\partial x} - \frac{\partial X}{\partial z} = 0, \qquad \frac{\partial Y}{\partial x} - \frac{\partial X}{\partial y} = 0. \qquad (1\text{-}24)$$

PROBLEMS

1. A particle of unit mass is sliding under the force of gravity along the parabola $y = 1 + x^2$ from the point $(2, 5)$ to the point $(0, 1)$. Calculate the work done by the gravitational force $\mathbf{g}$ during the motion. If the particle started from rest at $(2, 5)$, what is its velocity when it reaches $(0, 1)$?

2. The force acting on a particle at any point in space is

$$\mathbf{F} = \frac{x\mathbf{i} + y\mathbf{j} + z\mathbf{k}}{\sqrt{x^2 + y^2 + z^2}}.$$

Is the force field conservative?

3. If $V = V(r)$, where $r = (x^2 + y^2 + z^2)^{1/2}$, show that $\mathbf{F} = -(dV/dr)\mathbf{u}_r$. Here $\mathbf{u}_r$ is a unit vector along $\mathbf{r} = x\mathbf{i} + y\mathbf{j} + z\mathbf{k}$. This type of potential-energy function occurs in many problems in celestial mechanics.

1-5 Potential due to a sphere. A basic result proved by Newton† is that a sphere which is homogeneous in concentric layers attracts an exterior point mass as if all of the mass of the sphere were concentrated at its center. This fundamental result allows us to consider the attraction between the earth and the sun, for example, to be equivalent to that

---

* See W. Kaplan, *Advanced Calculus.* Reading, Mass.: Addison-Wesley Publishing Co., Inc., 1952, p. 279 ff.

† See the *Principia*, revised translation by F. Cajori. Berkeley: University of California Press, 1946, p. 193 ff.

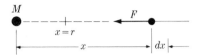

FIG. 1–6. Potential due to a point mass.

between two point masses. While this is only a very good first approximation, still it underlies the mathematical theory of nearly all problems in
celestial mechanics. In view of its importance, we shall demonstrate the
result.

The force per unit mass at any point a distance x from a mass M is given
by Newton's law of gravitation as $F = -GM/x^2$ (Fig. 1–6). As the particle is moved from $x = r$ to $x = \infty$, the amount of work done against
the force field is

$$-GM \int_r^\infty \frac{dx}{x^2} = -\frac{GM}{r} = U. \qquad (1\text{--}25)$$

This, by definition, is the *potential* at r. The potential difference between
two points $x = r_1$ and $x = r_2$ would be

$$-GM \left\{ \frac{1}{r_2} - \frac{1}{r_1} \right\},$$

and we observe that this is the work done by **F** in the motion of the unit
mass from $x = r_1$ to $x = r_2$. By comparison with Eq. (1–21) this is observed to be equivalent to the change in potential energy per unit mass
during the motion. It is clear that the potential at distance r from M and
the force there are related by

$$\mathbf{F} = -\frac{dU}{dr} \mathbf{u}_r. \qquad (1\text{--}26)$$

A section of spherical shell of radius a and unit thickness is pictured in
Fig. 1–7. The density ρ of the shell is constant. An element of surface area
on the shell is

$$d\sigma = a^2 \sin \phi \, d\phi d\theta.$$

If we now place a unit mass at $(0, 0, r)$, the magnitude of the force of
attraction between the element $d\sigma$ and the unit mass will be

$$dF = -\frac{G\rho \, d\sigma}{b^2},$$

where b is the distance between the element and $(0, 0, r)$. This force will
be directed as shown in Fig. 1–7. By symmetry, the components of these
vectors parallel to the xy-plane balance out when the elements $d\sigma$ are

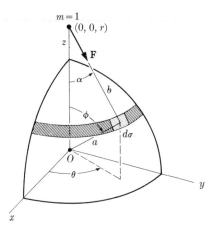

FIG. 1–7. Potential at exterior point due to spherical shell.

summed over the entire spherical shell. The z-components add together. Hence for the total force at $(0, 0, r)$ due to the shell, we have

$$F_z = - \int_S \frac{G\rho \, d\sigma \cos \alpha}{b^2}, \tag{1–27}$$

where α is the angle between the force vector $\mathbf{F}$ and the z-axis.

Integration of Eq. (1–27) is most easily performed by using b as the variable. We have

$$b^2 = a^2 + r^2 - 2ar \cos \phi,$$

$$\cos \alpha = \frac{r - z}{b} = \frac{r - a \cos \phi}{b} = \frac{r^2 - a^2 + b^2}{2br},$$

$$b \, db = ar \sin \phi \, d\phi,$$

$$d\sigma = \frac{ab \, db \, d\theta}{r} .$$

Therefore

$$F_z = - \frac{G\rho a}{2r^2} \int_{\theta=0}^{2\pi} \int_{b=r-a}^{r+a} \frac{r^2 + b^2 - a^2}{b^2} \, db \, d\theta.$$

Integration yields

$$F_z = - \frac{4\pi G\rho a^2}{r^2} . \tag{1–28}$$

But $4\pi\rho a^2 = M(a)$, the mass of the shell. Hence Eq. (1–28) states that F_z *is the same as though all of the mass of the shell were concentrated at its center.*

For a solid sphere of radius R in which the density is a function only of the distance from the center, the force per unit mass at an exterior point is

$$F = -\frac{4\pi G}{r^2}\int_{a=0}^{R}\rho a^2\,da. \qquad (1\text{--}29)$$

But since the mass of the sphere is

$$M = 4\pi\int_{a=0}^{R}\rho a^2\,da,$$

the total force exhibited by Eq. (1–29) is

$$F = -\frac{GM}{r^2}.$$

The solid sphere attracts an exterior unit mass as though all of its mass were concentrated at the center.

The potential, therefore, due to a spherical body homogeneous in concentric layers, for a point outside the sphere is

$$U = -\frac{GM}{r}, \qquad (1\text{--}30)$$

where r is the distance from the point to the center of the sphere.

Problems

1. The gravitational attraction upon a unit mass situated inside a spherical shell vanishes. Prove this statement, using an analysis similar to that leading to Eq. (1–28).

2. Using the result of Problem 1, prove that the force acting on a unit mass interior to a solid homogeneous sphere varies directly as the distance from the center of the sphere to the particle.

3. The mass of the earth is 5.98×10^{27} gm and its radius is 6.38×10^8 cm. If the earth is considered as a sphere, what is the potential difference between points at elevations of 1000 and 2000 km above its surface? [$G = 6.67 \times 10^{-8}$ dyne·cm²·gm⁻².] If a mass of 100 gm falls from rest from the second elevation to the first, what is its velocity at the 1000-km level?

4. Imagine a vertical shaft to be bored through the earth from pole to pole. A unit mass is dropped down the shaft. Describe the subsequent motion of the particle. (Assume the earth to be a homogeneous sphere.)

1–6 Systems of particles. Let n particles of differing masses be located relative to an origin O by their position vectors, as shown in Fig. 1–8. We assume that the origin O is fixed in space and that, relative to O, Newton's

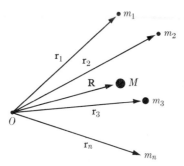

FIG. 1-8. Center of mass for a system of particles.

laws of motion are applicable. Let M denote the total mass of the system:

$$M = \sum_{j=1}^{n} m_j.$$

Then the *center of mass* of the n particles is defined by

$$\mathbf{R} = \frac{1}{M} \sum_{j=1}^{n} m_j \mathbf{r}_j. \qquad (1\text{--}31)$$

The reader may show that if $\mathbf{r} = x\mathbf{i} + y\mathbf{j} + z\mathbf{k}$ in a cartesian coordinate reference frame with origin at O, Eq. (1–31) is equivalent to the well-known equations

$$\bar{x} = \frac{1}{M} \sum_{j=1}^{n} m_j x_j, \qquad \bar{y} = \frac{1}{M} \sum_{j=1}^{n} m_j y_j, \qquad \bar{z} = \frac{1}{M} \sum_{j=1}^{n} m_j z_j.$$

In general, the force acting on each particle consists of an external part $\mathbf{F}_j$ and the totality of internal forces due to the other particles, $\sum_k \mathbf{f}_{j,k}$ ($j \neq k$). For the jth particle, therefore, by Newton's second law of motion,

$$m_j \ddot{\mathbf{r}}_j = \mathbf{F}_j + \sum_{k} \mathbf{f}_{j,k} \qquad (j \neq k), \qquad (1\text{--}32)$$

where the summation extends over $n - 1$ particles of the system.

Summing Eq. (1–32) over the entire system, we find

$$\sum_{j=1}^{n} m_j \ddot{\mathbf{r}}_j = \sum_{j=1}^{n} \mathbf{F}_j + \sum_{j,k=1}^{n} \mathbf{f}_{j,k} \qquad (j \neq k). \qquad (1\text{--}33)$$

But by Newton's third law of motion (Section 1–1), the internal forces are subject to the relationship $\mathbf{f}_{j,k} = -\mathbf{f}_{k,j}$. Hence $\sum_{j,k}^{n} \mathbf{f}_{j,k} = 0$. Furthermore, by comparison of the left-hand side of Eq. (1–33) with Eq. (1–31),

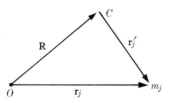

FIG. 1-9. Position relative to the center of mass.

it is evident that $\sum_{j=1}^{n} m_j \ddot{\mathbf{r}}_j = M\ddot{\mathbf{R}}$. Therefore

$$M\ddot{\mathbf{R}} = \sum_{j=1}^{n} \mathbf{F}_j = \mathbf{F}, \tag{1-34}$$

where $\mathbf{F}$ is, by definition, the resultant of all the external forces acting on the group of particles. This fundamental relationship states that *the motion of the center of mass is the same as if the entire mass of the system were concentrated there and acted upon by the resultant of the external forces.*

Consider now the angular or rotational motions of the n particles about O. By definition, Eq. (1-17), the total angular momentum of the group of particles about O is

$$\mathbf{L}_O = \sum_{j=1}^{n} \mathbf{r}_j \times m_j \dot{\mathbf{r}}_j. \tag{1-35}$$

Similarly, if we denote by $\mathbf{L}_C$ the angular momentum about the center of mass,

$$\mathbf{L}_C = \sum_{j=1}^{n} \mathbf{r}'_j \times m_j \dot{\mathbf{r}}'_j, \tag{1-36}$$

where $\mathbf{r}'_j$ is the position vector of m_j relative to the center of mass (Fig. 1-9). It is clear from the figure that

$$\mathbf{r}_j = \mathbf{R} + \mathbf{r}'_j$$

and hence that

$$\dot{\mathbf{r}}_j = \dot{\mathbf{R}} + \dot{\mathbf{r}}'_j.$$

Substituting these values in Eq. (1-35) and expanding, we obtain

$$\mathbf{L}_O = \sum_{j=1}^{n} m_j(\mathbf{R} \times \dot{\mathbf{R}}) + \sum_{j=1}^{n} m_j \mathbf{r}'_j \times \dot{\mathbf{R}} + \sum_{j=1}^{n} \mathbf{R} \times m_j \dot{\mathbf{r}}'_j$$

$$+ \sum_{j=1}^{n} m_j(\mathbf{r}'_j \times \dot{\mathbf{r}}'_j). \tag{1-37}$$

But, by the definition of the center of mass, $\sum_{j=1}^{n} m_j \mathbf{r}'_j = 0$ and

$\sum_{j=1}^{n} m_j \dot{\mathbf{r}}_j' = 0$. Also $\sum_{j=1}^{n} m_j (\mathbf{R} \times \dot{\mathbf{R}}) = \mathbf{R} \times M\dot{\mathbf{R}}$ is the angular momentum about O of the entire mass considered as concentrated at the center of mass. The second and third terms of Eq. (1–37) vanish and we have remaining

$$\mathbf{L}_O = \mathbf{R} \times M\dot{\mathbf{R}} + \sum_{j=1}^{n} \mathbf{r}_j' \times m_j \dot{\mathbf{r}}_j'. \qquad (1\text{–}38)$$

The last term of Eq. (1–38) is the angular momentum, $\mathbf{L}_C$, of the system about the center of mass. We are therefore led to another fundamental property of the rotational motion, namely, *the angular momentum about a fixed point O is equal to the sum of the angular momentum about O of a particle whose mass is the entire mass of the system situated at and moving with the center of mass, and the angular momentum of the system of particles about the center of mass.*

One further property of the rotational motion remains to be demonstrated. Writing $\mathbf{L}_C$ for the last term in Eq. (1–38) and differentiating with respect to the time, we find

$$\dot{\mathbf{L}}_O = \dot{\mathbf{R}} \times M\dot{\mathbf{R}} + \mathbf{R} \times M\ddot{\mathbf{R}} + \dot{\mathbf{L}}_C. \qquad (1\text{–}39)$$

The first term in this expression vanishes. Furthermore $\mathbf{R} = \mathbf{r}_j - \mathbf{r}_j'$. Substituting in Eq. (1–39), using Eq. (1–34), and rewriting, we have

$$\dot{\mathbf{L}}_O - \sum_{j=1}^{n} \mathbf{r}_j \times \mathbf{F}_j = \dot{\mathbf{L}}_C - \sum_{j=1}^{n} \mathbf{r}_j' \times \mathbf{F}_j. \qquad (1\text{–}40)$$

But by definition $\sum_{j=1}^{n} \mathbf{r}_j \times \mathbf{F}_j = \mathbf{N}_O$, the torque of the external force system about O. Similarly, $\sum_{j=1}^{n} \mathbf{r}_j' \times \mathbf{F}_j = \mathbf{N}_C$ is the torque about the center of mass. Therefore Eq. (1–40) becomes

$$\dot{\mathbf{L}}_O - \mathbf{N}_O = \dot{\mathbf{L}}_C - \mathbf{N}_C. \qquad (1\text{–}41)$$

By Newton's second law for rotational motion, Eq. (1–18), $\dot{\mathbf{L}}_O - \mathbf{N}_O = 0$. Therefore $\dot{\mathbf{L}}_C - \mathbf{N}_C = 0$ also, and we find that *the time rate of change of the angular momentum for motion relative to the center of mass equals the torque about the center of mass. Furthermore, this is true whether the center of mass is at rest or is in translational motion relative to a fixed primary inertial coordinate system.*

This result is very important. It means that we can study the rotational properties of a system of mass points independently of the translation of the group, provided we refer the description of the motion to the center of mass of the system. In studying the motions of the planets, for example, we can ignore the motion of the whole solar system in space and study only the rotational motion about the center of mass.

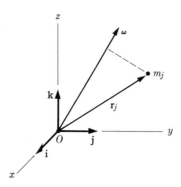

FIG. 1–10. Angular velocity of a mass particle.

Let the mass particles of the system be rigidly connected together so that the mutual distances between particles remains fixed. And let the system rotate about an instantaneous axis through the origin O with angular velocity $\boldsymbol{\omega}$ (Fig. 1–10). The origin is considered to be fixed in space or, if moving, to be the center of mass of the system. Then at any instant the linear velocity of mass m_j at position $\mathbf{r}_j$ is $\boldsymbol{\omega} \times \mathbf{r}_j$. Its angular momentum is

$$\mathbf{L} = \mathbf{r}_j \times m_j \mathbf{v}_j = m_j[\mathbf{r}_j \times (\boldsymbol{\omega} \times \mathbf{r}_j)].$$

The expansion of this triple vector product yields

$$\mathbf{L} = m_j[(\mathbf{r}_j \cdot \mathbf{r}_j)\boldsymbol{\omega} - (\mathbf{r}_j \cdot \boldsymbol{\omega})\mathbf{r}_j],$$

and hence for the assemblage of masses the total angular momentum is

$$\mathbf{L} = \boldsymbol{\omega} \sum_{j=1}^{n} m_j r_j^2 - \sum_{j=1}^{n} m_j(\mathbf{r}_j \cdot \boldsymbol{\omega})\mathbf{r}_j. \tag{1–42}$$

In the cartesian coordinate system shown, let

$$\mathbf{r} = x\mathbf{i} + y\mathbf{j} + z\mathbf{k}, \quad \boldsymbol{\omega} = \omega_x\mathbf{i} + \omega_y\mathbf{j} + \omega_z\mathbf{k}, \quad \mathbf{L} = L_x\mathbf{i} + L_y\mathbf{j} + L_z\mathbf{k}.$$

Substituting these into Eq. (1–42) and separating components yields

$$L_x = \omega_x \sum_{j=1}^{n} m_j(y_j^2 + z_j^2) - \omega_y \sum_{j=1}^{n} m_j x_j y_j - \omega_z \sum_{j=1}^{n} m_j x_j z_j,$$

$$L_y = -\omega_x \sum_{j=1}^{n} m_j y_j x_j + \omega_y \sum_{j=1}^{n} m_j(x_j^2 + z_j^2) - \omega_z \sum_{j=1}^{n} m_j y_j z_j, \tag{1–43}$$

$$L_z = -\omega_x \sum_{j=1}^{n} m_j z_j x_j - \omega_y \sum_{j=1}^{n} m_j z_j y_j + \omega_z \sum_{j=1}^{n} m_j(x_j^2 + y_j^2).$$

The quantities

$$\sum_j m_j(y_j^2 + z_j^2), \qquad \sum_j m_j(x_j^2 + z_j^2), \qquad \sum_j m_j(x_j^2 + y_j^2)$$

are called the *moments of inertia* of the system about the x-, y-, and z-axes respectively. They will be denoted by I_{xx}, I_{yy}, and I_{zz}. The remaining quantities

$$\sum_j m_j x_j y_j, \qquad \sum_j m_j x_j z_j, \qquad \sum_j m_j y_j z_j$$

are called *products of inertia*. They will be denoted by I_{xy}, I_{xz}, I_{yz}. These are the fundamental inertial parameters of the system of mass points. For a continuous medium, the summations are to be replaced by integrals over the volume which bounds the mass distribution. The character of the rotational motion of the assemblage of masses under the action of an external torque is determined by these parameters through Newton's second law for rotational motion, $\dot{\mathbf{L}} = \mathbf{N}$. They play the same part in rotational motion of the system that the mass plays in translational motion.

Problems

1. A pair of masses m_1 and m_2 ($m_2 = 2m_1$), linked by a rigid rod, whose mass is negligible compared with m_1 and m_2, is located in a vertical plane, as shown in Fig. 1–11, with m_2 at the origin and m_1 at $(0, a)$. The mass m_1 is at rest at $t = 0$ while the mass m_2 has, instantaneously, a linear velocity $\mathbf{v_0}$, as indicated. The system moves under the influence of the force of gravity, g. Determine the subsequent position of the center of mass and the rotational orientation of the system. Verify the properties for the system established in this section.

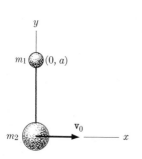

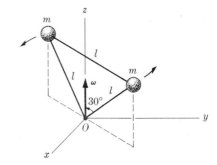

Fig. 1–11. Masses on a rigid rod.   Fig. 1–12. Rotating framework carrying two masses.

2. Two equal masses are mounted on an equilateral rigid framework, as shown in Fig. 1–12. The whole rotates with angular velocity $\boldsymbol{\omega}$ about the z-axis. Exhibit the moments and products of inertia for this pair of masses, and calculate the components of the angular momentum vector. Do the moments and products of inertia change with the time as the system rotates?

CHAPTER 2

CENTRAL FORCE MOTION

When the resultant force causing accelerated motion of a mass particle always passes through a fixed point, the ensuing motion is called *central force motion*. The fixed point is the *center of force*.

This type of motion predominates in the celestial universe. The planets move around the sun in orbits such that the force of attraction due to the sun always passes through the latter. One component of a double star pair revolves about the other component under the action of a gravitational central force.

In this chapter we shall derive several properties of central force motion which are independent of the precise analytical form of the force law. Most astronomical applications involve the inverse square law of Newton.

2–1 The law of areas. Consider a particle of mass m at a position $\mathbf{r}$ relative to a fixed origin O (Fig. 2–1). Let the particle describe the curve C under the action of a central force $\mathbf{F}$, which may be directed toward or away from O. We shall denote $\mathbf{F}$ by $F\mathbf{u}_r$ where $\mathbf{u}_r$ is a unit vector along $\mathbf{r}$. Then by Newton's second law for constant mass [Eq. (1–15)]

$$m\dot{\mathbf{v}} = F\mathbf{u}_r$$

and

$$\mathbf{r} \times m\dot{\mathbf{v}} = \mathbf{r} \times F\mathbf{u}_r = 0$$

by virtue of the collinearity of $\mathbf{r}$ and $\mathbf{u}_r$. Now from Eq. (1–12) the areal velocity $\dot{\mathbf{A}} = \frac{1}{2}\mathbf{r} \times \mathbf{v}$. Hence

$$\frac{d\dot{\mathbf{A}}}{dt} = \frac{1}{2}[(\dot{\mathbf{r}} \times \mathbf{v}) + \mathbf{r} \times \dot{\mathbf{v}}] = \frac{1}{2}\mathbf{r} \times \dot{\mathbf{v}} = 0$$

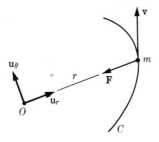

Fig. 2–1. Curvilinear central force motion.

19

by the analysis above. Therefore $\dot{\mathbf{A}}$ = a constant. Equation (1–13) shows, however, that the areal velocity is

$$\dot{\mathbf{A}} = \tfrac{1}{2}r^2\dot{\theta}\mathbf{u}_A \qquad (2\text{–}1)$$

where $\mathbf{u}_A$ is a unit vector perpendicular to $\mathbf{r}$ and $\mathbf{v}$, that is, perpendicular to the instantaneous plane defined by these vectors. Because $\mathbf{u}_A$ is a constant vector, we conclude that *the mass particle moving under a central force describes an orbit which lies in a plane.*

Let the magnitude of the constant areal velocity be $\tfrac{1}{2}h$. Then the area described in time t is given by

$$A = \tfrac{1}{2}ht + c, \qquad (2\text{–}2)$$

where c is a constant of integration.

From the above analysis we draw the conclusion that *for any central force Kepler's second law of planetary motion* (Section 1–1) *holds.* That is, *the area swept out by the radius vector is directly proportional to the time.* This is the *law of areas.*

The converse of this is also true, namely, if the area swept out by the radius vector is directly proportional to the time, the force is a central force. For, assuming $A = pt + q$, where p and q are constants, we have $\dot{A} = p$, and from Eq. (1–13) $r^2\dot{\theta} = 2p$. Therefore

$$\frac{d}{dt}\,(r^2\dot{\theta}) = 2r\dot{r}\dot{\theta} + r^2\ddot{\theta} = 0. \qquad (2\text{–}3)$$

But by Eq. (1–11) $2\dot{r}\dot{\theta} + r\ddot{\theta}$ is the acceleration component perpendicular to the radius vector. Since this vanishes by Eq. (2–3), there is no acceleration and hence no force perpendicular to r. The line of action of the entire acceleration, or force, passes through the origin.

2–2 Linear and angular velocities. Two other kinematic results follow from the fact that a force, or acceleration, is central. Let p (Fig. 2–2) denote the perpendicular distance from the origin O to the tangent T of the curve at a given point P. By Eqs. (1–12) and (2–2), we have

$$2\dot{\mathbf{A}} = \mathbf{r} \times \mathbf{v} = h\mathbf{u}_A.$$

But

$$\mathbf{r} \times \mathbf{v} = rv \sin \alpha\, \mathbf{u}_A \qquad \text{and} \qquad r \sin \alpha = p.$$

Therefore,

$$v = \frac{h}{p} \qquad (2\text{–}4)$$

the *linear speed v of a particle moving at a point P under the action of a central*

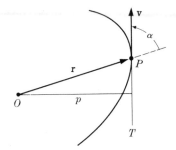

FIG. 2-2. Linear speed in central force motion.

force is inversely proportional to the perpendicular distance from O to the instantaneous tangent to the orbit at P.

The angular speed of the particle at P is given by

$$\dot{\theta} = \frac{h}{r^2}. \tag{2-5}$$

We observe that *the angular speed of a particle moving under a central force varies inversely as the square of the distance from the origin to the particle.*

2-3 Integrals of angular momentum and energy. Let the equation of motion of a mass m be

$$m\dot{\mathbf{v}} = F\mathbf{u}_r, \tag{2-6}$$

where F denotes the magnitude of a central force and $\mathbf{u}_r$ is the unit vector along $\mathbf{r}$ (Fig. 2-1). Then from Eqs. (1-18) and (2-6)

$$\dot{\mathbf{L}} = \mathbf{r} \times m\dot{\mathbf{v}} = \mathbf{r} \times F\mathbf{u}_r = 0. \tag{2-7}$$

This implies that the *angular momentum* $\mathbf{L}$ *of a particle moving under a central force remains constant in magnitude and direction.* The vector $\mathbf{L}$ is perpendicular to the orbital plane.

By comparing Eqs. (1-17), (1-12), and (1-13), we see that

$$\mathbf{L} = \mathbf{r} \times m\mathbf{v} = 2m\dot{\mathbf{A}} = mr^2\dot{\theta}\mathbf{u}_A$$

so that the magnitude of the angular momentum is

$$mr^2\dot{\theta} = mh. \tag{2-8}$$

Thus *one integral of the equations of motion of the mass particle is that of constant angular momentum, mh.*

Again, from Eq. (2–6), we write the scalar product

$$m\mathbf{v} \cdot \dot{\mathbf{v}} = F\mathbf{v} \cdot \mathbf{u}_r. \tag{2–9}$$

But

$$\mathbf{v} \cdot \dot{\mathbf{v}} = \frac{d}{dt}(\tfrac{1}{2}\mathbf{v} \cdot \mathbf{v}) = \frac{d}{dt}(\tfrac{1}{2}v^2)$$

and, by Eq. (1–10), because $\mathbf{u}_r$ is perpendicular to $\mathbf{u}_\theta$,

$$\mathbf{v} \cdot \mathbf{u}_r = (\dot{r}\mathbf{u}_r + r\dot{\theta}\mathbf{u}_\theta) \cdot \mathbf{u}_r = \dot{r}.$$

Therefore Eq. (2–9) becomes

$$\frac{d}{dt}(\tfrac{1}{2}mv^2) = F\frac{dr}{dt}. \tag{2–10}$$

Now suppose that F depends only on the length of the radius vector, that is, $F = F(r)$. Then upon integrating Eq. (2–10), we have

$$\tfrac{1}{2}mv^2 = \int F(r)\,dr + E, \tag{2–11}$$

where E is a constant of integration which depends upon the initial conditions of the motion.

The integral in Eq. (2–11) is the work done by F in the change of position of the particle along the orbit. When the analytical form for $F(r)$ is given, the integral can be calculated. We leave it to the reader to show that $\mathbf{F} = F(r)\mathbf{u}_r$ is a conservative force. There exists, therefore, a potential energy (Section 1–4) $V(r)$ such that $F(r) = -dV/dr$. Hence we may rewrite Eq. (2–11) in the form

$$\tfrac{1}{2}mv^2 + V(r) = E. \tag{2–12}$$

Equation (2–12) states that *the kinetic energy plus the potential energy of a particle moving under a central force is constant.* This is the law of conservation of energy for the system, and E constitutes a second integral of the equations of motion.

Another property of central force motion is demonstrated by Eq. (2–12). Solving for v, we have

$$v = \pm\sqrt{(2/m)(E - V)}. \tag{2–13}$$

Since the square root depends only on r through the function $V(r)$, we see that the speed in all orbits of the same total energy, *regardless of their shapes,* is the same at a given distance r from the center of force.

Problems

1. Prove that $\mathbf{F} = F(r)\mathbf{u}_r$ is a conservative force. [*Hint:* See Eqs. (1–24)].

2. A particle of unit mass moves along a straight line under the action of a force $F(r) = ar^{-2}e^{-br}$, $(a > 0, b > 0)$. It starts from rest at $r = r_0$. What is the potential energy of the particle? Is the force field conservative? What is the total energy? What is the speed of the particle at $r = 5r_0$?

2-4 The equation of the orbit.

Let the force be denoted by $F(r)$. Then the equations of motion obtained from Newton's second law are

$$m[\ddot{r} - r\dot{\theta}^2] = F(r),$$
$$mr^2\dot{\theta} = mh. \tag{2-14}$$

They follow from Eqs. (1–11) and (2–8). In their original form, these differential equations were each of the second order, hence their complete solution would result in four integration constants. But we have already exhibited two of these in the form of the angular momentum and energy integrals. Two more constants will result from the solution of Eqs. (2–14). Two initial conditions are still required, therefore, to fix the orbit completely.

Let $u = 1/r$ be the reciprocal radius vector. Then from the second of Eqs. (2–14), $\dot{\theta} = hu^2$. Also

$$\dot{r} = -h(du/d\theta) \qquad \text{and} \qquad \ddot{r} = -h^2u^2(d^2u/d\theta^2),$$

so that the first of Eqs. (2–14) becomes, after some simplification,

$$\frac{d^2u}{d\theta^2} + u = -\frac{F(1/u)}{mh^2u^2}. \tag{2-15}$$

This second-order differential equation for u as a function of θ yields the polar equation of the orbit when the proper force law, expressed in terms of u, is substituted.

Suppose that the force is one which varies as an integral power n of the distance: $F(r) = \alpha r^n$. Then $F(1/u) = \alpha u^{-n}$ and Eq. (2–15) becomes

$$\frac{d^2u}{d\theta^2} + u = -\frac{\alpha u^{-n-2}}{mh^2}. \tag{2-16}$$

This may be integrated directly. Multiplying both sides by $2(du/d\theta)$ and rewriting, we have

$$\frac{d}{d\theta}\left[\left(\frac{du}{d\theta}\right)^2 + u^2\right] = -\beta u^{-(n+2)}\frac{du}{d\theta},$$

where $\beta = 2\alpha/mh^2$. Integration yields

$$\left(\frac{du}{d\theta}\right)^2 + u^2 = \frac{\beta u^{-(n+1)}}{n+1} + c \qquad (n \neq -1), \qquad (2\text{-}17)$$

where c is a constant of integration.

Integrating a second time, we obtain

$$\int_{u_0}^{u} \frac{du}{\sqrt{c - u^2 + \beta u^{-(n+1)}/(n+1)}} = \theta - \theta_0 \qquad (n \neq -1), \qquad (2\text{-}18)$$

where the coordinates (u_0, θ_0) define an initial starting point in the orbit. When n is given, Eq. (2-18) defines u as a function of θ, namely, the polar equation of the orbit. It should be clear that the case $n = -1$ is excluded from Eq. (2-18). For $n = -1$, a logarithm in u replaces the power of u in the right-hand side of Eq. (2-17).

The integral in Eq. (2-18) is of the form

$$\int (a + bu^2 + cu^{-n-1})^{-1/2} \, du, \qquad (2\text{-}19)$$

where n is an integer, and it may be shown from a table of integrals that trigonometric functions will result if no power of u exceeds two. Therefore n is restricted by

$$-n - 1 = 0, 1, 2 \qquad \text{or} \qquad n = -1, -2, -3.$$

However, $n = -1$ was excluded, so we are left with $n = -2$ or -3.

When $n = 1$, the integral [Eq. (2-19)] assumes the form

$$\int (bu^4 + au^2 + c)^{-1/2} u \, du.$$

A substitution $v = u^2$ and $dv = 2u \, du$ reduces this to

$$\tfrac{1}{2}\int (bv^2 + av + c)^{-1/2} \, dv,$$

which can be integrated in terms of trigonometric functions. Hence we conclude that when a central force varies as r^n, where $n = +1, -2, -3$, the polar equation of the orbit can be expressed in terms of trigonometric functions. Under special circumstances higher powers of r yield orbits expressible in terms of circular functions. It can be shown* in general, however, that when $n = +5, +3, 0, -4, -5, -7$, the integral [Eq. (2-19)] may be evaluated in terms of elliptic functions.

---

* See, H. Goldstein, *Classical Mechanics*, Reading, Mass.: Addison-Wesley Publishing Co., Inc., 1950, pp. 74–76.

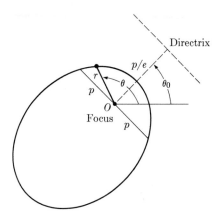

FIG. 2–3. Parameters for an elliptic orbit.

2–5 The inverse square force. The orbits in most astronomical applications arise from the inverse square force postulated by Newton. We shall illustrate the analysis of Section 2–4 by using $F(r) = -GMm/r^2$, where GM is the *power* of the force center and m is the mass being accelerated. The equations of motion, reduced by this force law, yield for the orbit

$$\frac{d^2u}{d\theta^2} + u = \frac{GM}{h^2}. \tag{2–20}$$

Rather than use the integral [Eq. (2–18)] here, we shall integrate Eq. (2–20) directly to obtain

$$u = \frac{GM}{h^2} + A \cos (\theta - \theta_0), \tag{2–21}$$

where θ_0 and A are constants of integration. Hence

$$r = \frac{(h^2/GM)}{1 + (Ah^2/GM) \cos (\theta - \theta_0)}. \tag{2–22}$$

This is the polar equation of the orbit. It will be recognized as the standard equation for a conic section

$$r = \frac{p}{1 + e \cos (\theta - \theta_0)}, \tag{2–23}$$

where e is the eccentricity and p/e is the distance from focus to directrix (Fig. 2–3). Comparison of Eqs. (2–22) and (2–23) shows that

$$p = \frac{h^2}{GM}, \qquad e = \frac{Ah^2}{GM}.$$

The parameters e and p determine the shape of the conic. From analytic geometry we know that when

$e < 1$, the conic is an ellipse;

$e = 1$, the conic is a parabola;

$e > 1$, the conic is a hyperbola.

These geometrical parameters obviously depend upon the integration constant A and the physical constants of the system, h, G, and M.

Reference to Eq. (2–17) will show that for the inverse square force

$$\left(\frac{du}{d\theta}\right)^2 + u^2 = \frac{2GMu}{h^2} + c. \tag{2-24}$$

This equation has a simple physical interpretation. The velocity components in the orbit are

$$\dot{r} = -h\frac{du}{d\theta} \qquad \text{and} \qquad r\dot{\theta} = hu.$$

Hence the speed v is

$$\left[\left(h\frac{du}{d\theta}\right)^2 + h^2u^2\right]^{1/2}$$

Furthermore $-GM/r = -GMu$ is the potential energy per unit mass as the reader may show. Therefore Eq. (2–24) states that the total energy of the system remains constant. That is,

$$\tfrac{1}{2}mv^2 - GMmu = \tfrac{1}{2}h^2cm = E, \tag{2-25}$$

where E is the total energy. Also $c = 2E/mh^2$.

At the end, or ends, of the transverse axis of the conic $\dot{r} = -h(du/d\theta) = 0$. From Eq. (2–24), therefore,

$$u^2 - \frac{2GMu}{h^2} - \frac{2E}{mh^2} = 0$$

and

$$u = \frac{GM}{h^2}[1 \pm \sqrt{1 + (2Eh^2/mG^2M^2)}]. \tag{2-26}$$

The values of u thus found are those at the ends of the transverse axis of the conic. From Eqs. (2–21) and (2–26), we find

$$u_{\max} = \frac{GM}{h^2} + A = \frac{GM}{h^2}[1 + \sqrt{1 + (2Eh^2/mG^2M^2)}],$$

$$u_{\min} = \frac{GM}{h^2} - A = \frac{GM}{h^2}[1 - \sqrt{1 + (2Eh^2/mG^2M^2)}].$$

Hence
$$A = \frac{GM}{h^2} \sqrt{1 + (2Eh^2/mG^2M^2)}.$$

But $e = Ah^2/GM$; therefore we arrive at a fundamental relation between the eccentricity and the total energy of the particle, namely,

$$e = \sqrt{1 + (2Eh^2/mG^2M^2)}. \qquad (2\text{–}27)$$

It is clear that if

(a) $E = 0$, $e = 1$ the orbit is a parabola,

(b) $E < 0$, $e < 1$ the orbit is an ellipse,

(c) $E > 0$, $e > 1$ the orbit is a hyperbola.

Case I. $E = 0$, $e = 1$ *the parabola.* Let q denote the distance from focus to vertex. Then

$$p = \frac{h^2}{GM} = 2q$$

and the equation of the orbit is

$$r = \frac{2q}{1 + \cos(\theta - \theta_0)}. \qquad (2\text{–}28)$$

The speed in the orbit at a distance r from the center of force is, by Eq. (2–25),

$$v_p = \sqrt{2GM/r}. \qquad (2\text{–}29)$$

This is the speed which would result if a particle moved under the inverse square force from an infinite distance to r. Or conversely, if the particle has this speed at a distance r, it will recede indefinitely far from the center of force. The speed v_p sometimes is called the *velocity of escape* from the force center.

Case II. $E < 0$, $e < 1$ *the ellipse.* Let q denote the radius vector of the vertex of the ellipse nearest the origin (Fig. 2–3), let q' denote the radius vector at maximum distance from the origin. The origin is, of course, the focus. Let the major axis of the ellipse be $2a$. Then

$$q = \frac{p}{1 + e} \quad \text{and} \quad q' = \frac{p}{1 - e},$$

and

$$q + q' = 2a.$$

From these equations we find that $p = a(1 - e^2)$, and the equation of the ellipse is

$$r = \frac{a(1 - e^2)}{1 + e\cos(\theta - \theta_0)}. \qquad (2\text{–}30)$$

Furthermore, since $p = h^2/GM$, the areal velocity constant is given by

$$h = \sqrt{GMa(1 - e^2)}.$$ (2–31)

Substituting this value into Eq. (2–27) and simplifying, we find the total energy

$$E = -\frac{GMm}{2a}.$$ (2–32)

Equation (2–25) then yields, for the orbital speed at a distance r from the force center,

$$v^2 = GM\left[\frac{2}{r} - \frac{1}{a}\right].$$ (2–33)

We are now in position to deduce an expression for the period in elliptic motion. Let A denote the area swept out by the radius vector in time t. Then by Eqs. (2–2) and (2–31)

$$A = \tfrac{1}{2}\sqrt{GMa(1 - e^2)}\, t + c,$$

where c is a constant of integration. In one period, P, the radius vector sweeps out an area

$$\pi ab = \pi a^2\sqrt{1 - e^2} = \tfrac{1}{2}\sqrt{GMa(1 - e^2)}\, P.$$

Here $b = a\sqrt{1 - e^2}$ is the semiminor axis. Therefore

$$P = \frac{2\pi a^{3/2}}{\sqrt{GM}}.$$ (2–34)

This is Kepler's third law (Section 1–1) when applied to the planetary system. In this application M is *very nearly* the same for each planet and is approximately the mass of the sun. It is clear that two planets having periods P_1 and P_2 and orbits with semimajor axes a_1 and a_2 fulfill the relation

$$\left(\frac{P_1}{P_2}\right)^2 = \left(\frac{a_1}{a_2}\right)^3$$

as Kepler's third law asserts.

Case III. $E > 0, e > 1$ *the hyperbola.* Again let $2a$ denote the transverse axis of the conic. Then the geometry of the orbit indicates that $p = a(e^2 - 1)$:

$$r = \frac{a(e^2 - 1)}{1 + e \cos (\theta - \theta_0)}.$$ (2–35)

The areal velocity constant is

$$h = \sqrt{GMa(e^2 - 1)}, \tag{2–36}$$

and the total energy will be

$$E = \frac{GMm}{2a}. \tag{2–37}$$

At a distance r from the force center, the speed will be given by

$$v^2 = GM\left[\frac{2}{r} + \frac{1}{a}\right]. \tag{2–38}$$

In the preceding analysis of motion under an inverse square force directed toward a fixed center, it is clear that a deduction of Kepler's first law of planetary motion (Section 1–1) is implied. We have seen that the differential equation defining the orbit does yield, under proper conditions of total energy, an elliptical path with the force center at one focus. This is precisely what Kepler deduced from observations of Mars, where the force center is the sun.

PROBLEMS

1. Determine the path followed by a particle of mass m subjected to a repelling force $F(r) = GMm/r^2$. What would be the speed of this particle at an infinite distance from the origin?

2. A particle of mass m moves in a circular orbit under an inverse square force of attraction $-GMm/r^2$. What is its speed as a function of r? How does the circular speed compare with the speed of escape at the same r?

3. A particle of mass m is projected from the point $(r_0, 0)$ with velocity v_0 perpendicular to the line $\theta = 0$. It is subjected to a force $F(r) = -mr^{-3}$. Find the orbit along which it moves. Study all cases which may arise.

4. A particle of mass m is moving in a force field for which the potential energy is $V(r) = \frac{1}{2}mr^2$. Show that the orbit will have an equation of the form

$$r^2 = A/(B + C \cos 2\theta).$$

This is an ellipse with its center at the origin.

5. A particle describes an orbit under the central force

$$F(r) = -m[(k/r^2) + (k'/r^3)],$$

where $k' \ll k$. Show that the orbit has the form $r = A/[1 + e \cos (\alpha\theta).]$ This can be interpreted as an ellipse with a moving major axis. Find the period of revolution of the moving axis.

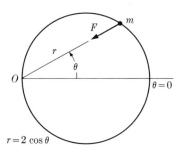

F IG . 2–4. Circular motion with origin on circumference.

2–6 From orbit to force law. The converse of the problem discussed in the preceding sections can be solved by use of Eq. (2–15). Suppose, for example, that a mass particle is moving on the circle $r = 2 \cos \theta$ under the action of a force directed toward the origin (Fig. 2–4). Then, by Eq. (2–15) with

$$\phi(u) = F(1/u),$$

we have

$$\phi(u) = -mh^2u^2\left[\frac{d^2u}{d\theta^2} + u\right]$$
$$= -mh^2u^2[8u^3]$$
$$= -8mh^2u^5.$$

Thus the force $F(r) = -8mh^2/r^5$, an inverse fifth-power law.

Kepler found that Mars described an ellipse with the sun at one focus. The equation for such a curve is

$$r = \frac{p}{1 + e \cos \theta} \qquad (2\text{–}39)$$

when the major axis of the ellipse coincides with the polar axis of coordinates. On the assumption that the force governing the motion is a central force, we can show directly from Eq. (2–15) that the law of force must be that of the inverse square.

From Eq. (2–39) with

$$u = \frac{1 + e \cos \theta}{p},$$

we have

$$F\left(\frac{1}{u}\right) = -mh^2u^2\left[\frac{1}{p}\right] = -\frac{mh^2u^2}{p}.$$

The force law is, therefore, $F(r) = -mh^2/pr^2$, an inverse square law.

Problems

1. Show that the equation for the central ellipse,

$$\frac{x^2}{a^2} + \frac{y^2}{b^2} = 1,$$

can be written as

$$u^2 = \frac{1 - e^2 \cos^2 \theta}{a^2(1 - e^2)}$$

in polar coordinates, with $1/r = u$. Show from the last equation that the force law followed by a particle moving in such an ellipse, with the center of the ellipse as the force center, is $F(r) = -kr$, where k is a constant.

2. A mass particle moves on the curve $r = a + b \cos \theta$, where a and b are constants and $a > b$. Find the law of force.

3. A mass particle moves along the spiral $r\theta = k$, where k is a constant. Under what force law does it move?

4. In the example of this section resulting in an inverse fifth-power law, the assumed orbit was a circle through the origin. Study the converse problem. Assume that $F(r) = -k/r^5$ and find the integral representing the orbit. Show that the circle is a special case which results when the initial conditions are suitably chosen. Can circular motion with the force center at the center of the circle result from this force law?

CHAPTER 3

THE TWO-BODY PROBLEM

In this chapter we shall assume that the masses involved are spherically symmetrical and are homogeneous in concentric layers. According to the result shown in Section 1–5, they will then attract one another as if the mass of each were concentrated at the center of the sphere. In other words, they behave gravitationally like two mass particles at a distance apart equal to the distance between centers. The two masses will be assumed to be sufficiently isolated from other masses in the universe so that the only force acting is the inverse square force of their mutual attraction along the line joining the centers. In astronomical applications the distances between the spheres will be large compared with the diameters of the spheres themselves.

A discussion of the dynamics of the resulting motion of the two masses brings to the fore two problems which are central in celestial mechanics.

(1) Given the position and velocity in space of a mass point as a function of the time, to find the elements of the orbit.

(2) Given the orbital elements, or parameters, defining the shape and orientation of the dynamical path, to find the position of the mass point in space at a given instant.

In this chapter we shall consider the second of these problems. The first will be taken up in some detail in Chapter 4. It is by far the more difficult.

3–1 Motion of the center of mass. Let O, Fig. 3–1, be an origin defining an inertial system in which Newton's laws of motion hold. Let the positions of the two masses be given by the vectors $\mathbf{r}_1$ and $\mathbf{r}_2$; and let $\mathbf{R}$ be the position vector of the center of mass of the pair. Furthermore let $\mathbf{r}$ be the position vector of m_2 relative to m_1.

By Newton's law of gravitation, the force on m_1 due to m_2 is

$$\frac{k^2 m_1 m_2}{r^2} \mathbf{u}_r;$$

that on m_2 due to m_1 is

$$-\frac{k^2 m_1 m_2}{r^2} \mathbf{u}_r.$$

Here $\mathbf{u}_r$ is a unit vector in the direction of $\mathbf{r}$, and k^2 is the constant of gravitation. The significance of the notation k^2 rather than the customary G for the gravitational constant will become apparent in the following discussion.

The equations of motion are

$$m_1\ddot{\mathbf{r}}_1 = + \frac{k^2 m_1 m_2}{r^3}\,\mathbf{r}, \tag{3-1}$$

$$m_2\ddot{\mathbf{r}}_2 = - \frac{k^2 m_1 m_2}{r^3}\,\mathbf{r}. \tag{3-2}$$

Adding Eqs. (3-1) and (3-2) and integrating twice, we obtain

$$m_1\mathbf{r}_1 + m_2\mathbf{r}_2 = \mathbf{c}_1 t + \mathbf{c}_2, \tag{3-3}$$

where $\mathbf{c}_1$ and $\mathbf{c}_2$ are vector constants. But the left-hand side of Eq. (3-3) is $M\mathbf{R}$ by the definition of the center of mass [Eq. (1-31)]. Therefore

$$\mathbf{R} = \frac{\mathbf{c}_1 t}{M} + \frac{\mathbf{c}_2}{M}, \tag{3-4}$$

a result which states that the *center of mass moves uniformly on a straight line in space*. Here M is the total mass of the system. This result is in conformity with Eq. (1-34) in which $\mathbf{F} = 0$ because no external forces are assumed to act on the system.

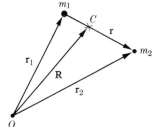

Fig. 3-1. Center of mass motion in a two-body problem.

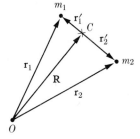

Fig. 3-2. Position vectors relative to the center of mass.

3-2 Relative motion. The motions of m_1 and m_2 relative to the center of mass can be found in the following way. Let $\mathbf{r}_1 = \mathbf{R} + \mathbf{r}_1'$ and $\mathbf{r}_2 = \mathbf{R} + \mathbf{r}_2'$, where $\mathbf{r}_1'$ and $\mathbf{r}_2'$ denote the position vectors of m_1 and m_2, respectively, with respect to the mass center C (Fig. 3-2). Then $\mathbf{r} = \mathbf{r}_2' - \mathbf{r}_1'$ and, since $\ddot{\mathbf{R}} = 0$, $m_1\ddot{\mathbf{r}}_1 = m_1\ddot{\mathbf{r}}_1'$ and $m_2\ddot{\mathbf{r}}_2 = m_2\ddot{\mathbf{r}}_2'$. Therefore Eqs. (3-1) and (3-2) become

$$m_1\ddot{\mathbf{r}}_1' = + \frac{k^2 m_1 m_2(\mathbf{r}_2' - \mathbf{r}_1')}{r^3}, \tag{3-5}$$

$$m_2\ddot{\mathbf{r}}_2' = - \frac{k^2 m_1 m_2(\mathbf{r}_2' - \mathbf{r}_1')}{r^3}. \tag{3-6}$$

But $m_1\mathbf{r}_1' + m_2\mathbf{r}_2' = 0$, and $\mathbf{r}_2'$ can be eliminated from Eq. (3–5) and $\mathbf{r}_1'$ can be eliminated from Eq. (3–6). The resulting equations are

$$m_1\ddot{\mathbf{r}}_1' = -k^2 m_1 m_2 \left[1 + \frac{m_1}{m_2}\right]\frac{\mathbf{r}_1'}{r^3}, \qquad (3\text{–}7)$$

$$m_2\ddot{\mathbf{r}}_2' = -k^2 m_1 m_2 \left[1 + \frac{m_2}{m_1}\right]\frac{\mathbf{r}_2'}{r^3}. \qquad (3\text{–}8)$$

But, since

$$r = \frac{M}{m_2}\,r_1' = \frac{M}{m_1}\,r_2',$$

we may write

$$\ddot{\mathbf{r}}_1' = -\frac{k^2 M}{r^3}\,\mathbf{r}_1' = -k^2 \left(\frac{m_2^3}{M^2}\right)\frac{\mathbf{r}_1'}{r_1'^3}, \qquad (3\text{–}9)$$

$$\ddot{\mathbf{r}}_2' = -\frac{k^2 M}{r^3}\,\mathbf{r}_2' = -k^2 \left(\frac{m_1^3}{M^2}\right)\frac{\mathbf{r}_2'}{r_2'^3}. \qquad (3\text{–}10)$$

These give the accelerations of m_1 and m_2 *relative to the center of mass.* It is clear that they are of the same form as Eqs. (3–1) and (3–2) with adjusted effective masses replacing m_2 and m_1, respectively.

Ostensibly we could find the positions of m_1 and m_2 at any instant by solving Eqs. (3–9) and (3–10) and by knowing the constants $\mathbf{c}_1$ and $\mathbf{c}_2$ of Eq. (3–4). The latter are not known, however, and there is no way to determine them absolutely because they are defined with respect to an origin fixed in space. Therefore in all that follows we shall be restricted to a solution for the relative motion of one mass with respect to another.

Let m_1 be considered the origin of the two-body system. Then from Eqs. (3–9) and (3–10) we obtain

$$\ddot{\mathbf{r}} = -\frac{k^2 M}{r^3}\,\mathbf{r}, \qquad (3\text{–}11)$$

where $\mathbf{r}$ is the relative radius vector. This expresses the acceleration of m_2 in its motion around m_1. In the planetary system, for example, we take m_1 to be the sun and m_2 to be a planet. In the case of an earth satellite, m_1 would be the mass of the earth and m_2 that of the satellite.

For computational purposes it is convenient to express the equations of relative motion in cartesian form. In terms of the unit vectors $\mathbf{i}$, $\mathbf{j}$, $\mathbf{k}$, we have $\mathbf{r} = x\mathbf{i} + y\mathbf{j} + z\mathbf{k}$. Hence Eq. (3–11) takes the form

$$\begin{aligned} \ddot{x} &= -k^2 M x (x^2 + y^2 + z^2)^{-3/2}, \\ \ddot{y} &= -k^2 M y (x^2 + y^2 + z^2)^{-3/2}, \\ \ddot{z} &= -k^2 M z (x^2 + y^2 + z^2)^{-3/2}. \end{aligned} \qquad (3\text{–}12)$$

The orientation of the xyz-axes in space, for astronomical purposes, will be considered in a later section.

The original differential equations of motion, Eqs. (3–1) and (3–2), in vector form each correspond to three second-order equations. The solution of each equation in cartesian coordinates introduces two constants of integration, which would necessarily be fixed by the initial conditions. There are obviously twelve such constants in the original system. By ignoring the motion of the center of gravity [Eq. (3–4)] we have reduced the number of constants by six. Hence the solution of Eqs. (3–12) will result in six remaining constants. If we know the position (three coordinates) and the velocity (three components) at any one instant, these six integration constants can be found. In astronomical applications, however, these data are not generally available. One must rely on the geometric coordinates of the moving mass, for at least three instants of time, and must deduce from these the required velocity components. Orbit theory has this as its central problem. We shall discuss it in Chapter 4.

3–3 The integral of areas. The relative motion of m_2 around m_1 is indeed a central force motion as defined in Chapter 2. Therefore the areal velocity, according to Eq. (2–1), is constant. That is,

$$\dot{\mathbf{A}} = \tfrac{1}{2}(\mathbf{r} \times \mathbf{v}) = \tfrac{1}{2}h\mathbf{u}_A, \tag{3–13}$$

where $\mathbf{u}_A$ is a unit vector perpendicular to the orbital plane defined by $\mathbf{r}$ and $\mathbf{v}$ and has a constant direction.

In cartesian coordinates we have, by Eqs. (1–14), the components of areal velocity

$$\tfrac{1}{2}(y\dot{z} - z\dot{y}) = \tfrac{1}{2}c_1,$$
$$\tfrac{1}{2}(z\dot{x} - x\dot{z}) = \tfrac{1}{2}c_2, \tag{3–14}$$
$$\tfrac{1}{2}(x\dot{y} - y\dot{x}) = \tfrac{1}{2}c_3,$$

where c_1, c_2, and c_3 are constants which are related to h by

$$\sqrt{c_1^2 + c_2^2 + c_3^2} = h. \tag{3–15}$$

Given the initial coordinates and velocity components of m_2, we can determine the constants c_1, c_2, and c_3. We shall assume here that they are known. They must, however, be related to the elements of the orbit.

In Fig. 3–3 let the orbital plane intersect the xy-plane in the line $N'ON$. This is called the *line of nodes*. If m_2 passes from below to above the xy-plane at N, we speak of the point N as the *ascending node* of the orbit; the point N' is the *descending node*.

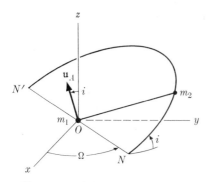

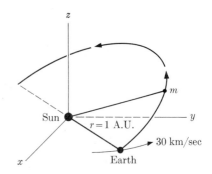

FIG. 3-3. Orientation of orbit in space.

FIG. 3-4. Motion of the earth and a mass particle.

The angle Ω, the *longitude of the ascending node*, is the angle measured counterclockwise from the positive x-axis to the line ON. It takes values from $0°$ to $360°$. The angle i, the *inclination* of the orbit, is the angle between the orbital plane and the xy-plane as shown. It is also the angle between the z-axis and the vector $\mathbf{u}_A$. The inclination may vary from $0°$ to $180°$.

In terms of Ω and i, the unit vector

$$\mathbf{u}_A = (\sin i \sin \Omega)\mathbf{i} + (-\sin i \cos \Omega)\mathbf{j} + (\cos i)\mathbf{k}. \qquad (3\text{-}16)$$

Therefore the areal velocity is

$$\dot{\mathbf{A}} = (\tfrac{1}{2}h \sin i \sin \Omega)\mathbf{i} + (-\tfrac{1}{2}h \sin i \cos \Omega)\mathbf{j} + (\tfrac{1}{2}h \cos i)\mathbf{k}. \qquad (3\text{-}17)$$

Comparing Eqs. (3-14) and (3-17), we see that

$$c_1 = h \sin i \sin \Omega,$$
$$c_2 = -h \sin i \cos \Omega, \qquad (3\text{-}18)$$
$$c_3 = h \cos i,$$
$$\sqrt{c_1^2 + c_2^2 + c_3^2} = h.$$

Given the values of c_1, c_2, and c_3 as determined from the initial conditions, we find that Eqs. (3-18) suffice to determine the Ω and i. Specification of these elements orients the orbital plane in space with respect to the cartesian coordinate system.

EXAMPLE. Consider the earth to be a point mass revolving around the sun (Fig. 3-4) at a speed of 30 km·sec^{-1}. The xy-plane is the plane of its orbit. The earth's mean distance is 1 *astronomical unit* (A.U.) which is 1.5×10^8 km. At $x = 0.707$, $y = 0.707$, and $z = 0$(A.U.), let a mass particle m be projected perpendicular to the xy-plane with a speed of 15 km·sec^{-1}. What is the inclination i and the longitude of the node Ω for the resulting orbit? Here

$$\dot{x} = -21 \text{ km·sec}^{-1};$$
$$\dot{y} = 21 \text{ km·sec}^{-1};$$
$$\dot{z} = 15 \text{ km·sec}^{-1}.$$

Hence, by Eqs. (3–14) and (3–15),

$$c_1 = 1.59 \times 10^9 = -c_2,$$
$$c_3 = 4.46 \times 10^9,$$
$$h = 5.00 \times 10^9 \text{ km}^2\text{·sec}^{-1}.$$

From these values and Eqs. (3–18), we find that

$$\Omega = 45° \qquad \text{and} \qquad i = 26°52'.$$

PROBLEMS

1. A projectile is launched 500 km above the earth's surface at longitude 45° E and latitude 30° N (Fig. 3–5) in such a way that

$$-\dot{x} = \dot{y} = \dot{z},$$

and its resultant speed is 7.6 km·sec^{-1}. The earth's radius is 6378 km. Find Ω and i for the subsequent trajectory of the projectile. Will the projectile orbit the earth? [Consider the earth a sphere and ignore its rotation.]

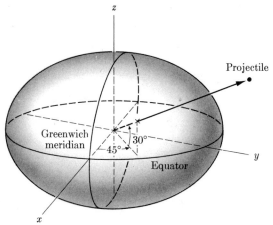

FIG. 3–5. Projectile around the earth.

2. A meteor is observed in the earth's atmosphere when the earth is at

$$x = 0.63593 \text{ A.U.,} \qquad y = -0.79094 \text{ A.U.,} \qquad z = 0.$$

At the same time the velocity components of the meteor are

$$\dot{x} = -32, \qquad \dot{y} = -5.3, \qquad \dot{z} = -3.1 \text{ km·sec}^{-1}.$$

Find the speed of the meteor and the values of h, Ω, and i for its orbit around the sun. Here the coordinates and velocity components are referred to a set of axes with the sun as the origin and the plane of the ecliptic as the xy-plane.

3–4 Elements of the orbit from initial position and velocity. Having established the orientation of the orbital plane in space through the constants c_1, c_2, and c_3 [Eqs. (3–14)], we now turn our attention to the size and shape of the orbit and its orientation in the plane of motion. The mathematical analysis required for this is given in Section 2–5. There it was shown that the path would be a conic section with the effective mass M at the center of force, namely the focus of the conic. In the two-body problem $M = m_1 + m_2$. We shall use $k^2 = G$ for the gravitational constant. In the problem at hand, m_1 is located at the focus of the conic, while m_2 is the moving mass.

The elements to be found are

a, the semimajor or semitransverse axis in the case
    of the ellipse or hyperbola, respectively; or
q, the distance from focus to vertex of the parabola;
e, the eccentricity;
ω, the argument of perihelion; this is the angle in the orbital plane
    from the line of nodes to the perihelion point;
T, the time of perihelion passage.

We have used the word "perihelion" here in a general sense, meaning the point of the orbit closest to the focus. In the case of a planet moving around the sun, perihelion is the correct designation for this point. In the case of an earth satellite, the corresponding term is *perigee*. For a satellite of Jupiter, the term would be *peri-Jove*.

Figure 3–6 illustrates an orbit in its relationship to the cartesian system of axes. The angle f, *measured from perihelion in the direction of motion of* m_2, is called the *true anomaly*. The equation of the conic in which m_2 moves can be written

$$r = \frac{p}{1 + e \cos f}, \qquad (3\text{–}19)$$

where, by comparison with Eq. (2–23) and Fig. 2–3, it is evident that $f = \theta - \theta_0$.

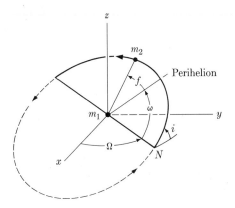

FIG. 3-6. True anomaly and argument of perihelion.

Let x_0, y_0, z_0 be the coordinates and $\dot{x}_0$, $\dot{y}_0$, $\dot{z}_0$ be the velocity components of m_2 at time $t = 0$. Then Eqs. (3-14) and (3-18) become

$$c_1 = y_0\dot{z}_0 - z_0\dot{y}_0 = h \sin i \sin \Omega,$$

$$c_2 = z_0\dot{x}_0 - x_0\dot{z}_0 = -h \sin i \cos \Omega, \qquad (3\text{-}20)$$

$$c_3 = x_0\dot{y}_0 - y_0\dot{x}_0 = h \cos i,$$

and these equations yield Ω, i, and h as indicated in Section 3-3.

Since the initial position $r_0 = (x_0^2 + y_0^2 + z_0^2)^{1/2}$ and initial speed $v_0 = (\dot{x}_0^2 + \dot{y}_0^2 + \dot{z}_0^2)^{1/2}$ are known, we have, by Eqs. (2-33) and (2-38),

$$\frac{1}{a} = \frac{2}{r_0} - \frac{v_0^2}{k^2 M} \qquad \text{for the ellipse,} \qquad (3\text{-}21)$$

$$\frac{1}{a} = \frac{v_0^2}{k^2 M} - \frac{2}{r_0} \qquad \text{for the hyperbola,} \qquad (3\text{-}22)$$

and

$$q = \frac{h^2}{2k^2 M} \qquad \text{for the parabola.} \qquad (3\text{-}23)$$

From the above values and the value of h, we can determine the eccentricity by

$$e^2 = 1 \mp \frac{h^2}{k^2 M a}, \qquad (3\text{-}24)$$

where the minus sign is to be used for the ellipse and the plus sign for the hyperbola.

The angle ω may be calculated in the following way. For convenience, we set $f + \omega = u$. Then we have (Fig. 3–6)

$$r \cos u = x \cos \Omega + y \sin \Omega,$$

$$r \sin u = (-x \sin \Omega + y \cos \Omega)\cos i + z \sin i. \tag{3–25}$$

Since Ω and i are known from Eqs. (3–20), and r_0 is known from the initial conditions, Eqs. (3–25) yield u_0 for the time $t = 0$.

Now from Eq. (3–19)

$$e \cos f = \frac{p}{r} - 1 \tag{3–26}$$

and, by differentiation with respect to the time,

$$-(e \sin f)\dot{f} = -\frac{p}{r^2}\dot{r}. \tag{3–27}$$

But $r^2\dot{f} \equiv r^2\dot{\theta} = h$ which is known. Furthermore, since

$$r^2 = x^2 + y^2 + z^2,$$

we have

$$r\dot{r} = x\dot{x} + y\dot{y} + z\dot{z}.$$

Hence Eq. (3–27) can be written, for $t = 0$,

$$e \sin f_0 = \frac{p}{h}\left[\frac{x_0\dot{x}_0 + y_0\dot{y}_0 + z_0\dot{z}_0}{r_0}\right]. \tag{3–28}$$

Dividing Eq. (3–28) by (3–26), we find, at $t = 0$,

$$\tan f_0 = \frac{p}{h}\left[\frac{x_0\dot{x}_0 + y_0\dot{y}_0 + z_0\dot{z}_0}{p - r_0}\right]. \tag{3–29}$$

Thus from u_0, as computed by Eqs. (3–25), and f_0 as given above, we find the argument of perihelion

$$\omega = u_0 - f_0. \tag{3–30}$$

It should be noted that in Eq. (3–29) we use $p = a(1 - e^2)$ for the ellipse and $p = a(e^2 - 1)$ for the hyperbola. For the parabola, $p = 2q$.

To determine the quadrant of f_0, we note the sign of the quantity $x_0\dot{x}_0 + y_0\dot{y}_0 + z_0\dot{z}_0$. Since this is equal to $r_0\dot{r}_0$ and $r_0 > 0$, its algebraic sign will depend on $\dot{r}_0$. If $\dot{r}_0 > 0$, that is, the radius vector is increasing, $0 < f_0 < \pi$. If $\dot{r}_0 < 0$, $\pi < f_0 < 2\pi$. The quadrant for ω can be calculated when that for u_0 has been established.

EXAMPLE. To illustrate the ideas described above, consider the problem sketched in Fig. 3–4 of the previous section. The initial position and speed are

$$x_0 = 0.707 \text{ A.U.}, \qquad \dot{x}_0 = -21 \text{ km·sec}^{-1},$$
$$y_0 = 0.707 \text{ A.U.}, \qquad \dot{y}_0 = 21 \text{ km·sec}^{-1},$$
$$z_0 = 0 \text{ A.U.}, \qquad \dot{z}_0 = 15 \text{ km·sec}^{-1}.$$

From these data and the information given in the example cited, we have

$$r_0 = 1 \text{ A.U.} = 1.5 \times 10^{13} \text{ cm},$$
$$v_0 = 33.3 \times 10^5 \text{ cm·sec}^{-1},$$
$$h = 5 \times 10^{19} \text{ cm}^2\text{·sec}^{-1},$$
$$\Omega = 45°,$$
$$i = 26°52'.$$

The attracting center is the sun, mass 2×10^{33} gm, and

$$k^2 \cong 6.7 \times 10^{-8} \text{ dyne·cm}^2\text{·gm}^{-2}.$$

Hence the power of the force center is

$$k^2 M = 1.34 \times 10^{26} \text{ cm}^3\text{·sec}^{-2}.$$

Therefore, from Eq. (3–21)

$$\frac{1}{a} = \frac{2}{1.5 \times 10^{13}} - \frac{1.11 \times 10^{13}}{1.34 \times 10^{26}} = 0.50 \times 10^{-13} \text{ cm}^{-1},$$

and the semimajor axis of the orbit is

$$a = 2 \times 10^{13} \text{cm} = 1.33 \text{ A.U.}$$

From Eq. (3–24) we have

$$e^2 = 1 - \frac{25 \times 10^{38}}{1.34 \times 10^{26} \times 2 \times 10^{13}} = 0.067$$

and, therefore, $e = 0.258$.

Application of Eqs. (3–25) will show that $\tan u_0 = 0$ and hence $u_0 = 0$. Furthermore, from Eq. (3–29), we find $\tan f_0 = 0$ and hence $f_0 = 0$. The mass particle was, therefore, launched at perihelion as is evident from elementary considerations. Let the reader demonstrate this. We conclude that $\omega = 0$.

The final element, the time of perihelion passage T, is of course the launching time $t = 0$ in our example.

Problems

1. In a cartesian coordinate system with origin at the sun, an object has the following position and velocity at $t = 0$:

$$x_0 = -0.08084 \text{ A.U.}, \qquad \dot{x}_0 = +0.02212 \text{ A.U./day},$$

$$y_0 = -0.45844 \text{ A.U.}, \qquad \dot{y}_0 = -0.00355 \text{ A.U./day},$$

$$z_0 = -0.03038 \text{ A.U.}, \qquad \dot{z}_0 = -0.00228 \text{ A.U./day}.$$

Find the elements of its orbit. Sketch the orbit.

2. When free of the earth's gravitational field, a space vehicle moves around the sun under the sole influence of the latter. At $t = 0$, the vehicle is located at

$$x_0 = 1.2 \text{ A.U.},$$

$$y_0 = 0,$$

$$z_0 = 0,$$

and has a velocity given by

$$\dot{x}_0 = 25.0 \text{ km·sec}^{-1},$$

$$\dot{y}_0 = 25.0 \text{ km·sec}^{-1},$$

$$\dot{z}_0 = 18.7 \text{ km·sec}^{-1}.$$

Find the elements of its orbit. If the motion is periodic, what is the period? What is the areal velocity constant? What is the total energy in this orbit?

3. Assuming that the earth is a sphere of radius 6378 km and mass 6×10^{27} gm, calculate the power of this planet as a center of force. Suppose that a satellite is launched from the equatorial plane at a height of 1000 km above the earth's surface and parallel to it. The initial velocity vector makes an angle of 45° with the equatorial plane. With what speed must the vehicle be launched in order that it move in an ellipse of $e = 0.2$? What are the elements of the elliptic orbit? [*Hint:* Choose the xy-axes in the plane of the equator and the z-axis pointing toward the north pole.]

3–5. Properties of the motion. The foregoing discussion together with that in Section 2–5 reveals several properties of two-body motion which should be emphasized. At a given distance r from the force center O (Fig. 3–7) the *speed in all elliptic orbits of the same major axis* is the same; only the direction of the velocity vector differs. This is clear from Eq. (2–33) in which it is evident that the speed at a given value of r depends only on a.

At the same distance r from the force center, the speed in a parabolic orbit is

$$v_p = k\sqrt{2M/r},$$

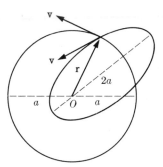

FIG. 3–7. Velocity vectors in orbits of different shape.

and that in the circular orbit is

$$v_c = k\sqrt{M/r}.$$

These results were deduced in Section 2–5. Thus the circular and parabolic velocities at a given point, a distance r from the center of force, mark the lower and upper limits, respectively, for the speed in elliptic orbits *passing through the same point*. When a mass is projected at **r** with a given velocity **v**, lying between these limits, the path it will follow will depend on the direction of **v**.

In elliptic motion Kepler's third law as expressed in Eq. (2–34) holds, namely,

$$P = \frac{2\pi a^{3/2}}{k\sqrt{M}}, \tag{3–31}$$

where it is clear that the period is independent of all orbital elements except the semimajor axis. In the application here, we note again that $M = m_1 + m_2$ which is the total mass of the two-body system.

PROBLEMS

1. A satellite around the earth is to have a 24-hour period. On the assumption that the earth is a sphere of mass 6×10^{27} gm and radius 6378 km, calculate the semimajor axis of its orbit. What projection speed will be required to make the orbit circular? [The mass of the satellite is negligible compared with that of the earth.]

2. An earth satellite is launched at a height of 622 km above the earth's surface and parallel to it. Later its apogee height is measured as 3622 km. On the assumption that the earth is spherical, what are the values of a and e for the satellite's orbit? What is the areal velocity constant? What is the speed of the satellite at apogee? What would the launching velocity have to be in order that the satellite escape from the earth?

3. The semimajor axis, a, of a planetary orbit is sometimes referred to as the "mean distance" of the planet from the sun. Calculate the mean value of the radius vector $\mathbf{r}$ with respect to the true anomaly f in the orbit. Calculate also the mean distance as a function of the time. Is the statement "mean distance" a precise or an approximate statement of the situation? What is your interpretation of the term "mean distance"? [*Hint:* Use Eq. (3–19) and the fact that $r^2\dot{f} = h$.]

3–6 The constant of gravitation. The constant of gravitation G as determined by laboratory measurements and in the cgs system is

$$G = (6.668 \pm 0.005) \times 10^{-8} \text{ dyne·cm}^2\text{·gm}^{-2}. \qquad (3\text{–}32)$$

This is obviously known to an accuracy of only one part in about 1300. Such accuracy is not sufficient for astronomical purposes. Instead it has been customary from the time of Gauss (circa 1800) to adopt a value in more appropriate units for describing the dynamical properties of the solar system.

Equation (3–31) is useful in defining the astronomical constant k, called the *Gaussian gravitational constant*. Its value is

$$k = 0.01720209895. \qquad (3\text{–}33)$$

The units on which this value is based are: (a) the mean solar day as the unit for time; (b) the astronomical unit (A.U.) as the unit for distance; and (c) the mass of the sun as the unit of mass. In Eq. (3–31), written as $P = 2\pi a^{3/2}/k\sqrt{1 + m_2}$ and applied to the earth-moon system, we take $P = 365.2563835$ mean solar days, $a = 1$ A.U., and $m_2 = 1/354710$ solar masses. These were the values originally used by Gauss.* Their substitution yields the value of k given in Eq. (3–33).

The Gaussian constant obviously depends upon the values of a and m_2 adopted for the earth-moon system. Since the time of Gauss, these have been improved considerably. Rather than change k, however, it has been customary to keep k fixed and to modify the unit of distance so that Eq. (3–31) will always be satisfied.

The mean daily motion of a planet in its orbit is defined to be $n = 2\pi/P$, where P is the period. From Eq. (3–31), therefore, we have

$$n = \frac{2\pi}{P} = \frac{k\sqrt{1 + m_2}}{a^{3/2}}. \qquad (3\text{–}34)$$

If P is in mean solar days, n is in radians per day. For convenience in later applications, Eq. (3–34) may be written $n^2 a^3 = k^2(1 + m_2)$.

---

* C. F. Gauss, *Theoria Motus Corporum Coelestium*, translated by C. H. Davis. Boston: Little, Brown and Company, 1857, p. 2.

In many problems it is convenient to use a system of units in which $k = 1$. To obtain this, we set $a = 1$, $1 + m_2 = 1$ in Eq. (3–34), and adjust the unit of time appropriately. For example, if $a = 1$ A.U., $1 + m_2 = 1$ solar mass, and $k = 1$, we take the unit of time as $365.2563835/2\pi$ or 58.1323589 mean solar days. This would be a *canonical system* of units for the earth-sun two-body problem. Obviously, in such a system of units $n = 1$. For purely theoretical investigations canonical units are especially useful.

PROBLEMS

The equation of motion of one body around a center of force of power k^2M is given in Eq. (3–11) as $\ddot{\mathbf{r}} + (k^2M/r^3)\mathbf{r} = 0$. When applied to heliocentric motion $M \cong 2 \times 10^{33}$ gm; when applied to geocentric motion, $M \cong 6 \times 10^{27}$ gm. If r is in cm and t is in seconds, $k^2 = 6.67 \times 10^{-8}$.

1. What unit of time, τ, would be necessary to reduce the above equation to the form $d^2\mathbf{r}/d\tau^2 + \mathbf{r}/r^3 = 0$ for heliocentric motion if r is in A.U.? Compare it with the value 58.1323 mean solar days mentioned in the text.

2. What unit of time, τ, would be required to reduce the equation of motion to the same form, but for geocentric motion, with r in units of earth radii? (1 earth radius $= 6378$ km.)

3–7 Kepler's equation. Motion in an elliptic orbit is by far the most important in the solar system. In this and the following sections, therefore, we shall consider the problem: we are given the elements a, e, i, ω, Ω, T of an elliptic orbit, to find the polar coordinates of the moving mass at any time t. These coordinates are the radius vector, r, and the true anomaly, f. An auxiliary relation known as Kepler's equation is useful in this connection.

Consider the elliptic orbit shown in Fig. 3–8 and an auxiliary circle whose diameter is the major axis of the ellipse. The mass m_1 is at the focus F,

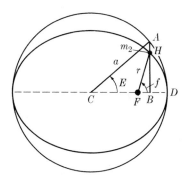

FIG. 3–8. Eccentric circle and eccentric anomaly.

and the moving mass m_2 traverses the ellipse in the counterclockwise direction. Let BA be a perpendicular to CD through the position of the mass m_2. Then we define an auxiliary variable, E, *the eccentric anomaly*, as shown in the figure. As f, the true anomaly, changes by 2π radians, so does E.

It is clear from Fig. 3–8 and the properties of the ellipse that

$$r \cos f = a \cos E - ae, \qquad r \sin f = a \sin E - HA. \qquad (3\text{–}35)$$

Furthermore, it can be shown that

$$\frac{BH}{BA} = \frac{b}{a} = \sqrt{1 - e^2},$$

where b is the semiminor axis of the ellipse. Therefore,

$$HA = BA - BH = BA(1 - \sqrt{1 - e^2}).$$

Hence the second of Eqs. (3–35) can be written

$$r \sin f = a \sin E \sqrt{1 - e^2}. \qquad (3\text{–}36)$$

Squaring Eq. (3–36) and adding to the square of the first of Eqs. (3–35) yields, after some reduction,

$$r = a(1 - e \cos E). \qquad (3\text{–}37)$$

Once we find E as a function of the time, the value of r follows from Eq. (3–37).

To find E as a function of t, we shall use a geometric argument. By elementary calculus it can be shown (Fig. 3–8) that

$$\frac{\text{area } BDH}{\text{area } BDA} = \frac{b}{a} = \sqrt{1 - e^2}. \qquad (3\text{–}38)$$

But area $BDH =$ area $DFH -$ area BFH and area $BDA =$ area $DCA -$ area BCA. Furthermore, by Kepler's second law [Eqs. (2–2) and (2–31)],

$$\text{area } DFH = \tfrac{1}{2}na^2\sqrt{1 - e^2}\,(t - T), \qquad (3\text{–}39)$$

where n is the mean daily motion given by Eq. (3–34), T is the time of perihelion passage, and t is the instant under consideration. Hence we may write Eq. (3–38) as

$$\sqrt{1 - e^2} = \frac{\tfrac{1}{2}na^2\sqrt{1 - e^2}\,(t - T) - \tfrac{1}{2}r^2 \sin f \cos f}{\tfrac{1}{2}a^2 E - \tfrac{1}{2}a^2 \sin E \cos E}.$$

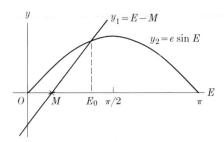

FIG. 3-9. Graphical solution of Kepler's equation.

By using Eqs. (3–35) and (3–36) we may reduce this to

$$n(t - T) = E - e \sin E. \tag{3-40}$$

This transcendental equation in E is called *Kepler's equation*. The quantity $n(t - T) = M$ is defined to be the *mean anomaly*. It is the angle which the radius vector would have described if it had been moving uniformly with the average rate $2\pi/P$. When $t - T$ is given, M is defined and Eq. (3–40) can be solved for E. We leave as an exercise for the reader to show that Kepler's equation can be obtained directly by integrating the energy equation for an elliptic orbit after substituting for r the new variable E given by Eq. (3–37).

A first approximation to the solution of Kepler's equation can be found graphically. We write Eq. (3–40) as

$$E - M = e \sin E, \tag{3-41}$$

where M is given and E is to be found. Let $y_1 = E - M$ and $y_2 = e \sin E$. Then we plot the two curves as shown in Fig. 3-9. By Eq. (3–41), it is apparent that the abscissa of their intersection is a first approximation, E_0, for the eccentric anomaly.

When e is small, it is obvious that E does not differ greatly from M at any instant. A series expansion then can be used profitably to obtain E to the desired accuracy. This may be obtained as follows. To a first approximation $E \sim M$. Therefore we may write as a second approximation

$$E_1 = M + e \sin M$$

which is an approximation to the first order in e. Resubstituting this in Kepler's equation, we have

$$E_2 = M + e \sin E_1 = M + e \sin (M + e \sin M).$$

But the right-hand side can be written

$$M + e \sin M \cos (e \sin M) + e \cos M \sin (e \sin M). \qquad (3\text{--}42)$$

The terms in parentheses are small, and we may write

$$\cos (e \sin M) = 1 - \frac{e^2 \sin^2 M}{2!} + \cdots,$$

$$\sin (e \sin M) = e \sin M - \frac{e^3 \sin^3 M}{3!} + \cdots.$$

Substituting in Eq. (3–42) and collecting like powers of e, we obtain as a third approximation

$$E_2 = M + e \sin M + \frac{e^2}{2} \sin 2M + \cdots \qquad (3\text{--}43)$$

Proceeding in this way, we can expand E into a power series in e with coefficients of the form $\sin pM$ $(p = 0, 1, 2, \ldots)$ and of the desired accuracy. A development of the series to the sixth order in e is given elsewhere.* For our purposes, we shall write the series to the terms in e^3 only. Thus

$$E = M + e \sin M + \frac{e^2}{2} \sin 2M + \frac{e^3}{8} (3 \sin 3M - \sin M) + \cdots \qquad (3\text{--}44)$$

When e exceeds about 0.2, the series developed above converges too slowly to be useful. In this case an approximate value of E can be obtained by the graphical analysis mentioned above and then corrected differentially. Suppose the approximate value of E is E_0. Then by Kepler's equation, we can compute a corresponding mean anomaly

$$M_0 = E_0 - e \sin E_0. \qquad (3\text{--}45)$$

Now M is a continuous function of E, say $M = \phi(E)$, which may be expanded into a Taylor's series about the point $E = E_0$. Thus

$$M = \phi(E_0) + \phi'(E_0)(E - E_0) + \frac{\phi''(E_0)}{2!} (E - E_0)^2 + \cdots, \qquad (3\text{--}46)$$

where primes denote the derivatives of $\phi(E)$ with respect to E. Let $E - E_0 = \Delta E_0$ and neglect powers 2 and greater in Eq. (3–46). Further-

* F. R. Moulton, *Celestial Mechanics*. New York: The Macmillan Company, 1914, p. 169.

more, $\phi(E_0) = M_0$ is given by Eq. (3–45). Then to this order of approximation

$$M - M_0 = \phi'(E_0)\,\Delta E_0 = (1 - e\cos E_0)\,\Delta E_0.$$

Solving for ΔE_0, we have

$$\Delta E_0 = \frac{M - M_0}{1 - e\cos E_0}, \qquad (3\text{–}47)$$

and thus we find a new value of E,

$$E_1 = E_0 + \Delta E_0.$$

The method can be reapplied using E_1 in Eq. (3–47) in place of E_0. Repetition will yield as accurate a value as may be desired.

Well over a hundred methods have been devised for the solution of Kepler's equation. The advent of high-speed computing machines has expedited the use of iterative methods.* For obtaining approximate starting values, tables such as those by Bauschinger are useful.†

Questions of convergence of the series for E given in Eq. (3–44) and in other expansions whose coefficients are trigonometric functions of M are treated elsewhere.‡ For example, it can be shown that when $e > 0.6627\ldots$, the expansion of E in powers of e does not converge for all values of M. When e is very nearly 1, the series method of finding E is practically useless. The graphical and successive approximation method, however, is still valid and useful. Other analytical methods are available. A discussion of these will be given in Section 3–11.

EXAMPLE 1. With $M = 62°$ and $e = 0.1$, find E. From Bauschinger's *Tafeln* p. 67, we find $E - M = 5°.28$. Hence, $E = 67°16'.8$. Using Eq. (3–44), we find

$$E = 62° + \frac{180}{\pi}\,\{0.088295 + 0.005 \times 0.82904 + 0.000125 \times (-1.19654)\}$$

to terms of order e^3. The factor $180/\pi$ is necessary to reduce the terms in radians to degrees. We find, finally, by the series method $E = 67°17'.3$.

---

* See, for example, P. Herget, *The Computation of Orbits.* Cincinnati, Ohio: Privately printed, 1948, p. 33. Also D. Brouwer and G. M. Clemence, *Methods of Celestial Mechanics.* New York and London: Academic Press, 1961, p. 84 ff.

† J. Bauschinger, *Tafeln zur Theoretischen Astronomie, Zweite Auflage.* Leipzig: Wilhelm-Engelmann, 1934, Table 11.

‡ See H. C. Plummer, *An Introductory Treatise on Dynamical Astronomy.* Cambridge: Cambridge University Press, 1918.

EXAMPLE 2. With the same data as above, we shall use a successive approximation method. We "guess" $E_0 = 62°$ and find from Kepler's equation

$$M_0 = 62° - 0.1 \times \frac{180}{\pi} \times \sin 62° = 56°.9411.$$

Then by Eq. (3–47), we find

$$\Delta E_0 = \frac{5.0589}{1 - 0.04695} = 5°.3081,$$

and hence

$$E_1 = 62° + 5°.3055 = 67°.3081.$$

Insertion of E_1 into Kepler's equation yields

$$M_1 = 67°.3055 - 0.1 \times \frac{180}{\pi} \times \sin 67°.3055 = 62°.0221.$$

Reapplication of the method yields

$$\Delta E_1 = \frac{-0.0221}{1 - 0.03858} = -0°.0230.$$

Hence

$$E_2 = 67°.28511, \qquad M_2 = 61°.9999.$$

The last value is very close to the given value of M_2. Further correction of E_2 results in a very small change. The value of E_3 becomes $67°17'.11$. This we shall assume to be as accurate a value as desired.

PROBLEMS

1. The energy equation for two-body motion of m_2 around m_1 can be written

$$\dot{r}^2 = \frac{n^2 a^2}{r^2} [a^2 e^2 - (a - r)^2].$$

Using the change of variable from r to E defined by $r = a(1 - e \cos E)$, deduce Kepler's equation by direct integration.

2. The planet Mercury, period $P = 87.9693$ days, passed perihelion on May 20 at 0^h. What was the eccentric anomaly of the planet on May 31? The eccentricity of Mercury's orbit is 0.21.

3. When observed in 1929, Comet Schwassman-Wachman II had an elliptical orbit of period $P = 6.42$ years and eccentricity 0.40. At what value of E would the comet be found 2.00 years after it passed perihelion? What would be its radius vector at that time?

3–8 Position in the elliptical orbit. In the preceding section we have obtained an expression for the radius vector in terms of the eccentric anomaly, $r = a(1 - e \cos E)$. It remains to express the true anomaly f as a function of E.

From the first of Eqs. (3–35), we have

$$a \cos E = ae + r \cos f, \qquad (3\text{–}48)$$

but from the polar equation of the orbit [Eq. (3–19)]

$$r = \frac{a(1 - e^2)}{1 + e \cos f}.$$

Hence, combining this with Eq. (3–48), we may write

$$\cos E = \frac{e + \cos f}{1 + e \cos f}.$$

Therefore,

$$1 - \cos E = \frac{(1 - e)(1 - \cos f)}{1 + e \cos f},$$

$$1 + \cos E = \frac{(1 + e)(1 + \cos f)}{1 + e \cos f},$$

and, by division,

$$\tan^2 \left(\frac{E}{2}\right) = \left(\frac{1 - e}{1 + e}\right) \tan^2 \left(\frac{f}{2}\right).$$

Thus we have

$$\tan \left(\frac{f}{2}\right) = \left(\frac{1 + e}{1 - e}\right)^{1/2} \tan \left(\frac{E}{2}\right). \qquad (3\text{–}49)$$

There is no ambiguity in the sign of the square root because $\tan (f/2)$ and $\tan (E/2)$ always have the same sign. To illustrate the application of these equations, consider the following example.

EXAMPLE. An earth satellite in an orbit whose plane coincides with that of the earth's equator is 1000 km above the earth's surface at perigee and 2000 km high at apogee. What are the values of a and e for its orbit, and what will be its polar coordinates 1.5 hours after it passes perigee? We shall assume for simplicity that the earth is a sphere of radius 6378 km. Figure 3–10 illustrates the problem. The mass of the earth is 6×10^{27} gm and $G = 6.67 \times 10^{-8}$ dyne·cm²·gm^{-2}. The center of force is now the center of the earth, and this is the focus of the elliptic orbit. Therefore

$$q = a(1 - e) = 7378 \text{ km},$$
$$q' = a(1 + e) = 8378 \text{ km},$$

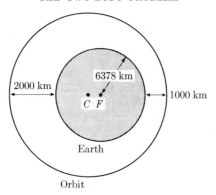

FIG. 3–10. Close earth satellite orbit.

from which we find the elements

$$a = 7878 \text{ km} \qquad \text{and} \qquad e = 0.0635.$$

The period P is given by Eq. (2–34), Kepler's third law, as

$$P = 0.08036 \text{ days} = 1.929 \text{ hours,}$$

and hence the mean daily motion is

$$n = 78.190 \text{ rad/day.}$$

For the instant 1.5 hours after perigee passage, we find the mean anomaly

$$M = 78.190 \times \frac{1.5}{24} = 4.8869 \text{ rad} \qquad \text{or} \qquad M = 279°59'.6.$$

For illustrative purposes, we assume M to be the first approximation to E, namely E_0. Then the sequence of calculations by Eqs. (3–45) and (3–47) yields

$$E_0 = M = 4.8869,$$
$$M_0 = 4.9494,$$
$$\Delta E_0 = -0.0632,$$
$$E_1 = 4.8236,$$
$$M_1 = 4.8866,$$
$$\Delta E_1 = +.0002,$$
$$E_2 = 4.8238,$$
$$M_2 = 4.8868.$$

This last value agrees with the stipulated M within the accuracy assumed here. Therefore we adopt for E at the instant of observation:

$$E = 4.8238 \text{ rad} = 276°23'.0.$$

In making this calculation, a table of sines with the argument in radians is useful.

With the value of E thus found, we find by Eq. (3–37) that

$$r = 7878 \ (1 - e \cos E) = 7822.49 \text{ km},$$

and, by Eq. (3–49),

$$\tan\left(\frac{f}{2}\right) = \left(\frac{1.0635}{0.9365}\right)^{1/2} \tan\left(\frac{E}{2}\right),$$

$$\frac{f}{2} = 136°22'.4,$$

so that

$$f = 272°44'.8.$$

The satellite, then, has polar coordinates (r, f) at the instant specified.

PROBLEMS

1. On June 7, 1960, the eccentricity of the orbit of the satellite Explorer I was 0.106. The semimajor axis was 7.52×10^3 km. Calculate (a) the period of the satellite and the mean daily motion, and (b) its position in the orbit one hour after it passed perigee. [Assume the earth to be a sphere of radius 6378 km; mass 6×10^{27} gm; take $G = 6.67 \times 10^{-8}$.]

2. Comet Forbes, (1929 II) has the following orbital elements:

$$a = 3.45482 \text{ A.U.},$$

$$e = 0.552735,$$

$$P = 6.42154 \text{ yr},$$

$$T = 1948 \text{ September } 16.194.$$

What were the radius vector and the true anomaly on November 1.000, 1949?

3. A space probe is to be sent from the earth to Mars on an elliptical path. Assume that the orbits of these planets are circular, of radii 1.00 and 1.52 A.U., respectively, and are coplanar. The orbit of the probe is to be tangent to the planetary orbits. (a) Find the values of a and e for the probe's orbit. (b) Find the period of the motion on the assumption that the mass of the probe is negligible compared with that of the sun. How long will it take the probe to reach the orbit of Mars? (c) What will be the polar coordinates of the probe 90 days after it left the earth's orbit? [Neglect the influence of the earth and Mars on the motion of the probe.]

3–9 Position in a parabolic orbit. The orbital arc described by a newly discovered comet near perihelion is usually so short that one cannot distinguish immediately whether the orbit is a parabola, an ellipse, or a hyperbola. Because the parabolic orbit is easily calculated from the observations, it is usually assumed as a first approximation. As the object is observed over a longer and longer arc, a definitive orbit will ultimately be required. This most likely will be an elongated ellipse. For obtaining the initial ephermeris of positions, we must obtain the polar coordinates of the object in its parabolic path.

The equation of the parabolic path (Fig. 3–11) is

$$r = \frac{2q}{1 + \cos f} = q \sec^2 \left(\frac{f}{2}\right), \tag{3–50}$$

an expression which follows from Eq. (3–19). The motion of the mass m_2 is counterclockwise with the true anomaly f measured from perihelion, V.

From the discussion of Section 2–5, Case I, we see that the areal velocity constant for the parabolic path is

$$h = k\sqrt{2Mq}. \tag{3–51}$$

The mass of a comet is usually negligible compared with that of the sun, so that M is the solar mass. If q is in astronomical units and k is the Gaussian constant, $M = 1$.

From the areal velocity law $r^2 \dot{f} = h$, we then obtain, by combining Eqs. (3–50) and (3–51),

$$q^2 \dot{f} \sec^4 \left(\frac{f}{2}\right) = k\sqrt{2Mq}$$

or

$$\sec^4 \left(\frac{f}{2}\right) df = \frac{k\sqrt{2M}}{q^{3/2}} dt,$$

and by integration,

$$\tan \left(\frac{f}{2}\right) + \frac{1}{3} \tan^3 \left(\frac{f}{2}\right) = k\sqrt{\frac{M}{2q^3}} (t - T), \tag{3–52}$$

where T is the time of perihelion passage.

This is a cubic equation in tan $(f/2)$ which can be solved for f as a function of t with a digital computer or by graphical or tabular methods.* A direct solution of the equation has been given by Moulton.† We note

---

* J. Bauschinger, *Tafeln zur Theoretischen Astronomie*, p. 9 ff.
† F. R. Moulton, *Celestial Mechanics*, p. 156 ff.

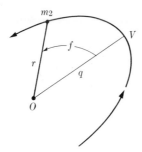

FIG. 3–11. Parameters in a parabolic orbit.

here the resulting chain of calculation by means of auxiliary quantities:

$$\cot s = \frac{3k(t - T)}{(2q)^{3/2}}, \qquad (3\text{–}53)$$

$$\cot w = \left[\cot\left(\frac{s}{2}\right)\right]^{1/3}, \qquad (3\text{–}54)$$

$$\tan\left(\frac{f}{2}\right) = 2\cot 2w, \qquad (3\text{–}55)$$

where the mass of the sun has been taken as 1.

Having solved Eq. (3–52) for $\tan (f/2)$, one can find the radius vector readily from the relation

$$r = q\sec^2\left(\frac{f}{2}\right) = q\left[1 + \tan^2\left(\frac{f}{2}\right)\right]. \qquad (3\text{–}56)$$

PROBLEMS

1. Comet Barnard (1889 III) was found to have an orbit with $q = 1.102$ A.U., $e = 0.957$, and $P = 218.3$ years. Calculate the position of the comet 3 years after perihelion passage on the assumption that its orbit was parabolic. How does this position compare with that obtained from the elliptic elements?

2. Compare the radii vectors and the true anomalies, for $t - T = 50$ days, of two objects having the same T under the following circumstances:

Object A has an orbit with $e = 0.5$ and $q = 1.5$,
Object B has an orbit with $e = 1$ and $q = 1.5$.

The focus is identical for the two orbits.

3–10 Position in a hyperbolic orbit.   When a meteoroid enters the atmosphere of the earth, its path is hyperbolic with the earth's center at one focus. To find the position of the object in the hyperbola is a problem similar to that discussed for the ellipse in Section 3–8.

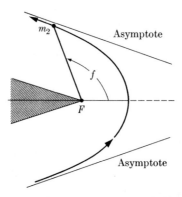

Fig. 3–12. Geometry of a hyperbolic orbit.

The equation of the path is

$$r = \frac{a(e^2 - 1)}{1 + e \cos f} \quad (e > 1), \qquad (3\text{--}57)$$

where f is, as usual, the true anomaly. Obviously f can vary in this case only between the limits defined by a vanishing of the denominator in Eq. (3–57). That is,

$$\left[-180° + \cos^{-1}\left(\frac{1}{e}\right) \right] < f < \left[180° - \cos^{-1}\left(\frac{1}{e}\right) \right]. \qquad (3\text{--}58)$$

Thus f is restricted to the region outside that shown shaded in Fig. 3–12.

Instead of a geometrical argument for obtaining f and r as functions of the time, we shall use here an analytical one.

Kepler's second law for the hyperbola is [see Eq. (2–36)]

$$r^2 \dot{f} = \sqrt{k^2 M a(e^2 - 1)}, \qquad (3\text{--}59)$$

and for the energy equation [Eq. (2–38)],

$$\dot{r}^2 + r^2 \dot{f}^2 = k^2 M \left[\frac{2}{r} + \frac{1}{a} \right]. \qquad (3\text{--}60)$$

Substitution of $\dot{f}$ from Eq. (3–59) into Eq. (3–60) yields a separable differential equation similar to that shown in Problem 1, Section 3–7, namely,

$$\dot{r}^2 = \frac{n^2 a^2}{r^2} [(a + r)^2 - a^2 e^2], \qquad (3\text{--}61)$$

where

$$n^2 = \frac{k^2 M}{a^3}. \qquad (3\text{--}62)$$

The quantity n plays a role here analogous to that in the elliptic case. Of course, the relationship of n to the period P in the latter case is not present.

Corresponding to the eccentric anomaly E of the elliptic orbit, we introduce here an auxiliary variable F defined by

$$r = a[e \cosh F - 1]. \qquad (3\text{-}63)$$

Then $dr = ae \sinh F \, dF$ and Eq. (3–61) becomes, upon separation,

$$n \, dt = (e \cosh F - 1) \, dF,$$

which can be integrated to yield

$$n(t - T) = e \sinh F - F = M.$$

This is a relation similar to Kepler's equation. It is to be solved for F when $M = n(t - T)$ is given.

A graphical process similar to that introduced in Section 3–7 can be used to obtain an approximate value of F. For example, we plot, with F as abscissa, the straight line

$$y_1 = \frac{1}{e} (F + M) \qquad (3\text{-}64)$$

and the hyperbolic sine curve

$$y_2 = \sinh F. \qquad (3\text{-}65)$$

The abscissa of the point where $y_1 = y_2$ is the desired approximate value of F.

Differential corrections to this value of F may be obtained in a manner analogous to that described in Section 3–7.

The radius vector is given by Eq. (3–63) when F is known. And from the relation

$$r = \frac{a(e^2 - 1)}{1 + e \cos f} = a[e \cosh F - 1], \qquad (3\text{-}66)$$

we can derive the expression

$$\tan \left(\frac{f}{2} \right) = \left(\frac{e + 1}{e - 1} \right)^{1/2} \tanh \left(\frac{F}{2} \right), \qquad (3\text{-}67)$$

which yields f when F has been found.

3–11 Position in near-parabolic orbits. When the eccentricity $e \sim 1$, the methods discussed above for finding the polar coordinates of an object in an elliptic or hyperbolic orbit are not practicable. Unless extensive modifications are made in the *form* of Kepler's equation, its solution is nearly indeterminate. Many instances of highly elliptical orbits occur in the solar system, especially among the comets and, more recently, among the artificial satellites, lunar probes, and solar probes. Therefore the problem of finding the position of an object in such an orbit is not un-important.

Kepler's equation can be written [see Eq. (3–34)] in the form

$$n(t - T) = \frac{k\sqrt{1 + m_2}}{a^{3/2}} (t - T) = E - e \sin E, \qquad (3\text{–}68)$$

where m_2 is the moving mass. By introducing the perihelion distance $q = a(1 - e)$ in place of a, we have

$$\frac{k\sqrt{1 + m_2}}{q^{3/2}} (t-T) = \frac{E - e \sin E}{(1 - e)^{3/2}}. \qquad (3\text{–}69)$$

If $e \to 1$ and $E \to 0$, it is clear that the right-hand side of Eq. (3–69) becomes an indeterminate form. The left-hand side of the equation, however, resembles the expression

$$\frac{k\sqrt{1 + m_2}}{\sqrt{2q^3}} (t - T)$$

for the parabola as exhibited in Eq. (3–52). Therefore we shall first indicate a relationship between Eq. (3–52) and an analogous equation for the ellipse. Secondly, we shall exhibit Kepler's equation in a modified form which will permit calculating f and r when the value of $e \sim 1$.

Let $x = \tan (f/2)$. Then the equation for the elliptical orbit can be recast as follows:

$$x^2 = \tan^2\left(\frac{f}{2}\right) = \frac{1 - \cos f}{1 + \cos f},$$

$$\cos f = \frac{1 - x^2}{1 + x^2},$$

$$r = \frac{a(1 - e^2)}{1 + e \cos f} = \frac{q(1 + e)}{1 + e[(1 - x^2)/(1 + x^2)]} = \frac{q(1 + x^2)}{1 + [(1 - e)/(1 + e)]x^2}.$$

Finally, with

$$y = \left(\frac{1 - e}{1 + e}\right) x^2,$$

we have

$$r = \frac{q(1 + x^2)}{1 + y}. \qquad (3\text{–}70)$$

By referring to Eq. (3–49), the student should note immediately that $y = \tan^2 (E/2)$.

Now, by Kepler's second law for the ellipse,

$$r^2\dot{f} = k\sqrt{(1 + m_2)(1 - e^2)a} = k\sqrt{(1 + m_2)(1 + e)q}, \quad (3\text{–}71)$$

and from the definition of x, we have

$$\tfrac{1}{2}\sec^2\left(\frac{f}{2}\right)\dot{f} = \dot{x}. \qquad (3\text{–}72)$$

Substitution of Eqs. (3–72) and (3–70) into Eq. (3–71) yields a separable differential equation analogous to that preceding Eq. (3–52),

$$\frac{(1 + x^2)\,dx}{(1 + y)^2} = \frac{k\sqrt{(1 + m_2)(1 + e)}}{2q^{3/2}}\,dt, \qquad (3\text{–}73)$$

where we note that y is a function of x.

Expanding $(1 + y)^{-2}$ by the binomial theorem and multiplying by $(1 + x^2)$ yields an infinite series

$$(1 + x^2)(1 + y)^{-2} = 1 + (1 - 2\alpha)x^2 + (3\alpha^2 - 2\alpha)x^4$$
$$+ (3\alpha^2 - 4\alpha^3)x^6 + (5\alpha^4 - 4\alpha^3)x^8 + \cdots,$$

where

$$\alpha = \frac{1 - e}{1 + e}.$$

Integration of this series, term by term, from 0 to x and resubstitution of $y/x^2 = \alpha$, yields

$$x[1 - \tfrac{2}{3}y + \tfrac{3}{5}y^2 - \tfrac{4}{7}y^3 + \tfrac{5}{9}y^4 - \cdots]$$
$$+ \frac{x^3}{3}[1 - \tfrac{6}{5}y + \tfrac{9}{7}y^2 - \tfrac{12}{9}y^3 + \cdots]$$
$$= \frac{k\sqrt{(1 + m_2)(1 + e)}}{2q^{3/2}}(t - T), \quad (3\text{–}74)$$

where $t = T$ when $x = 0$.

Equation (3–74) is similar in form to the equation [Eq. (3–52)]

$$x + \tfrac{1}{3}x^3 = \frac{k\sqrt{(1 + m_2)}\,(t - T)}{\sqrt{2q^3}}$$

for the parabola. Note that if $e = 1$ in Eq. (3–74), the terms in y vanish and Eq. (3–74) becomes identical with Eq. (3–52). Thus there is a smooth transition from the ellipse of high eccentricity to the parabola, through Kepler's second law.

The series coefficients for x and $x^3/3$ converge rapidly if y is small, as it will be when $e \sim 1$ and E is not too large. For larger values of E, however, the convergence is slow. Equation (3–74) indicates that a method of solving for $x = \tan(f/2)$, as in the case of the parabola, and applying corrective measures to give the corresponding values of f for the ellipse are feasible. The method we outline here is due to Gauss.*

Kepler's equation may be written in the form

$$E - e \sin E = (1 - e)\{\tfrac{9}{10}E + \tfrac{1}{10}\sin E\} + \left(\frac{1 + 9e}{10}\right)\{E - \sin E\} = R,$$

$$(3-75)$$

where

$$R = \frac{k\sqrt{1 + m_2}\,(1 - e)^{3/2}(t - T)}{q^{3/2}}.$$

$$(3-76)$$

The series expansions of the terms in braces in Eq. (3–75) are

$$\tfrac{9}{10}E + \tfrac{1}{10}\sin E = E - \tfrac{1}{60}E^3 + \tfrac{1}{1200}E^5 - \cdots,$$

$$(3-77)$$

$$E - \sin E = \tfrac{1}{6}E^3 - \tfrac{1}{120}E^5 + \tfrac{1}{5040}E^7 - \cdots.$$

$$(3-78)$$

Hence, with respect to E, the second expansion is, at most, of the third order, and the first expansion is of the first order.

We now introduce the auxiliary variables

$$A = \frac{15[E - \sin E]}{9E + \sin E} = \tfrac{1}{4}E^2 - \tfrac{1}{120}E^4 - \tfrac{1}{20160}E^6 - \cdots,$$

$$(3-79)$$

$$B = \frac{9E + \sin E}{20\sqrt{A}} = 1 + \tfrac{3}{3800}E^4 + \cdots,$$

$$(3-80)$$

and it is clear that $B \approx 1$. Furthermore, if desired, B can be tabulated as a function of A by eliminating E between Eqs. (3–79) and (3–80).

Substitution of A and B for the appropriate combinations of terms in Eq. (3–75) yields

$$A^{1/2} + \left(\frac{1 + 9e}{1 - e}\right)\frac{A^{3/2}}{15} = \frac{k\sqrt{1 + m_2}\,(1 - e)^{1/2}(t - T)}{2Bq^{3/2}}.$$

$$(3-81)$$

Let

$$\tan(\tfrac{1}{2}w) = \sqrt{\frac{1 + 9e}{5(1 - e)}}\,A.$$

Then Eq. (3–81) becomes

$$\tan(\tfrac{1}{2}w) + \tfrac{1}{3}\tan^3(\tfrac{1}{2}w) = \frac{k\sqrt{1 + m_2}}{B\sqrt{2q^3}}\sqrt{\frac{1 + 9e}{10}}\,(t - T).$$

$$(3-82)$$

---

* C. F. Gauss, *Theoria Motus Corporum Coelestium*, p. 46 ff. See, also, the discussion by P. Herget, *Computation of Orbits*, pp. 34–37.

This is identical in form to Eq. (3–52) for the parabola with the auxiliary variable w replacing f.

The method for solving Eq. (3–82) consists of an iteration procedure. As a first approximation, B can be taken as 1. Then with e, q, t, and T given, the right-hand side of Eq. (3–82) is known so that $\tan\left(\frac{1}{2}w\right)$ can be found by Barker's tables or in the manner outlined for the parabola in Section 3–9. With this value, one can obtain the first approximation to A from

$$A = \frac{5(1-e)}{1+9e}\tan^2\left(\tfrac{1}{2}w\right). \tag{3–83}$$

With this value of A and the tables giving B as a function of A, a new approximation to B can be obtained. Tables for this purpose have been published by Herget,[*] Stracke,[†] Bauschinger,[‡] and others. One must note in applying the table by Herget that the B defined by him is the reciprocal of the B defined in Eq. (3–80).

The computation can be repeated with the new value of B to get a revised A, and so forth. When the final values of A and B have been found, together with $\tan\left(\frac{1}{2}w\right)$, the polar coordinates in the orbit can be calculated according to the following sequence.

Let $y = \tan^2(E/2)$ so that

$$E = 2\tan^{-1}\sqrt{y}$$

and

$$\sin E = 2\sin\left(\frac{E}{2}\right)\cos\left(\frac{E}{2}\right) = \frac{2\sqrt{y}}{1+y}.$$

Then

$$E = 2\sqrt{y}\,[1 - \tfrac{1}{3}y + \tfrac{1}{5}y^2 - \tfrac{1}{7}y^3 + \cdots],$$

$$\sin E = 2\sqrt{y}\,[1 - y + y^2 - y^3 + y^4 - \cdots],$$

and by substitution into Eq. (3–79), the auxiliary quantity A can be written

$$A = 15\left[\frac{E - \sin E}{9E + \sin E}\right] = y - \tfrac{4}{5}y^2 + \tfrac{24}{35}y^3 - \tfrac{1592}{2625}y^4 + \cdots$$

or

$$\frac{A}{y} = 1 - \tfrac{4}{5}y + \tfrac{24}{35}y^2 - \tfrac{1592}{2625}y^3 + \cdots. \tag{3–84}$$

---

[*] P. Herget, *Computation of Orbits*, Table V.

[†] G. Stracke, *Bahnbestimmung der Planeten und Kometen*. Berlin: Julius Springer, 1929, Table 10.

[‡] J. Bauschinger, *Tafeln zur Theoretischen Astronomie, Zweite Auflage*. Leipzig: Wilhelm Engelmann, 1934, Tables 15, 16, and 17.

If we invert this series, we obtain

$$\frac{A}{y} = 1 - \tfrac{4}{5}A + \tfrac{8}{175}A^2 + \tfrac{8}{525}A^3 + \cdots$$

$$= 1 - \tfrac{4}{5}A + C, \tag{3-85}$$

where C is the sum of the terms of order 2 and higher.

By Eq. (3-49),

$$\tan^2\left(\frac{f}{2}\right) = \left(\frac{1+e}{1-e}\right)\tan^2\left(\frac{E}{2}\right) = \left(\frac{1+e}{1-e}\right)y. \tag{3-86}$$

Substituting for y in terms of A from Eq. (3-85) and using Eq. (3-83), we find

$$\tan^2\left(\frac{f}{2}\right) = \left[\frac{5(1+e)}{1+9e}\right]\left[\frac{1}{1 - \tfrac{4}{5}A + C}\right]\tan^2\left(\frac{w}{2}\right). \tag{3-87}$$

Since the quantities on the right-hand side of this equation are known, $\tan(f/2)$ can be found.

The radius vector r follows immediately from Eq. (3-70). That is,

$$r = q\left(1 + \tan^2\frac{f}{2}\right)(1 + y)^{-1}. \tag{3-88}$$

Herget* has tabulated $(1 + y)^{-1}$ as a function of A so that r can be found easily when f is known.

PROBLEMS

1. Prove that the series in y given in Eq. (3-74) converge.

2. Repeat, for the hyperbola, the analysis exhibited in Eqs. (3-70) to (3-74).

3. The orbital parameters of the probe Lunik III, with respect to the earth as center of force, were $q = 45,000$ km, $e = 0.8$, $T = 4.125$ October 1959. Calculate a first approximation to A and $\tan(w/2)$ for 14.125 October 1959. On the assumption that this value of A is the final one, find f and r for the given date. [Neglect the mass of the probe compared with that of the earth.] What is the period of the probe? What is its apogee distance?

4. Evaluate f and r for the Lunik III data of Problem 3 by the method discussed in Sections 3-7 and 3-8. Compare the results with those deduced in Problem 3.

3-12 Position on the celestial sphere. The preceding sections have been devoted to finding the polar coordinates of a celestial object in its orbit when the elements of the orbit are given. We now consider the

---

* P. Herget, *Computation of Orbits*, Table V.

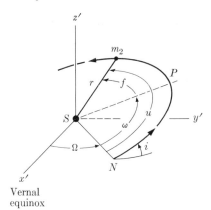

FIG. 3–13. Orbit in heliocentric reference frame.

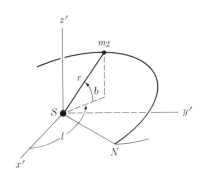

FIG. 3–14. Heliocentric longitude and latitude.

actual position of the object on the sky at any time t. That is, we seek for a planet or satellite or other object the spherical coordinates with origins at the center of the sun (the *heliocentric* coordinates) and at the center of the earth (the *geocentric* coordinates). We shall omit refinements and corrections to the coordinates due to precession, nutation, aberration, and so forth. The reader is referred to other sources for a discussion of these.*

(a) *Heliocentric coordinates.* Let the orbit be situated in a rectangular coordinate system as pictured in Fig. 3–13. The origin is the sun; the x'-axis points toward the vernal equinox; the $x'y'$-plane is the plane of the earth's orbit (*ecliptic plane*). The z'-axis points to the north side of the ecliptic. The ascending node of the orbit is at N; the perihelion point is P, and, at any instant t, the moving mass m_2 is at the position shown. *Then the heliocentric longitude, l, of m_2 is the angle from the vernal equinox toward the east in the plane of the ecliptic to the projection of the radius vector on this plane* (Fig. 3–14). Similarly, the *heliocentric latitude, b, is the angle from ecliptic to object in a plane perpendicular to the ecliptic.* It is considered positive when the object is north of the ecliptic plane and negative when the object is south. Obviously

$$0° \leq l < 360°,$$

$$-90° \leq b \leq +90°.$$

Let $u = \omega + f$, as shown in Fig. 3–13. Then from the figure it should be clear that the projection of the radius vector along SN is $r \cos u$, but

---

* See D. Brouwer and G. M. Clemence, *Methods of Celestial Mechanics*, Chapters VI and VII.

from Fig. 3–14 we observe it to be $r \cos b \cos (l - \Omega)$. Hence

$$\cos u = \cos b \cos (l - \Omega). \tag{3–89}$$

Similarly, using projections perpendicular to SN, we have, in the ecliptic plane,

$$\sin u \cos i = \cos b \sin (l - \Omega), \tag{3–90}$$

and perpendicular to the ecliptic plane

$$\sin u \sin i = \sin b. \tag{3–91}$$

From Eqs. (3–89), (3–90), and (3–91), we find

$$\tan (l - \Omega) = \cos i \tan u,$$
$$\tan b = \tan i \sin (l - \Omega). \tag{3–92}$$

When u, i, and Ω are known, Eqs. (3-89) to (3-92) determine uniquely the heliocentric latitude and longitude of the object.

The *rectangular ecliptic heliocentric coordinates* of the moving mass m_2 are given by

$$x' = r \cos u \cos \Omega - r \sin u \sin \Omega \cos i,$$
$$y' = r \cos u \sin \Omega + r \sin u \cos \Omega \cos i, \tag{3–93}$$
$$z' = r \sin u \sin i,$$

as the reader may verify by inspection of Fig. 3–13. In using these equations one can employ to advantage the eccentric anomaly E in place of r by means of the relation $r = a(1 - e \cos E)$.

The fundamental reference plane for positions, *as seen from the earth*, is the plane of the earth's equator. This plane is inclined at an angle $\epsilon = 23°27'$ to the plane of the ecliptic. Therefore an auxiliary set of axes is required with the sun at the origin, the x-axis aligned toward the vernal equinox, and the z-axis inclined at an angle ϵ to the z'-axis, as shown in Fig. 3–15.

Then in this *heliocentric equatorial system* of coordinates

$$x = x',$$
$$y = y' \cos \epsilon + z' \sin \epsilon, \tag{3–94}$$
$$z = -y' \sin \epsilon + z' \cos \epsilon.$$

Substitution of Eqs. (3–93) into Eq. (3–94) yields directly the rectangular heliocentric equatorial coordinates of the moving object.

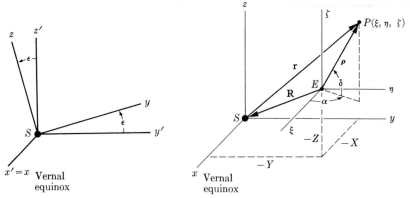

FIG. 3-15. Rotation to heliocentric equatorial coordinate system.

FIG. 3-16. Geocentric equatorial coordinates.

The transformation from x, y, z to x', y', z' is readily found to be

$$x' = x,$$
$$y' = y \cos \epsilon - z \sin \epsilon, \qquad (3\text{-}95)$$
$$z' = y \sin \epsilon + z \cos \epsilon.$$

Equations (3–94) and (3–95) permit one system of coordinates to be changed readily into the other.

(b) *Geocentric coordinates.* The heliocentric rectangular equatorial system can now be related to that of a parallel system with the origin at the center of the earth. The *American Ephemeris and Nautical Almanac* gives for each day in the year the geocentric equatorial rectangular coordinates, X, Y, Z, of the sun's center. Let ξ, η, ζ denote the corresponding coordinates for a moving object (Fig. 3–16). Let ρ be the distance of the object P from the center of the earth and r its distance from the center of the sun. Then

$$\xi = x + X,$$
$$\eta = y + Y, \qquad (3\text{-}96)$$
$$\zeta = z + Z$$

are the desired geocentric equatorial rectangular coordinates of P. If $\mathbf{r}$, $\boldsymbol{\rho}$, $\mathbf{R}$ denote the vectors shown in the figure, we have

$$\boldsymbol{\rho} = \mathbf{r} + \mathbf{R}, \qquad (3\text{-}97)$$

which is the vector equivalent of Eqs. (3–96).

TABLE 3–1

t(1961)	Jan. 1.0	Jan. 21.0	Feb. 10.0
$t-T$ (days)	94.0426	114.0426	134.0426
M (deg)	27.70216	33.59387	39.48497
E (deg)	51.53727	59.93960	67.6400
f (deg)	82°11′16″	92°23′23″	100°10′06″
$u = \omega + f$	237°14′19″	247°28′07″	255°13′09″
r (A.U.)	1.498	1.642	1.785
$\cos u$	−0.541142	−0.383642	−0.254841
$\sin u$	−0.840931	−0.923482	−0.966983
$\cos \Omega$	−0.884045	—	—
$\sin \Omega$	−0.467403	—	—
$\cos i$	+0.997968	—	—
$\sin i$	+0.063720	—	—
$x' = x$ (A.U.)	+0.129036	−0.150414	−0.402984
y'	+1.49030	+1.63224	+1.73540
z'	−0.080269	−0.096622	−0.109985
y (A.U.)	+1.399159	+1.535884	+1.635842
z	+0.519425	+0.560090	+0.589701
X Y 1950.0 Z	+0.174024 −0.887806 −0.385009	+0.500539 −0.777344 −0.337105	+0.765523 −0.571350 −0.246951
ξ (A.U.)	+0.303060	+0.350125	+0.362539
η	+0.511353	+0.758590	+1.064492
ζ	+0.134416	+0.222985	+0.341931
ρ (A.U.)	0.60942	0.86470	1.1753
$\tan \alpha$	1.68729	2.16663	2.93621
$\sin \delta$	0.220564	0.257876	0.290931
α	$3^h57^m23^s$	$4^h20^m54^s$	$4^h44^m46^s$
δ	+12°44′32″	+14°56′39″	+16°54′51″

The polar coordinates of P are now readily found. Let these be ρ, α, δ (Fig. 3–16). Then

$$\xi = \rho \cos \delta \cos \alpha, \qquad \eta = \rho \cos \delta \sin \alpha, \qquad \zeta = \rho \sin \delta. \quad (3\text{--}98)$$

From these it follows that

$$\tan \alpha = \eta/\xi, \qquad \sin \delta = \zeta/\rho, \qquad \rho = (\xi^2 + \eta^2 + \zeta^2)^{1/2}. \quad (3\text{--}99)$$

The angle α is the right ascension of the object; the angle δ is its declination. The former is the angle *in the plane of the equator from the vernal equinox eastward to the projection of the geocentric radius vector ρ on the equatorial plane.* The latter is the *angular distance, $+$ north and $-$ south, from the plane of the equator and perpendicular to it, to the radius vector ρ.* It should be emphasized that these angular coordinates are as viewed *from the center of the earth.* For nearby objects, such as artificial satellites of the earth, further corrections are required to obtain the position on the sky as seen from a point on the earth's surface.

Occasionally it is desirable to use a polar coordinate geocentric system of coordinates with the ecliptic as the fundamental plane. In this system *celestial longitude, λ, is the angular distance in degrees along the ecliptic eastward from the vernal equinox to the projection of the radius vector ρ on the ecliptic. Celestial latitude, β, is the angular distance, $+$ north and $-$ south, measured from the plane of the ecliptic, and perpendicular to it, to the radius vector.* The relationships between α, δ and λ, β are

$$\cos \lambda \cos \beta = \cos \delta \cos \alpha,$$
$$\sin \lambda \cos \beta = \sin \delta \sin \epsilon + \cos \delta \cos \epsilon \sin \alpha, \qquad (3\text{–}100)$$
$$\sin \beta = \sin \delta \cos \epsilon - \cos \delta \sin \epsilon \sin \alpha.$$

The *American Ephemeris and Nautical Almanac* tabulates for each day in the year the celestial longitude L, the celestial latitude B, and the sun's geocentric radius vector R. The latitude B is, of course, very nearly zero.

EXAMPLE. As a final illustration of the analysis of this chapter, as well as of this section, we shall calculate the positions of a recently discovered object for three dates. The heliocentric orbital data are as follows:

$$
\left.
\begin{aligned}
T &= \text{1960 September 28.9574 E.T.,} \\
\omega &= 155°.0509, \\
\Omega &= 207°.8658, \\
i &= 3°.6699,
\end{aligned}
\right\} \quad \text{Equinox 1950.0}
$$

$$
\begin{aligned}
q &= 1.048545 \text{ A.U.,} \\
e &= 0.531284, \\
a &= 2.237055 \text{ A.U.,} \\
P &= 3.35 \text{ yr,} \\
n &= 0.2945703 \text{ deg/day.}
\end{aligned}
$$

The 1961 positions of the object are desired for January 1.0, January 21.0, and February 10.0. The analysis in tabulated form (Table 3–1) follows

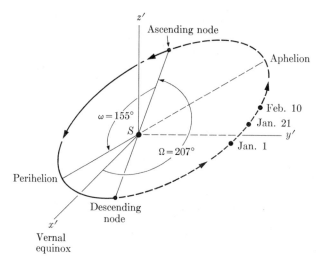

FIG. 3–17. Orbit illustrated by the example.

from the basic equations given in this chapter. Figure 3–17 shows the orbit and the positions calculated.

PROBLEMS

1. The position of an object is given in its orbit by Eqs. (3–35) and (3–36), namely,

$$r \cos f = a \cos E - ae,$$

$$r \sin f = b \sin E,$$

where $b = a\sqrt{1 - e^2}$ is the semiminor axis. In Fig. 3–18, SP is the direction to perihelion; SQ is the direction for $f = 90°$; SR is perpendicular to the orbit. The sun is at S and the xy-plane is the plane of the earth's equator. Let P_x,

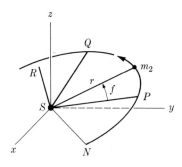

FIG. 3–18. Rectangular directions for Problem 1.

P_y, P_z be the direction cosines of SP; Q_x, Q_y, Q_z be those of SQ; R_x, R_y, R_z be those of SR. Express the coordinates x, y, and z in terms of E and the direction cosines.

2. The orbital elements of Comet 1944 II Comas Solá are

$$P = 8.50 \text{ yr}, \qquad \omega = 38°.9,$$
$$q = 1.766 \text{ A.U.}, \qquad \Omega = 65°.7,$$
$$e = 0.576, \qquad i = 13°.7.$$

Calculate the position of the perihelion point (a) in the heliocentric ecliptic system; and (b) in the heliocentric equatorial system. What are the direction cosines P_x, P_y, P_z, for this comet (see Problem 1)?

3. Calculate the right ascension and declination of Comet Comas Solá (Problem 2) for the instant 0.50 years after perihelion passage. The required geocentric equatorial coordinates of the sun are:

$$X = +0.9319043; \qquad Y = -0.3090872; \qquad Z = -0.1340491.$$

CHAPTER 4

COMPUTATION OF ORBITS

The preceding three chapters have dealt with one of the basic problems of celestial mechanics, that is, given the elements of an orbit, to find the position of the celestial object at any time. In the present chapter we shall sketch the principles underlying the second type of problem, namely, given the observations of a celestial object, to determine the elements of its orbit.

In Section 3–4 it was shown how the orbital elements can be determined when the components of velocity and the space coordinates of the body are known at an initial time t_0. Knowledge of the cartesian coordinates from which this solution follows implies that the distance of the body is known. Actually, in general, this is not known. We observe the angular coordinates (α, δ) of the body as seen from the earth. We have no idea how far away it is. If it moves around the sun, or around another planet, a guess about its distance from the center of force can be obtained from Kepler's third law. Still the velocity components are not known and must be estimated. Thus the problem of determining the orbital elements *de novo* from observations of its position in the sky is not a simple one.

There are six orbital elements to be determined. Hence six independent quantities must be observed. These, in the commonest instance, are the coordinates (α, δ) at each of three times. We shall assume in our discussion of the problem that these positions have been corrected for aberration, precession, nutation, and other variations due to irregularities in the earth's motion.* It is obvious that all of the coordinates to be used for such a solution must be referred to the same coordinate system. Customarily one uses as the reference system the standard equinox of 1950.0.

4–1 The radius vector is known. Before embarking on a discussion of the general problem, we shall consider the rather trivial case in which the radius vector from the center of force to the moving body is known. In brief we know its spherical coordinates at each of three times.

For simplicity we shall assume that the object is moving around the sun with a period P in an ellipse. We assume that its heliocentric longitude, heliocentric latitude, and radius vector (l, b, r) are known at times t_1, t_2, t_3. Then the radius vector at each time is $\mathbf{r} = x'\mathbf{i} + y'\mathbf{j} + z'\mathbf{k}$, where $x' = r$

---

* See P. Herget, *The Computation of Orbits*. Cincinnati, Ohio: Privately printed, 1948, Chapter 2, for a discussion of these corrections.

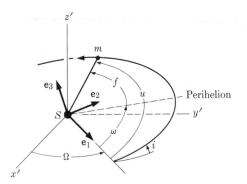

FIG. 4–1. Unit vectors for orbit computation.

$\cos b \cos l$, $y' = r \cos b \sin l$, $z' = r \sin b$. Let these be denoted by $\mathbf{r}_1$, $\mathbf{r}_2$, $\mathbf{r}_3$, where $t_1 < t_2 < t_3$. Let $\mathbf{e}_1$, $\mathbf{e}_2$, $\mathbf{e}_3$, be three mutually perpendicular unit vectors, as shown in Fig. 4–1. The first is directed along the line of nodes toward the ascending node; the second is perpendicular to $\mathbf{e}_1$ in the plane of the orbit; and the third is perpendicular to the orbital plane. The triad forms a right-handed system in which $\mathbf{e}_3 = \mathbf{e}_1 \times \mathbf{e}_2$. Then

$$
\begin{aligned}
\mathbf{e}_1 &= \cos \Omega \, \mathbf{i} + \sin \Omega \, \mathbf{j}, \\
\mathbf{e}_2 &= -(\sin \Omega \cos i)\mathbf{i} + (\cos \Omega \cos i)\mathbf{j} + (\sin i)\mathbf{k}, \qquad (4\text{–}1) \\
\mathbf{e}_3 &= (\sin \Omega \sin i)\mathbf{i} - (\cos \Omega \sin i)\mathbf{j} + (\cos i)\mathbf{k},
\end{aligned}
$$

where $\mathbf{i}$, $\mathbf{j}$, and $\mathbf{k}$ are unit vectors along the x'-, y'-, and z'-axes, respectively.

From the known values of $\mathbf{r}_1$ and $\mathbf{r}_3$, we may obtain a unit vector

$$
\frac{\mathbf{r}_1 \times \mathbf{r}_3}{|\mathbf{r}_1 \times \mathbf{r}_3|} = A_1\mathbf{i} + A_2\mathbf{j} + A_3\mathbf{k}.
$$

This is perpendicular to the orbit and must be identical with $\mathbf{e}_3$. Therefore, by comparison with the last of Eqs. (4–1), we have

$$
\begin{aligned}
A_1 &= \sin \Omega \sin i, \\
A_2 &= -\cos \Omega \sin i, \qquad (4\text{–}2) \\
A_3 &= \cos i.
\end{aligned}
$$

From these it follows that

$$
\tan \Omega = -\frac{A_1}{A_2}, \qquad (4\text{–}3)
$$

$$
\cos i = A_3, \qquad (4\text{–}4)
$$

and thus Ω and i are determined. These elements orient the orbit in space.

Obviously any pair of the vectors $\mathbf{r}_1$, $\mathbf{r}_2$, $\mathbf{r}_3$ can be used in such a calculation. The only stipulation is that they be noncollinear.

Let u denote the angle from the line of nodes in the plane of the orbit to the moving mass (Fig. 4–1), then the equation of the ellipse can be written

$$r = \frac{a(1 - e^2)}{1 + e \cos f} = \frac{a(1 - e^2)}{1 + e \cos (u - \omega)}, \qquad (4\text{–}5)$$

where f is the true anomaly. Substituting the three values r_1, r_2, r_3 in Eq. (4–5), rearranging terms and subtracting, we have

$$e \cos \omega(r_1 \cos u_1 - r_2 \cos u_2) + e \sin \omega(r_1 \sin u_1 - r_2 \sin u_2) = r_2 - r_1,$$
$$\qquad (4\text{–}6)$$
$$e \cos \omega(r_1 \cos u_1 - r_3 \cos u_3) + e \sin \omega(r_1 \sin u_1 - r_3 \sin u_3) = r_3 - r_1.$$

However, $r \cos u = \mathbf{r} \cdot \mathbf{e}_1$ and $r \sin u = \mathbf{r} \cdot \mathbf{e}_2$. Therefore, Eqs. (4–6) can be written

$$e \cos \omega[(\mathbf{r}_1 - \mathbf{r}_2) \cdot \mathbf{e}_1] + e \sin \omega[(\mathbf{r}_1 - \mathbf{r}_2) \cdot \mathbf{e}_2] = r_2 - r_1,$$
$$\qquad (4\text{–}7)$$
$$e \cos \omega[(\mathbf{r}_1 - \mathbf{r}_3) \cdot \mathbf{e}_1] + e \sin \omega[(\mathbf{r}_1 - \mathbf{r}_3) \cdot \mathbf{e}_2] = r_3 - r_1.$$

The dot products in brackets are quantities computable from Eqs. (4–1), (4–3), (4–4), and the values of $\mathbf{r}$. Hence Eqs. (4–7) can be solved for $e \cos \omega$ and $e \sin \omega$. If the three radius vectors are noncollinear, as specified previously, the determinant of the coefficients of $e \cos \omega$ and $e \sin \omega$ in Eqs. (4–7) does not vanish, and unique values of these unknowns can be found.

Let the solutions of Eqs. (4–7) be $e \cos \omega = B_1$, $e \sin \omega = B_2$, then

$$e = (B_1^2 + B_2^2)^{1/2}, \qquad (4\text{–}8)$$

$$\omega = \tan^{-1}\left(\frac{B_2}{B_1}\right). \qquad (4\text{–}9)$$

The algebraic signs of $e \cos \omega$ and $e \sin \omega$ will determine the quadrant of ω because $e > 0$.

The semimajor axis, a, now follows from Eq. (4–5) which may be rearranged in the form

$$a = \frac{r + (\mathbf{r} \cdot \mathbf{e}_1)e \cos \omega + (\mathbf{r} \cdot \mathbf{e}_2)e \sin \omega}{1 - e^2} \qquad (4\text{–}10)$$

or, alternatively,

$$a = \frac{r + B_1(\mathbf{r} \cdot \mathbf{e}_1) + B_2(\mathbf{r} \cdot \mathbf{e}_2)}{1 - e^2}. \qquad (4\text{–}11)$$

We may confirm the value of a by using Kepler's third law [Eq. (3-31)]. If the period is not known, the value of a, calculated from Eq. (4-11), can be used with Kepler's law to find P.

To find the time of perihelion passage, T, Kepler's equation, $M = E - e \sin E$, can be used to find first the mean anomaly M. Obviously E can be calculated from $r = a(1 - e \cos E)$. With M given for one time of observation, the value of T follows from

$$M = \frac{2\pi}{P} (t - T). \qquad (4\text{-}12)$$

Thus the elements a, e, i, ω, Ω, T for the orbit can be calculated from the known space coordinates of the moving celestial object. In reality we could have performed the analysis using only two positions together with the constancy of the areal velocity as a third condition. But the resulting calculations are more complex.

EXAMPLE. The heliocentric coordinates of a moving object for three dates are given in the accompanying table. Its mean daily motion is $n = 2\pi/P = 4°.0923$.

Date	l	b	r(A.U.)
June 1.000	142°45′40″	+6°58′43″	0.34200
June 6.000	166°37′56″	+6°08′47″	0.37022
June 11.000	186°58′43″	+4°35′51″	0.39867

Find the elements of its orbit.

For illustrative purposes, we shall carry only five-place accuracy in the calculations. A considerably greater precision in practice is required for such computation.

Date	r	$x' = r \cos b \cos l$	$y' = r \cos b \sin l$	$z' = r \sin b$
June 1	0.34200	−0.27025	+0.20542	+0.04155
June 6	0.37022	−0.35812	+0.08510	+0.03964
June 11	0.39867	−0.39444	−0.04828	+0.03195

$$\mathbf{r_1} = -0.27025\mathbf{i} + 0.20542\mathbf{j} + 0.04155\mathbf{k},$$

$$\mathbf{r_2} = -0.35812\mathbf{i} + 0.08510\mathbf{j} + 0.03964\mathbf{k}, \qquad (4\text{-}13)$$

$$\mathbf{r_3} = -0.39444\mathbf{i} - 0.04828\mathbf{j} + 0.03195\mathbf{k}.$$

Hence, we have

$$\mathbf{r}_1 \times \mathbf{r}_2 = \begin{vmatrix} \mathbf{i} & \mathbf{j} & \mathbf{k} \\ -0.27025 & 0.20542 & 0.04155 \\ -0.35812 & 0.08510 & 0.03964 \end{vmatrix},$$

$$\frac{\mathbf{r}_1 \times \mathbf{r}_2}{|\mathbf{r}_1 \times \mathbf{r}_2|} = 0.09023\mathbf{i} - 0.08184\mathbf{j} + 0.99254\mathbf{k}, \tag{4-14}$$

$$\mathbf{i} = \cos^{-1}(0.99254) = 7°0', \tag{4-15}$$

$$\Omega = \tan^{-1}\left(\frac{0.09023}{0.08184}\right) = 47°47'.6. \tag{4-16}$$

Therefore

$$\mathbf{e}_1 = 0.67181\mathbf{i} + 0.74072\mathbf{j},$$
$$\mathbf{e}_2 = -0.73519\mathbf{i} + 0.66680\mathbf{j} + 0.12187\mathbf{k}, \tag{4-17}$$
$$\mathbf{e}_3 = 0.09023\mathbf{i} - 0.08184\mathbf{j} + 0.99254\mathbf{k}.$$

It is obvious that $\mathbf{e}_3$ and the vector given in Eq. (4–14) are identical, as they should be. Then

$$\mathbf{r}_1 - \mathbf{r}_2 = 0.08787\mathbf{i} + 0.12032\mathbf{j} + 0.00191\mathbf{k},$$
$$\mathbf{r}_1 - \mathbf{r}_3 = 0.12419\mathbf{i} + 0.25370\mathbf{j} + 0.00960\mathbf{k}. \tag{4-18}$$

From Eqs. (4–18) and (4–17),

$$(\mathbf{r}_1 - \mathbf{r}_2) \cdot \mathbf{e}_1 = 0.14815,$$
$$(\mathbf{r}_1 - \mathbf{r}_2) \cdot \mathbf{e}_2 = 0.01586,$$
$$(\mathbf{r}_1 - \mathbf{r}_3) \cdot \mathbf{e}_1 = 0.27135,$$
$$(\mathbf{r}_1 - \mathbf{r}_3) \cdot \mathbf{e}_2 = 0.07904.$$

Therefore, by Eqs. (4–7),

$$0.14815\, e \cos \omega + 0.01586\, e \sin \omega = 0.02822,$$
$$0.27135\, e \cos \omega + 0.07904\, e \sin \omega = 0.05667.$$

Solving these equations, we obtain $e \sin \omega = 0.09966$ and $e \cos \omega = 0.17981$ so that

$$e = 0.2056, \tag{4-19}$$
$$\omega = 28° 59'.8. \tag{4-20}$$

Hence, using $\mathbf{r}_1$, $\mathbf{e}_1$, and $\mathbf{e}_2$ with the values of e, $e \sin \omega$, and $e \cos \omega$ found above, we find by Eq. (4–11)

$$a = \frac{0.34200 - (0.02940)(0.17981) + (0.34072)(0.09966)}{1 - 0.04226}$$

or

$$a = 0.38702 \text{ A.U.} \tag{4–21}$$

With this value of a and the value of e given in Eq. (4–19), we obtain at time $t_1 = $ June 1.000:

$$r_1 = a(1 - e \cos E_1) = 0.38702(1 - 0.2056 \cos E_1),$$

which yields

$$\cos E_1 = 0.56576 \quad \text{and} \quad E_1 = 55°32'.7.$$

From Kepler's equation (E_1 is converted to radians),

$$M_1 = E_1 - e \sin E_1 = 0.96944 - (0.2056)(0.82457)$$
$$= 0.79991 \text{ rad.}$$

Therefore, Eq. (4–12) yields ($n = 4°.092339 = 0.07142$ rad)

$$t_1 - T = \frac{M_1}{n} = \frac{0.79991}{0.07142} = 11.200,$$

and since $t_1 = $ June 1.000 = May 32.000, we have

$$T = \text{May } 20.800. \tag{4–22}$$

In summary, therefore, the elements of the orbit are

$$a = 0.38702 \text{ A.U.}, \quad \Omega = 47°47'.6,$$
$$e = 0.2056, \quad \omega = 28°59'.8,$$
$$i = 7°0', \quad T = \text{May } 20.8.$$

As a check on the value of a we use the period $P = 2\pi/n = 87.975$ days. By Kepler's third law [Eq. (3–31)]

$$P = \frac{2\pi a^{3/2}}{k\sqrt{1 + m}}.$$

Therefore, since $m \ll 1$, we find $a^{3/2} = k/n$. Hence

$$a = \left(\frac{0.017202}{0.07142}\right)^{2/3} = (0.24086)^{2/3} \quad \text{or} \quad a = 0.38712,$$

which agrees sufficiently well with the value of a listed above.

PROBLEMS

1. The heliocentric ecliptic positions of a planet whose period is 686.98 days are as follows.

Date	l	b	r(A.U.)
July 4	181°42'10''	+1°21'55''	1.64830
Sept. 2	209°12'08''	+0°38'05''	1.59849
Nov. 1	238°55'46''	−0°18'39''	1.52637

Determine the elements of the planetary orbit.

2. The space probe Pioneer V was launched March 11, 1960, into an orbit around the sun. Subsequently by radio transmission and from the geometry of the earth's orbit it was determined that the heliocentric coordinates of Pioneer V were as follows.

Date (1960)	l	b	r(A.U.)
April 1	190°10'	−1°10'.4	0.98122
April 15	204°47'	−1°55'.7	0.96690
May 1	220°00'	−2°34'.7	0.94679

Determine the elements of the orbit of Pioneer V. From the elements calculate the geocentric position and distance of the probe on January 1, 1961. The geocentric equatorial coordinates of the sun on January 1, 1961, are $X = +0.17662$, $Y = −0.88738$, $Z = −0.38482$.

4–2 Laplace's method. The problem treated in the preceding section is unrealistic in the sense that for most astronomical applications the length of the radius vector is not known. Only the angular position of the object in the sky as seen from the earth is recorded. Such an observation obviously locates the object somewhere on a line through the earth. Exactly where, we do not know. In this section, the method devised by Laplace, near the beginning of the nineteenth century, for finding the preliminary orbit of a celestial body from three observations of position will be described.

The equation of relative motion of a planet, say, around the sun [Eq. (3–11)] can be expressed in the form

$$\ddot{\mathbf{r}} = -\frac{\mathbf{r}}{r^3} \qquad (4\text{–}23)$$

by choosing the units of mass, distance, and time appropriately. Here $\mathbf{r}(t)$ is the radius vector from sun to planet at time t. This equation is obviously expressed in heliocentric coordinates. The conditions which determine the arbitrary constants in its solution, however, are expressed in terms of geocentric coordinates because the observations are made from the earth. The solution of the problem must contain a mechanism for making the transformation of coordinates from the geocentric to the heliocentric system.

Let $\mathbf{r}_0$ be the heliocentric radius vector of the planet at an initial epoch t_0. Let $\mathbf{r}$ denote its position at time t. Then we can write the solution of Eq. (4–23) in the form of a Taylor's series

$$\mathbf{r} = \mathbf{r}_0 + \dot{\mathbf{r}}_0 \tau + \frac{1}{2!} \ddot{\mathbf{r}}_0 \tau^2 + \cdots, \qquad (4\text{–}24)$$

where $\tau = k(t - t_0)$. The differentiability of $\mathbf{r}(t)$ at $t = t_0$ is assumed; the resulting time derivatives evaluated at this epoch are denoted by the subscripts.

By means of Eq. (4–23), we can eliminate $\ddot{\mathbf{r}}_0$ from Eq. (4–24) in terms of $\mathbf{r}_0$ and r_0. Then successive differentiations and the use of Eq. (4–23) result in

$$\dddot{\mathbf{r}}_0 = 3r_0^{-4}\dot{r}_0\mathbf{r}_0 - r_0^{-3}\dot{\mathbf{r}}_0,$$

$$\ddddot{\mathbf{r}}_0 = (-2r_0^{-6} - 12r_0^{-5}\dot{r}_0^2)\mathbf{r}_0 + 6r_0^{-4}\dot{r}_0\dot{\mathbf{r}}_0. \qquad (4\text{–}25)$$

In this way successive derivatives can all be expressed in terms of $\mathbf{r}_0$ and $\dot{\mathbf{r}}_0$.

Substitution of Eq. (4–25) into Eq. (4–24) reduces the latter to a linear form

$$\mathbf{r} = f\mathbf{r}_0 + g\dot{\mathbf{r}}_0, \qquad (4\text{–}26)$$

where

$$f = 1 - \tfrac{1}{2}\tau^2 r_0^{-3} + \tfrac{1}{2}\tau^3 r_0^{-4}\dot{r}_0 - \tfrac{1}{12}\tau^4(r_0^{-6} + 6r_0^{-5}\dot{r}_0^2) + \cdots, \qquad (4\text{–}27)$$

$$g = \tau - \tfrac{1}{6}\tau^3 r_0^{-3} + \tfrac{1}{24}\tau^4 r_0^{-4}\dot{r}_0 - \cdots, \qquad (4\text{–}28)$$

$$\tau = k(t - t_0).$$

In principle, therefore, if the series for f and g in Eqs. (4–27) and (4–28) converge, we can find $\mathbf{r}(t)$ given the position and velocity vectors $\mathbf{r}_0$ and $\dot{\mathbf{r}}_0$ at the initial epoch t_0. The problem is to find these vectors from the observations.

In Fig. 4–2, let x, y, and z denote a rectangular heliocentric equatorial coordinate system. The symbol S represents the sun; the x-axis is directed toward the vernal equinox.

Let a parallel geocentric system be centered on the earth at E. Then the unit vector $\mathbf{u}$ defining the position of the mass m, say, a planet, is given by

$$\mathbf{u} = \cos\alpha\cos\delta\mathbf{i} + \sin\alpha\cos\delta\mathbf{j} + \sin\delta\mathbf{k}, \qquad (4\text{–}29)$$

where $\mathbf{i}$, $\mathbf{j}$, and $\mathbf{k}$ are unit vectors along the ξ, η, ζ axes, respectively.

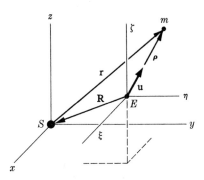

FIG. 4-2. Vector relationships for orbit computation.

The observational data are: (α_1, δ_1) at time t_1; (α_0, δ_0) at time t_0; (α_3, δ_3) at time t_3. These observations can be expressed by Eq. (4-29) in terms of the unit vectors $\mathbf{u}_1$, $\mathbf{u}_0$, and $\mathbf{u}_3$. We assume that $t_1 < t_0 < t_3$.

From the figure it is apparent that

$$\mathbf{r} = \boldsymbol{\rho} - \mathbf{R} = \rho\mathbf{u} - \mathbf{R}, \tag{4-30}$$

and hence

$$\dot{\mathbf{r}} = \dot{\rho}\mathbf{u} + \rho\dot{\mathbf{u}} - \dot{\mathbf{R}}, \tag{4-31}$$

$$\ddot{\mathbf{r}} = \ddot{\rho}\mathbf{u} + 2\dot{\rho}\dot{\mathbf{u}} + \rho\ddot{\mathbf{u}} - \ddot{\mathbf{R}}. \tag{4-32}$$

But from Eq. (4-23), we have $\ddot{\mathbf{r}} = -r^{-3}\mathbf{r}$. Equation (4-32) then can be written

$$\ddot{\rho}\mathbf{u} + 2\dot{\rho}\dot{\mathbf{u}} + \rho\ddot{\mathbf{u}} = \ddot{\mathbf{R}} - r^{-3}\mathbf{r}. \tag{4-33}$$

We now take the triple scalar product $\mathbf{u} \times \dot{\mathbf{u}} \cdot$ of both sides of Eq. (4-33) remembering that such a product which contains two identical elements vanishes. Thus we find

$$\rho[\mathbf{u} \times \dot{\mathbf{u}} \cdot \ddot{\mathbf{u}}] = [\mathbf{u} \times \dot{\mathbf{u}} \cdot \ddot{\mathbf{R}}] - r^{-3}[\mathbf{u} \times \dot{\mathbf{u}} \cdot \mathbf{r}].$$

This can be simplified still further by substituting in the last bracket $\mathbf{r} = \rho\mathbf{u} - \mathbf{R}$. We find finally

$$\rho[\mathbf{u} \times \dot{\mathbf{u}} \cdot \ddot{\mathbf{u}}] = [\mathbf{u} \times \dot{\mathbf{u}} \cdot \ddot{\mathbf{R}}] + \frac{[\mathbf{u} \times \dot{\mathbf{u}} \cdot \mathbf{R}]}{r^3}. \tag{4-34}$$

This equation is of the form

$$\rho = A + Br^{-3}, \tag{4-35}$$

where

$$A = \frac{\mathbf{u} \times \dot{\mathbf{u}} \cdot \ddot{\mathbf{R}}}{\mathbf{u} \times \dot{\mathbf{u}} \cdot \ddot{\mathbf{u}}} \qquad B = \frac{\mathbf{u} \times \dot{\mathbf{u}} \cdot \mathbf{R}}{\mathbf{u} \times \dot{\mathbf{u}} \cdot \ddot{\mathbf{u}}} \tag{4-36}$$

A second relation between ρ and r is evident from Fig. 4–2. By the cosine law

$$r^2 = R^2 + \rho^2 - 2\rho(\mathbf{u} \cdot \mathbf{R}). \tag{4-37}$$

The problem is to solve Eqs. (4–35) and (4–37) simultaneously for ρ and r at time t_0. This implies a knowledge of the scalars A and B, which in turn depend upon the unit vectors and the position vector of the sun.

The *American Ephemeris* gives for each day in the year the cartesian coordinates of the sun from which $\mathbf{R} = X\mathbf{i} + Y\mathbf{j} + Z\mathbf{k}$ can be computed. In fact, the *Ephemeris* gives the magnitude of this vector and also the geocentric equatorial coordinates of the sun so that its position is known. Furthermore, we know that $\ddot{\mathbf{R}} = -R^{-3}\mathbf{R}$. Hence this substitution can be made in A.

Let $\tau_1 = k(t_1 - t_0)$ and $\tau_3 = k(t_3 - t_0)$ be the time intervals between the middle and the first and last observations. Then we may write, by Taylor's expansion,

$$\mathbf{u}_1 = \mathbf{u}_0 + \dot{\mathbf{u}}_0\tau_1 + \tfrac{1}{2}\ddot{\mathbf{u}}_0\tau_1^2 + \cdots,$$
$$\mathbf{u}_3 = \mathbf{u}_0 + \dot{\mathbf{u}}_0\tau_3 + \tfrac{1}{2}\ddot{\mathbf{u}}_0\tau_3^2 + \cdots. \tag{4-38}$$

If the observations are not too far apart in time, these expansions can be truncated to include only the terms through degree two in τ. They may be written

$$\mathbf{u}_1 - \mathbf{u}_0 = \dot{\mathbf{u}}_0\tau_1 + \tfrac{1}{2}\ddot{\mathbf{u}}_0\tau_1^2,$$
$$\mathbf{u}_3 - \mathbf{u}_0 = \dot{\mathbf{u}}_0\tau_3 + \tfrac{1}{2}\ddot{\mathbf{u}}_0\tau_3^2. \tag{4-39}$$

Here $\mathbf{u}_1, \mathbf{u}_0, \mathbf{u}_3, \tau_1, \tau_3$ are known, and hence we can solve for the unknowns $\dot{\mathbf{u}}_0$ and $\ddot{\mathbf{u}}_0$. These then are incorporated into Eqs. (4–36) to yield A and B at $t = t_0$.

A convenient way to solve Eqs. (4–39) is the following: Let

$$\frac{\mathbf{u}_1 - \mathbf{u}_0}{\tau_1} \equiv \mathbf{u}(1, 0) \qquad \text{and} \qquad \frac{\mathbf{u}_3 - \mathbf{u}_0}{\tau_3} \equiv \mathbf{u}(3, 0).$$

Then Eqs. (4–39) can be written

$$\mathbf{u}(1, 0) = \dot{\mathbf{u}}_0 + \tfrac{1}{2}\tau_1\ddot{\mathbf{u}}_0, \tag{4-40}$$

$$\mathbf{u}(3, 0) = \dot{\mathbf{u}}_0 + \tfrac{1}{2}\tau_3\ddot{\mathbf{u}}_0, \tag{4-41}$$

from which we find

$$\dot{\mathbf{u}}_0 = \frac{\tau_3\mathbf{u}(1, 0) - \tau_1\mathbf{u}(3, 0)}{\tau_3 - \tau_1},$$

$$\ddot{\mathbf{u}}_0 = \frac{2[\mathbf{u}(3, 0) - \mathbf{u}(1, 0)]}{\tau_3 - \tau_1}. \tag{4-42}$$

When more than three observations are given, the series expansions [Eqs. (4–38)] can be carried to higher order terms. The higher order terms in $\mathbf{u}$ and its derivatives can be eliminated with resultant higher accuracy for the $\dot{\mathbf{u}}_0$ and $\ddot{\mathbf{u}}_0$.

Eqs. (4–35) and (4–37) can be solved by an iteration process. Assume a value, say r_1, in Eq. (4–35) and calculate the corresponding value of ρ, say ρ_1. This value substituted in Eq. (4–37) yields a revised value of r, say r_2. Repeat the calculation with this value of r and obtain a new value ρ_2. The rapidity with which this converges will depend upon the astuteness of the computer in guessing the initial estimate of r. If the mean daily motion or the period of the object can be estimated, a first guess for r might be obtained from Kepler's third law.

The nature of this solution can be visualized graphically. Let $r^2 = s$. Then Eq. (4–35) can be written

$$s = \left(\frac{B}{\rho - A} \right)^{2/3}.$$

The graph of s against ρ is shown in Fig. 4–3, curve I. It has a vertical asymptote at $\rho = A$.

In a similar way Eq. (4–37) can be written

$$s = \rho^2 - 2(\mathbf{u} \cdot \mathbf{R})\rho + R^2.$$

The graph of this is the parabola II shown in Fig. 4–3. There *may* be, in general, three intersections of curves I and II. One of these values of s, and hence of r, is the one to be used to begin the iterative process for obtaining the exact numerical solution described above.

Let us examine more closely the values of r^2 corresponding to the intersections of curves I and II in Fig. 4–3. The student may show that one of these can be ascribed to $r = R$, the radius vector of the earth's orbit.

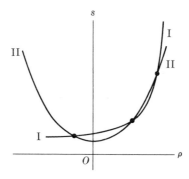

Fig. 4–3. Graphical solution of equations for r_0 and ρ_0.

Another may correspond to such a large or such a small value of r that the solution is obviously spurious. The third value of r is then the one with which the iterative process can be started. The slopes of curves I and II in the neighborhood of the adopted solution may be useful in deciding how rapidly the iteration process converges.

We shall now assume that r_0 and ρ_0 are known from the above calculations. These must obviously satisfy Eq. (4–30). To obtain $\dot{\mathbf{r}}_0$, we need to evaluate $\dot{\rho}_0$. This may be found by operating on Eq. (4–32) with the product $[\cdot(\mathbf{u} \times \ddot{\mathbf{u}})]$. We have, after deleting the products which vanish,

$$2\dot{\rho}[\dot{\mathbf{u}} \cdot \mathbf{u} \times \ddot{\mathbf{u}}] = [\ddot{\mathbf{R}} \cdot \mathbf{u} \times \ddot{\mathbf{u}}] + \frac{1}{r^3}[\mathbf{R} \cdot \mathbf{u} \times \ddot{\mathbf{u}}]. \qquad (4\text{–}43)$$

The quantities in the brackets and the value r_0 at $t = t_0$ are known. Therefore $\dot{\rho}_0$ can be calculated. From Eq. (4–31), we then have

$$\dot{\mathbf{r}}_0 = \dot{\rho}_0\mathbf{u}_0 + \rho_0\dot{\mathbf{u}}_0 - \dot{\mathbf{R}}_0. \qquad (4\text{–}44)$$

With $\mathbf{r}_0$ and $\dot{\mathbf{r}}_0$ given by the above analysis, we can find $\mathbf{r}$ at any other time t by means of Eq. (4–26). Thus the Laplacian method yields the requisite values of $\mathbf{r}_1, \mathbf{r}_0$, and $\mathbf{r}_3$ from which the preliminary orbital elements can be calculated by the method described in Section 4–1. Or, alternatively, the initial velocity and radius vector can be used according to the method described in Section 3–4.

The following example will illustrate the calculations required by Laplace's method. We shall assume that all corrections necessary to reduce the observed positions to true geocentric positions have been applied. For simplicity, we shall use five-place accuracy only. In any practical application of this or any other method for obtaining orbital elements, considerably greater accuracy is required.

EXAMPLE. Given the following geocentric positions and corresponding times, find the elements of the preliminary orbit of the object:

Date (1961)	α	δ
Nov. 15.0	$22^\text{h}39^\text{m}27^\text{s}.5$	$-10°53'50''.5$
Dec. 2.0	$22^\text{h}47^\text{m}48^\text{s}.1$	$-11°46'29''.5$
Dec. 12.0	$22^\text{h}55^\text{m}01^\text{s}.1$	$-11°55'57''.3$

Let t_1, t_0, and t_3 denote the times of the observations, and $t_3 > t_0 > t_1$. Table XI of the *American Ephemeris* gives a conversion of time units to are units for application to the values of α. Therefore we find the following.

	t_1	t_0	t_3
α	$22^h39^m27^s.5$ $339°51'52''.5$	$22^h47^m48^s.1$ $341°57'01''.5$	$22^h55^m01^s.1$ $343°45'16''.5$
$\sin \alpha$ $\cos \alpha$	-0.34424 $+0.93888$	$-0.30984 \cdot$ $+0.95080$	-0.27975 $+0.96007$
δ	$-10°53'50''.5$	$-11°46'29''.5$	$-11°55'57''.3$
$\sin \delta$ $\cos \delta$	-0.18905 $+0.98197$	-0.20407 $+0.97896$	-0.20676 $+0.97839$

By Eq. (4–29), we find the unit vectors

	u_1	u_0	u_3
i	$+0.92195$	$+0.93078$	$+0.93932$
j	-0.33803	-0.30332	-0.27370
k	-0.18905	-0.20407	-0.20676

and their differences

	$u_1 - u_0$	$u_3 - u_0$
i	-0.00883	$+0.00854$
j	-0.03471	$+0.02962$
k	$+0.01502$	-0.00269

$$\tau_1 = k(t_1 - t_0) = -0.29243, \qquad \tau_3 = k(t_3 - t_0) = +0.17202.$$

Using these values in Eqs. (4–42), we find the following.

	$\dot{u}_0$	$\ddot{u}_0$
i	$+0.04246$	$+0.08389$
j	$+0.15235$	$+0.23014$
k	-0.02888	$+0.15368$

For the same three dates, the *American Ephemeris* gives the following rectangular geocentric equatorial coordinates of the sun (1950.0).

	$R_1(t_1)$	$R_0(t_0)$	$R_3(t_3)$
X	-0.605812	-0.346707	-0.178284
Y	-0.717297	-0.846706	-0.888332
Z	-0.311058	-0.367176	-0.385229

Treating these in the same way we did the vectors **u**, we find the following values by Eqs. (4-42).

	$R_1 - R_0$	$R_3 - R_0$	$\dot{R}_0$	$\ddot{R}_0$
i	-0.25911	$+0.16842$	$+0.94462$	$+0.40053$
j	$+0.12941$	-0.04163	-0.31627	$+0.86350$
k	$+0.05612$	-0.01805	-0.13715	$+0.37455$

Hence, by Eqs. (4-36)

$$\mathbf{u}_0 \times \dot{\mathbf{u}}_0 \cdot \ddot{\mathbf{u}}_0 = \begin{vmatrix} +0.93078 & -0.30332 & -0.20407 \\ +0.04246 & +0.15235 & -0.02888 \\ +0.08389 & +0.23014 & +0.15368 \end{vmatrix}$$

$$= +0.03131.$$

In a similar way, by replacing $\ddot{\mathbf{u}}_0$ by $\mathbf{R}_0$ and $\ddot{\mathbf{R}}_0$, respectively, we find

$$\mathbf{u}_0 \times \dot{\mathbf{u}}_0 \cdot \mathbf{R}_0 = -0.08604, \qquad \mathbf{u}_0 \times \dot{\mathbf{u}}_0 \cdot \ddot{\mathbf{R}}_0 = +0.089628.$$

Thus Eq. (4-35) becomes

$$\rho_0 = 2.8670 - 2.7484 r_0^{-3}. \tag{4-45}$$

Furthermore, by Eq. (4-37),

$$r_0^2 = \mathbf{R}_0 \cdot \mathbf{R}_0 + \rho_0^2 - 2\rho_0(\mathbf{u}_0 \cdot \mathbf{R}_0)$$

$$= 0.97194 + \rho_0^2 - 0.01809\rho_0. \tag{4-46}$$

We observe that for r_0 very large $\rho_0 \rightarrow 2.8670$, and that in Eq. (4-46) r_0^2 cannot differ by much more than one from ρ_0^2. Therefore we try $r_0 = 3.0000$ as a starting value. Thus, by Eq. (4-46),

$$\left. \begin{array}{l} r_0 = 3.0000 \\ r_0^2 = 9.0000 \end{array} \right\} \rho_0 = 2.76518 \rightarrow r_0^2 = 8.56814.$$

This is reasonably close. Further, systematically applied trials yield

$$\rho_0 = 2.7562, \qquad r_0 = 2.9163.$$

These are the distances in astronomical units from earth to object and from sun to object at the time of the middle observation.

Using the value of ρ_0, and Eq. (4-30), we find the heliocentric radius vector to be

$$\mathbf{r}_0 = 2.91210\mathbf{i} + 0.01071\mathbf{j} - 0.19527\mathbf{k}.$$

The value of $\dot\rho_0$ remains to be calculated. Evaluation of the determinants required in Eq. (4–43) follows the same procedure used for those needed in Eq. (4–34). We find

$$\dot{\mathbf{u}}_0 \cdot \mathbf{u}_0 \times \ddot{\mathbf{u}}_0 = -0.03131,$$

$$\tfrac{1}{2}\ddot{\mathbf{R}}_0 \cdot \mathbf{u}_0 \times \ddot{\mathbf{u}}_0 = -0.02420,$$

$$\tfrac{1}{2}\mathbf{R}_0 \cdot \mathbf{u}_0 \times \ddot{\mathbf{u}}_0 = +0.02374.$$

These lead to

$$\dot\rho_0 = 0.77282 - \frac{0.75822}{r_0^3},$$

and hence upon substitution of the value found for r_0,

$$\dot\rho_0 = +0.74225.$$

Equation (4–44) then yields for the heliocentric velocity vector

$$\dot{\mathbf{r}}_0 = -0.13673\mathbf{i} + 0.51104\mathbf{j} - 0.09392\mathbf{k}.$$

With the values of $\mathbf{r}_0$ and $\dot{\mathbf{r}}_0$ found by the preceding analysis, we are now in position to calculate $\mathbf{r}_1$ and $\mathbf{r}_3$. By Eqs. (4–27) and (4–28), we find

$$f_1 = +0.99814, \qquad g_1 = -0.29226,$$
$$f_3 = +0.99941, \qquad g_3 = +0.17199.$$

Therefore [Eq. (4–26)] at times t_1 and t_3, respectively, we have

$$\mathbf{r}_1 = 0.99814\,\mathbf{r}_0 - 0.29226\,\dot{\mathbf{r}}_0, \qquad \mathbf{r}_3 = 0.99941\,\mathbf{r}_0 + 0.17199\,\dot{\mathbf{r}}_0.$$

In rectangular heliocentric *equatorial* coordinates the three position vectors of the object are, therefore,

$$\mathbf{r}_1 = 2.94664\mathbf{i} - 0.13867\mathbf{j} - 0.16746\mathbf{k},$$

$$\mathbf{r}_0 = 2.91210\mathbf{i} + 0.01071\mathbf{j} - 0.19527\mathbf{k},$$

$$\mathbf{r}_3 = 2.88686\mathbf{i} + 0.09860\mathbf{j} - 0.21131\mathbf{k}.$$

We leave the transformation of these into heliocentric *ecliptic* coordinates and the calculation of the orbital elements by the method of Section 4–1 as an exercise for the student. Figure 4–4 illustrates the successive positions of the earth and the object as seen projected on the equatorial plane.

Having found the right ascension and declination corresponding to each of the calculated positions $\mathbf{r}_1$ and $\mathbf{r}_3$, we may compare these with the observed α and δ for the two times. This will indicate how accurately the preliminary orbit based on $\mathbf{r}_0$ and $\dot{\mathbf{r}}_0$ fits the observations. Suppose the

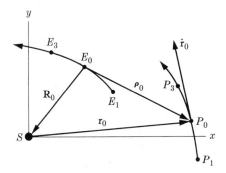

FIG. 4–4. Orbital positions of object calculated in the example.

deviations of the calculated from the observed positions are larger than are warranted from the known errors in the observed quantities. Then corrections must be applied to improve the preliminary orbital elements.

It is obvious from the method used above that the middle observation is exactly satisfied by the intermediate elements $\mathbf{r}_0$ and $\dot{\mathbf{r}}_0$ which have been found. However, the observations at t_1 and t_3 enter the calculations only through the approximations to the derivatives $\dot{\mathbf{u}}_0$, $\ddot{\mathbf{u}}_0$, $\dot{\mathbf{R}}_0$, $\ddot{\mathbf{R}}_0$, and so forth, obtained from Eqs. (4–42). Therefore, we would not expect the values of $\mathbf{r}_1$ and $\mathbf{r}_3$ predicted by means of the formula $\mathbf{r} = f\mathbf{r}_0 + g\dot{\mathbf{r}}_0$ to represent the observations at t_1 and t_3 exactly. On the other hand, calculation of $\mathbf{r}$ by means of these series [Eqs. (4–27), (4–28)] insures that the predicted first and third positions are *dynamically* consistent with the middle one. These positions accurately represent those the body would have if it were moving strictly in accordance with the intermediate elements $\mathbf{r}_0$ and $\dot{\mathbf{r}}_0$. The predicted positions at t_1 and t_3 satisfy the dynamical but not the geometrical conditions of the motion. We refer the student to other sources* for the details of a modified Laplacian method to make more direct use of the observed data at t_1 and t_3 and for consideration of the problem of improvement in the orbital elements.

In carrying out more refined orbital calculations, the recorded times of observations must be corrected for the time difference between the positions of the earth and sun. Light travels one A.U. in 0.00577 days; hence the *planetary aberration correction*, as it is called, is given by t(true) $= t$(obs) $- 0^\mathrm{d}.00577\rho$, where ρ is in A.U.

There are pitfalls arising in the calculation of an orbit by the Laplacian method or by any other method. Indeterminate cases arise in which three observations are insufficient. We shall examine some of them briefly. Suppose, for example, that the inclination of the orbit is zero. Then i

---

* P. Herget, *Computation of Orbits.*

and Ω need not be found. This leaves four elements, a, e, ω, and T, to be determined. The observations, however, of α, δ, when reduced to heliocentric coordinates, all have $b = 0°$, and hence we are left with only the three longitudes. A fourth observation is required in order to obtain a solution for the remaining unknown.

Suppose again that (a) the three observations are on a great circle and (b) the sun crosses this great circle during the time interval spanned by the observations. Then the situation is analogous to that of an object moving in the ecliptic plane. The sun, the earth, and the object are in nearly the same plane during the period of the observations. Again the solution is indeterminate and more observations are necessary. Methods for treating these exceptional cases are presented in standard treatises on orbit calculation.

PROBLEMS

1. Calculate the preliminary elements of the orbit for the object discussed in the example above.

2. For the object in the example, use the position and velocity vectors $\mathbf{r}_0$ and $\dot{\mathbf{r}}_0$, transformed to the heliocentric ecliptic coordinate system, to obtain the orbital elements by the method of Section 3–4.

3. The positions of an unidentified object are as follows.

1959 Date (U.T.)	$\alpha(1950)$	$\delta(1950)$
June 5.95391	$20^h17^m8^s.4$	$-38°38'20''.4$
June 9.90717	$19^h51^m57^s.8$	$-37°31'30''.0$
June 11.90557	$19^h40^m26^s.9$	$-36°53'56''.8$

For the same dates, the geocentric equatorial coordinates of the sun are as follows (in A.U.).

X	Y	Z
+0.2730601	+0.8966519	+0.3888416
+0.2080829	+0.9116112	+0.3953504
+0.1748719	+0.9125075	+0.3957174

Remember that $\tau = k(t - t_0)$, where $k = 0.017202099$. Find the orbital elements of the moving object.

4–3 Gauss's method. It should be clear that the Laplacian method discussed in Section 4–2 yields an orbit which fits the middle observation exactly. The positions predicted for times t_1 and t_3, however, depend upon

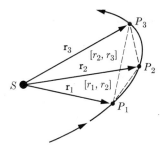

FIG. 4–5. Triangular areas in the Gaussian method.

the truncated series for f and g. Hence they agree with the observed positions only approximately. In the Gaussian method to be described, the observed positions at t_1 and t_3 enter the calculations directly. Therefore they serve immediately to strengthen the solution.

Let $\mathbf{r}_1$, $\mathbf{r}_2$, $\mathbf{r}_3$ be the unknown heliocentric equatorial position vectors at times t_1, t_2, and t_3. Because the motion takes place in a plane, one of these is a linear combination of the other two. We write, therefore,

$$\mathbf{r}_2 = c_1\mathbf{r}_1 + c_3\mathbf{r}_3, \tag{4–47}$$

and it is assumed that $\mathbf{r}_1$, $\mathbf{r}_2$, and $\mathbf{r}_3$ are not collinear.

As in Section 4–2, set $\mathbf{r} = \rho\mathbf{u} - \mathbf{R}$, where $\mathbf{u}$ is a unit vector denoting the geocentric position of the celestial object [Eq. (4–29)]. Then Eq. (4–47) can be written

$$c_1\rho_1\mathbf{u}_1 - \rho_2\mathbf{u}_2 + c_3\rho_3\mathbf{u}_3 = c_1\mathbf{R}_1 - \mathbf{R}_2 + c_3\mathbf{R}_3. \tag{4–48}$$

If the values of c_1 and c_3 are known, this equation in component form furnishes three simultaneous equations in ρ_1, ρ_2, and ρ_3, the geocentric distances of the object at the times of observation.

This is a geometric relationship. The values of c_1 and c_3 must be determined in such a way that, as the object moves along its orbit, the dynamical conditions are fulfilled; that is, $\ddot{\mathbf{r}}_i = -r_i^{-3}\mathbf{r}_i$ $(i = 1, 2, 3)$.

The quantities c_1 and c_3 have interesting geometrical interpretations. Taking the vector products of Eq. (4–47) by $\mathbf{r}_1$ and by $\mathbf{r}_3$, we find

$$\mathbf{r}_1 \times \mathbf{r}_2 = c_3\mathbf{r}_1 \times \mathbf{r}_3, \qquad \mathbf{r}_2 \times \mathbf{r}_3 = c_1\mathbf{r}_1 \times \mathbf{r}_3.$$

But $|\mathbf{r}_1 \times \mathbf{r}_2|$ is twice the area of the triangle SP_1P_2 (Fig. 4–5); $|\mathbf{r}_2 \times \mathbf{r}_3|$ is twice the area of SP_2P_3; and $|\mathbf{r}_1 \times \mathbf{r}_3|$ is twice the area SP_1P_3. Furthermore, since the vectors $\mathbf{r}_1$, $\mathbf{r}_2$, and $\mathbf{r}_3$ are coplanar, the cross products mentioned are collinear. Therefore, denoting the areas involved by $[r_1, r_2]$, $[r_2, r_3]$, and $[r_1, r_3]$, we see that

$$c_1 = \frac{[r_2, r_3]}{[r_1, r_3]} \quad \text{and} \quad c_3 = \frac{[r_1, r_2]}{[r_1, r_3]}. \qquad (4\text{--}49)$$

The solutions for c_1 and c_3 devised by Gauss* made use of *sector-triangle ratios*. These are the ratios of the sectors of the ellipse bounded by the radius vectors of the corresponding triangles. Let (r_1, r_3), (r_2, r_3), and (r_1, r_2) denote the sectors of the ellipse so bounded. Then the sector-triangle ratios are

$$\bar{y}_1 = \frac{(r_2, r_3)}{[r_2, r_3]}; \qquad \bar{y}_2 = \frac{(r_1, r_3)}{[r_1, r_3]}; \qquad \bar{y}_3 = \frac{(r_1, r_2)}{[r_1, r_2]}. \qquad (4\text{--}50)$$

We may write, therefore,

$$c_1 = \frac{(r_2, r_3)}{\bar{y}_1} \frac{\bar{y}_2}{(r_1, r_3)} = \frac{(t_3 - t_2)\bar{y}_2}{(t_3 - t_1)\bar{y}_1},$$

$$\qquad\qquad\qquad\qquad\qquad\qquad\qquad\qquad (4\text{--}51)$$

$$c_3 = \frac{(r_1, r_2)}{\bar{y}_3} \frac{\bar{y}_2}{(r_1, r_3)} = \frac{(t_2 - t_1)\bar{y}_2}{(t_3 - t_1)\bar{y}_3}.$$

The last terms in these equations follow from Kepler's second law, namely that the areas of the sectors swept out by the radius vector are proportional to the times.

The evaluation of c_1 and c_3 obviously rests upon a method of calculating the ratios $\bar{y}_2/\bar{y}_1$ and $\bar{y}_2/\bar{y}_3$. Such methods are presented in standard works on orbit computation, and we shall not go into detail here.† In brief, it is possible to obtain series expansions for c_1 and c_3 which fulfill the dynamical conditions of the motion.

Let

$$T_1 = k(t_3 - t_2),$$

$$T_2 = k(t_3 - t_1),$$

$$T_3 = k(t_2 - t_1)$$

---

* C. F. Gauss, *Theoria Motus Corporum Coelestium*, translated by C. H. Davis. Boston: Little, Brown and Co., 1857.

† See, for example, K. P. Williams, *The Calculation of the Orbits of Asteroids and Comets*. Bloomington, Indiana: The Principia Press, Inc., 1934, Chapter VII. Also P. Herget, *The Computation of Orbits*, p. 54 ff.

denote the time intervals between observations. Then the series expansions, truncated as was done in the Laplacian method, are

$$c_1 = \frac{T_1}{T_2} + \frac{1}{6}\left(\frac{T_1}{T_2}\right)\left(1 - \frac{T_1^2}{T_2^2}\right)\left(\frac{T_2^2}{r_2^3}\right) = a_1 + \frac{b_1}{r_2^3},$$

$$c_3 = \frac{T_3}{T_2} + \frac{1}{6}\left(\frac{T_3}{T_2}\right)\left(1 - \frac{T_3^2}{T_2^2}\right)\left(\frac{T_2^2}{r_2^3}\right) = a_3 + \frac{b_3}{r_2^3}. \tag{4-52}$$

The quantities a_1, b_1, a_3, and b_3 can be calculated directly from the times of observation.

Now we operate upon Eq. (4–48) to isolate the term $\rho_2 \mathbf{u}_2$. Taking the triple scalar product of both sides of Eq. (4–48) by $\cdot \mathbf{u}_1 \times \mathbf{u}_3$, we find

$$-\rho_2[\mathbf{u}_2 \cdot \mathbf{u}_1 \times \mathbf{u}_3] = c_1[\mathbf{R}_1 \cdot \mathbf{u}_1 \times \mathbf{u}_3] - [\mathbf{R}_2 \cdot \mathbf{u}_1 \times \mathbf{u}_3] + c_3[\mathbf{R}_3 \cdot \mathbf{u}_1 \times \mathbf{u}_3],$$

and upon substituting the values of c_1 and c_3 from Eqs. (4–52), there results

$$\rho_2[\mathbf{u}_1 \cdot \mathbf{u}_2 \times \mathbf{u}_3] = \left(a_1 + \frac{b_1}{r_2^3}\right)[\mathbf{R}_1 \cdot \mathbf{u}_1 \times \mathbf{u}_3] - [\mathbf{R}_2 \cdot \mathbf{u}_1 \times \mathbf{u}_3]$$

$$+ \left(a_3 + \frac{b_3}{r_2^3}\right)[\mathbf{R}_3 \cdot \mathbf{u}_1 \times \mathbf{u}_3],$$

which yields

$$\rho_2 = A + \frac{B}{r_2^3}, \tag{4-53}$$

where

$$A = \frac{a_1[\mathbf{R}_1 \cdot \mathbf{u}_1 \times \mathbf{u}_3] - [\mathbf{R}_2 \cdot \mathbf{u}_1 \times \mathbf{u}_3] + a_3[\mathbf{R}_3 \cdot \mathbf{u}_1 \times \mathbf{u}_3]}{[\mathbf{u}_1 \cdot \mathbf{u}_2 \times \mathbf{u}_3]},$$

$$B = \frac{b_1[\mathbf{R}_1 \cdot \mathbf{u}_1 \times \mathbf{u}_3] + b_3[\mathbf{R}_3 \cdot \mathbf{u}_1 \times \mathbf{u}_3]}{[\mathbf{u}_1 \cdot \mathbf{u}_2 \times \mathbf{u}_3]}. \tag{4-54}$$

Also we have

$$r_2^2 = \rho_2^2 + R_2^2 - 2(\mathbf{u}_2 \cdot \mathbf{R}_2)\rho_2. \tag{4-55}$$

The two equations [(4–53) and (4–55)] are the counterparts of Eqs. (4–35) and (4–37) of Section 4–2. They are to be solved simultaneously for ρ_2 and r_2.

Operating on Eq. (4–48) with $\cdot \mathbf{u}_2 \times \mathbf{u}_3$, we obtain

$$c_1\rho_1[\mathbf{u}_1 \cdot \mathbf{u}_2 \times \mathbf{u}_3] = c_1[\mathbf{R}_1 \cdot \mathbf{u}_2 \times \mathbf{u}_3] - [\mathbf{R}_2 \cdot \mathbf{u}_2 \times \mathbf{u}_3] + c_3[\mathbf{R}_3 \cdot \mathbf{u}_2 \times \mathbf{u}_3]. \tag{4-56}$$

Similarly, we have

$$c_3\rho_3[\mathbf{u}_3 \cdot \mathbf{u}_1 \times \mathbf{u}_2] = c_1[\mathbf{R}_1 \cdot \mathbf{u}_1 \times \mathbf{u}_2] - [\mathbf{R}_2 \cdot \mathbf{u}_1 \times \mathbf{u}_2] + c_3[\mathbf{R}_3 \cdot \mathbf{u}_2 \times \mathbf{u}_3].$$

$$(4\text{--}57)$$

Because r_2 has been determined, the quantities c_1 and c_3 are known from Eqs. (4–52), and hence Eqs. (4–56) and (4–57) yield directly ρ_1 and ρ_3.

It is clear that geometrically the observations at all three times are satisfied by the values of ρ so found. However, the values of c_1 and c_3 were determined from truncated series expressions and, therefore, the dynamical conditions imposed upon the solution are only approximately fulfilled. In Eqs. (4–52), defining c_1 and c_3, the truncation error would enter the values of b_1 and b_3. More accurate formulas for computing c_1 and c_3, when r_1, r_2, and r_3 are approximately known, are available.* With these more accurate values, we can obtain new values of b_1 and b_3 given by

$$b_1 = (c_1' - a_1)r_2^3, \qquad b_3 = (c_3' - a_3)r_2^3,$$

where c_1' and c_3' are the revised values of c_1 and c_3.

The formulas given by Gibbs† for c_1 and c_3 are

$$c_1 = \frac{T_1}{T_2}\left[\frac{1 + B_1 r_1^{-3}}{1 - B_2 r_2^{-3}}\right],$$

$$c_3 = \frac{T_3}{T_2}\left[\frac{1 + B_3 r_3^{-3}}{1 - B_2 r_2^{-3}}\right],$$

$$(4\text{--}58)$$

where

$$B_1 = \tfrac{1}{12}(mn + n - m)T_2^2,$$

$$B_2 = \tfrac{1}{12}(mn + 1)T_2^2,$$

$$B_3 = \tfrac{1}{12}(mn - n + m)T_2^2,$$

$$(4\text{--}59)$$

$$m = \frac{T_1}{T_2} \quad \text{and} \quad n = \frac{T_3}{T_2}.$$

These formulas may be used to improve the values of ρ_1, ρ_2, and ρ_3, and hence of r_1, r_2, and r_3. It should be noted that the times to be used in an

* See, for example, R. T. Crawford, *Determination of Orbits of Comets and Asteroids.* New York: McGraw-Hill Book Company, Inc., 1930, pp. 109 ff.

† W. Gibbs, "On the Determination of Elliptical Orbits," *Memoirs National Academy of Science*, Vol. IV, 1888.

improvement of this type should be corrected for light time by using the expression

$$t_{corr} = t_{obs} - 0.00577\rho,$$

where ρ is the distance computed in the first approximation.

From this point on, the calculation is again that of determining the orbital elements from the known values of r_1, r_2, and r_3.

PROBLEMS

1. Apply Gauss's method to the data used in the example discussed in Section 4–2.

2. A minor planet was observed as follows:

Date (1961 0^h E.T.)	α(1950)	δ(1950)
Nov. 1.0	$4^h02^m01^s.30$	$+11°38'42''.8$
Nov. 11.0	$3^h52^m35^s.17$	$+11°15'58''.7$
Nov. 27.0	$3^h35^m49^s.42$	$+10°51'18''.4$

The geocentric rectangular equatorial coordinates of the sun for the same dates (in A.U.) were as follows:

X	Y	Z
−0.7802476	−0.5626925	−0.2440132
−0.6598348	−0.6771343	−0.2936387
−0.4271833	−0.8159774	−0.3538531

By Gauss's method, find the elements of its preliminary orbit.

CHAPTER 5

THE THREE- AND n-BODY PROBLEMS

The complexity of motion arising when more than two bodies move under their mutual gravitational attractions increases rapidly with the number of objects concerned. As we have seen in the preceding chapters, the two-body problem can be formulated mathematically in such a way that, given the initial position and velocity of one body relative to the other, we can predict its position and velocity in space at any later time. This represents a closed mathematical solution to the problem. When more than two bodies are involved, it is impossible, in general, to formulate such a solution. Certain special cases can be so treated.

The planets of the solar system constitute a classic example of the n-body problem. As the positions of the planets change during their orbital motion around the sun, the gravitational forces acting on a given member of the system change also. In the case of the solar system, however, the sun is the dominant center of force. Hence the resulting planetary motions approximate closely the motions which would be observed if the sun and each planet comprised a pure two-body system. Deviations from the two-body motion due to the action of the other planets are called *perturbations*.

For a satellite of small mass moving around the earth, the dominant force center is the earth itself. But the sun, the moon, and even the earth's lack of sphericity cause deviations from two-body motion of the satellite.

In this chapter we shall outline mathematically the principal features of the three- and n-body problems.

5–1 Motion of the center of mass. We assume that the masses concerned are spherically symmetrical in homogeneous layers so that they attract one another like point masses. For simplicity in description we shall restrict

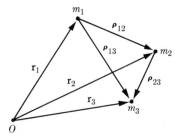

Fig. 5–1. Vector relations in three-body problem.

attention to three masses, m_1, m_2, and m_3, located in a primary fixed reference system by the position vectors $\mathbf{r}_1$, $\mathbf{r}_2$, and $\mathbf{r}_3$ (Fig. 5–1). Generalization to n bodies can be made readily from the analysis. The only forces acting are the mutual Newtonian attractions of the bodies on each other.

The equations of motion are

$$m_1\ddot{\mathbf{r}}_1 = k^2 \left\{ \frac{m_1 m_2}{\rho_{12}^3} \boldsymbol{\rho}_{12} + \frac{m_1 m_3}{\rho_{13}^3} \boldsymbol{\rho}_{13} \right\}, \tag{5–1}$$

$$m_2\ddot{\mathbf{r}}_2 = k^2 \left\{ \frac{m_2 m_3}{\rho_{23}^3} \boldsymbol{\rho}_{23} - \frac{m_2 m_1}{\rho_{12}^3} \boldsymbol{\rho}_{12} \right\}, \tag{5–2}$$

$$m_3\ddot{\mathbf{r}}_3 = k^2 \left\{ - \frac{m_3 m_2}{\rho_{23}^3} \boldsymbol{\rho}_{23} - \frac{m_3 m_1}{\rho_{13}^3} \boldsymbol{\rho}_{13} \right\}, \tag{5–3}$$

where the $\boldsymbol{\rho}_{i,j}$ are the vectors joining the masses, as shown in Fig. 5–1.

Adding Eqs. (5–1), (5–2), and (5–3) and integrating twice, we obtain

$$m_1\mathbf{r}_1 + m_2\mathbf{r}_2 + m_3\mathbf{r}_3 = \mathbf{c}_1 t + \mathbf{c}_2, \tag{5–4}$$

where $\mathbf{c}_1$ and $\mathbf{c}_2$ are vector constants of integration. But by definition the position of the center of mass, $\mathbf{R}$, of the three mass points is given by

$$\mathbf{R} = \frac{m_1\mathbf{r}_1 + m_2\mathbf{r}_2 + m_3\mathbf{r}_3}{M},$$

where $M = m_1 + m_2 + m_3$. Therefore it is apparent from Eq. (5–4) that

$$\mathbf{R} = \frac{\mathbf{c}_1}{M} t + \frac{\mathbf{c}_2}{M}, \tag{5–5}$$

an equation which states that the *center of mass either remains at rest or moves uniformly in space on a straight line.* This constitutes a first integral of the equations of motion and involves six arbitrary constants, namely the three components of each of the vectors $\mathbf{c}_1$ and $\mathbf{c}_2$.

If there are n bodies in the system, the differential equation for the ith member would be

$$m_i\ddot{\mathbf{r}}_i = k^2 \sum_{j=1}^{n-1} \frac{m_i m_j}{\rho_{i,j}^3} \boldsymbol{\rho}_{i,j} \quad (i, j = 1, 2, 3, \ldots, n; \quad i \neq j), \tag{5–6}$$

where $\boldsymbol{\rho}_{i,j}$ is the vector *from m_i to m_j.* Remembering that $\boldsymbol{\rho}_{i,j} = -\boldsymbol{\rho}_{j,i}$, we have, by summing Eq. (5–6) over i,

$$\sum_{i=1}^{n} m_i\ddot{\mathbf{r}}_i = 0.$$

Two integrations of this equation lead to a relationship similar to Eq. (5–4), namely

$$\sum_{i=1}^{n} m_i \mathbf{r}_i = \mathbf{c}_1 t + \mathbf{c}_2,$$

and again, since

$$\mathbf{R} = \frac{1}{M} \sum_{i=1}^{n} m_i \mathbf{r}_i,$$

we have

$$\mathbf{R} = \frac{\mathbf{c}_1}{M} t + \frac{\mathbf{c}_2}{M}, \tag{5–7}$$

where

$$M = \sum_{i=1}^{n} m_i.$$

Thus in the case of n bodies subjected only to their own mutual gravitational attractions, the center of mass either moves uniformly in space on a straight line or remains at rest. Equations (5–5) and (5–7) are identical to Eq. (3–4) of the two-body problem discussed in Chapter 3.

5–2 The angular momentum, or areal velocity, integrals. Let $\mathbf{u}_{12}$, $\mathbf{u}_{13}$, and $\mathbf{u}_{23}$ be unit vectors in the directions of $\boldsymbol{\rho}_{12}, \boldsymbol{\rho}_{13}$, and $\boldsymbol{\rho}_{23}$ (Fig. 5–1). Then Eqs. (5–1), (5–2), and (5–3) can be written

$$m_1 \dot{\mathbf{v}}_1 = k^2 \left\{ \frac{m_1 m_2}{\rho_{12}^2} \mathbf{u}_{12} + \frac{m_1 m_3}{\rho_{13}^2} \mathbf{u}_{13} \right\}, \tag{5–8}$$

$$m_2 \dot{\mathbf{v}}_2 = k^2 \left\{ \frac{m_2 m_3}{\rho_{23}^2} \mathbf{u}_{23} - \frac{m_2 m_1}{\rho_{12}^2} \mathbf{u}_{12} \right\}, \tag{5–9}$$

$$m_3 \dot{\mathbf{v}}_3 = k^2 \left\{ - \frac{m_3 m_2}{\rho_{23}^2} \mathbf{u}_{23} - \frac{m_3 m_1}{\rho_{13}^2} \mathbf{u}_{13} \right\}. \tag{5–10}$$

Taking the vector products of Eqs. (5–8) to (5–10), respectively, by $\mathbf{r}_1, \mathbf{r}_2, \mathbf{r}_3$ and adding, we obtain

$$\sum_{i=1}^{3} \mathbf{r}_i \times m_i \dot{\mathbf{v}}_i = k^2 \left\{ \frac{m_1 m_2}{\rho_{12}^2} (\mathbf{r}_1 - \mathbf{r}_2) \times \mathbf{u}_{12} + \frac{m_2 m_3}{\rho_{23}^2} (\mathbf{r}_2 - \mathbf{r}_3) \times \mathbf{u}_{23} \right.$$
$$\left. + \frac{m_3 m_1}{\rho_{13}^2} (\mathbf{r}_1 - \mathbf{r}_3) \times \mathbf{u}_{13} \right\}. \tag{5–11}$$

But $\mathbf{r}_1 - \mathbf{r}_2$ is collinear with $\mathbf{u}_{12}$; $\mathbf{r}_2 - \mathbf{r}_3$ is collinear with $\mathbf{u}_{23}$; and $\mathbf{r}_1 - \mathbf{r}_3$ is collinear with $\mathbf{u}_{13}$. Therefore the vector products and, hence, the entire right-hand side of Eq. (5–11) vanishes. Furthermore, the left-

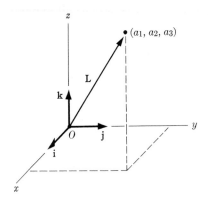

FIG. 5–2. The angular momentum vector.

hand side can be written

$$\frac{d}{dt}\left\{\sum_{i=1}^{3} \mathbf{r}_i \times m_i\mathbf{v}_i\right\} = 0. \tag{5–12}$$

The quantity in braces is the total angular momentum of the system of three mass points about the origin O [see Eq. (1–35)]. We shall denote it by $\mathbf{L}$. Equation (5–12) states that

$$\mathbf{L} = \text{constant vector.} \tag{5–13}$$

We have thus obtained a second integral of the equations of motion. The vector $\mathbf{L}$ involves three arbitrary scalar constants. Equation (5–13) expresses the *conservation of angular momentum* for the system of three masses.

In a cartesian coordinate system with origin at O (Fig. 5–2), let us denote the angular momentum vector by

$$\mathbf{L} = a_1\mathbf{i} + a_2\mathbf{j} + a_3\mathbf{k}.$$

Then the cartesian equations equivalent to Eq. (5–13) are

$$\sum_{i=1}^{3} m_i[y_i\dot{z}_i - z_i\dot{y}_i] = a_1,$$

$$\sum_{i=1}^{3} m_i[z_i\dot{x}_i - x_i\dot{z}_i] = a_2, \tag{5–14}$$

$$\sum_{i=1}^{3} m_i[x_i\dot{y}_i - y_i\dot{x}_i] = a_3.$$

The brackets appearing in these equations are the projections of the areal velocities of the various bodies upon the three coordinate planes. Hence they are called *the integrals of area*. In two-body motion these expressions have a counterpart in Eqs. (3–14) of Section 3–3. If we denote by A_{i1}, A_{i2}, A_{i3} the projections of the areas swept out by the radius vector of the mass m_i upon the yz-, xz-, and xy-planes, respectively, Eqs. (5–14) may be written

$$\sum_{i=1}^{3} m_i \dot{A}_{i1} = a_1,$$

$$\sum_{i=1}^{3} m_i \dot{A}_{i2} = a_2,$$

$$\sum_{i=1}^{3} m_i \dot{A}_{i3} = a_3.$$

These may be integrated to yield

$$\sum_{i=1}^{3} m_i A_{i1} = a_1 t + b_1,$$

$$\sum_{i=1}^{3} m_i A_{i2} = a_2 t + b_2, \qquad (5\text{--}15)$$

$$\sum_{i=1}^{3} m_i A_{i3} = a_3 t + b_3.$$

Hence we may summarize the geometric equivalent of the conservation of angular momentum in the form: *the sums of the products of the masses and the projections of the areas swept out by the corresponding radius vectors increase uniformly with the time.*

As the three bodies move, their velocity and position vectors are always so oriented that the vector **L** maintains a fixed direction in space and has the constant magnitude $(a_1^2 + a_2^2 + a_3^2)^{1/2}$. The line along which **L** is directed is called the *invariable line*. Associated with the invariable line is a plane perpendicular to it through the center of mass of the system called the *invariable plane*, a term introduced by Laplace. The invariable plane is characterized by the following properties: (a) the angular momentum about any line in the plane is zero; (b) the angular momentum about a line normal to the plane is a maximum. The direction numbers of the normal to the invariable plane are a_1, a_2, and a_3 in our notation.

In the solar system the orbital angular momentum contributed by Jupiter and Saturn constitutes nearly 87% of that of the whole system.

As a consequence of this contribution and because the orbital planes of these two major planets are nearly in the ecliptic, the vector $\mathbf{L}$ is directed only about $1°35'$ from the pole of the latter. The invariable plane lies between the orbital planes of these two major planets. Because the masses, positions, and velocities of members of the solar system are known with considerable accuracy at a given time, the constants a_1, a_2, and a_3 for this system can be found with considerable accuracy. Hence the invariable plane of the solar system is relatively well determined.

What has been said here for the three-body system can be generalized readily to the n-body problem.

PROBLEMS

1. Show that the plane through the origin, perpendicular to the vector $\mathbf{L}$, will have the equation $a_1x + a_2y + a_3z = 0$.

2. Find the angular momentum of the system of three masses about a line whose direction cosines are λ, μ, ν. Show that if this line coincides with L, the angular momentum is $(a_1^2 + a_2^2 + a_3^2)^{1/2}$, but if the line lies in the plane $a_1x + a_2y + a_3z = 0$, the angular momentum is zero.

5-3 The integral of energy. Another integral of the equations of motion in the three-body problem is that of energy analogous to Eq. (2-12) of Section 2-3. Let us take the scalar products of Eqs. (5-8), (5-9), and (5-10) by $\dot{\mathbf{r}}_1$, $\dot{\mathbf{r}}_2$, and $\dot{\mathbf{r}}_3$, respectively, and add the results. We find

$$\sum_{i=1}^{3} m_i \dot{\mathbf{r}}_i \cdot \dot{\mathbf{v}}_i = k^2 \left\{ \frac{m_1 m_2}{\rho_{12}^2} \mathbf{u}_{12} \cdot (\dot{\mathbf{r}}_1 - \dot{\mathbf{r}}_2) + \frac{m_1 m_3}{\rho_{13}^2} \mathbf{u}_{13} \cdot (\dot{\mathbf{r}}_1 - \dot{\mathbf{r}}_3) \right.$$
$$\left. + \frac{m_2 m_3}{\rho_{23}^2} \mathbf{u}_{23} \cdot (\dot{\mathbf{r}}_2 - \dot{\mathbf{r}}_3) \right\}.$$

$$(5\text{-}16)$$

Furthermore,

$$\dot{\mathbf{r}}_1 - \dot{\mathbf{r}}_2 = -\dot{\boldsymbol{\rho}}_{12}; \qquad \dot{\mathbf{r}}_1 - \dot{\mathbf{r}}_3 = -\dot{\boldsymbol{\rho}}_{13}; \qquad \dot{\mathbf{r}}_2 - \dot{\mathbf{r}}_3 = -\dot{\boldsymbol{\rho}}_{23}$$

and

$$\dot{\boldsymbol{\rho}}_{i,j} = \frac{d}{dt}(\rho_{i,j}\mathbf{u}_{i,j}) = \dot{\rho}_{i,j}\mathbf{u}_{i,j} + \rho_{i,j}\dot{\mathbf{u}}_{i,j} \qquad \text{for } (i, j = 1, 2, 3; \quad i \neq j).$$

Because $\mathbf{u}_{ij}$ is a unit vector, $\dot{\mathbf{u}}_{ij} \cdot \mathbf{u}_{ij} = 0$ and $\mathbf{u}_{ij} \cdot \mathbf{u}_{ij} = 1$. Using these relations in Eq. (5-16), we have

$$\sum_{i=1}^{3} m_i \dot{\mathbf{r}}_i \cdot \dot{\mathbf{v}}_i = -k^2 \left\{ \frac{m_1 m_2}{\rho_{12}^2} \dot{\rho}_{12} + \frac{m_1 m_3}{\rho_{13}^2} \dot{\rho}_{13} + \frac{m_2 m_3}{\rho_{23}^2} \dot{\rho}_{23} \right\}. \quad (5\text{-}17)$$

This may be written

$$\frac{d}{dt}\left[\frac{1}{2}\sum_{i=1}^{3} m_i \dot{\mathbf{r}}_i^2\right] = k^2 \frac{d}{dt}\left[\frac{m_1 m_2}{\rho_{12}} + \frac{m_1 m_3}{\rho_{13}} + \frac{m_2 m_3}{\rho_{23}}\right]. \qquad (5\text{–}18)$$

The kinetic energy of the system is by definition

$$T = \frac{1}{2}\sum_{i=1}^{3} m_i \dot{\mathbf{r}}_i^2 = \frac{1}{2}\sum_{i=1}^{3} m_i v_i^2, \qquad (5\text{–}19)$$

where v_i is the speed of the ith mass. We define the potential energy of the system by

$$V = -k^2 \left\{\frac{m_1 m_2}{\rho_{12}} + \frac{m_1 m_3}{\rho_{13}} + \frac{m_2 m_3}{\rho_{23}}\right\}. \qquad (5\text{–}20)$$

Then integration of Eq. (5–18) yields the fundamental property

$$T + V = E \text{ (a constant)}. \qquad (5\text{–}21)$$

This is the integral of energy. Equation (5–21) expresses the *conservation of energy* for the system of three masses.

Again the result derived here for three masses can be generalized to the n-body problem.

5–4 Summary of properties : n-body problem. In the preceding sections, we have derived important properties of the three-body motion which can be generalized to the n-body problem. The following is a summary of these properties.

(a) By Eq. (5–20) the potential energy of the system is

$$V = -k^2 \sum_{i,j=1}^{n} \frac{m_i m_j}{\rho_{i,j}} \qquad (i \neq j).$$

This depends only on the *relative distances* of the mass points from each other. Its value is invariant under a translation of the origin of the coordinate system and under a rotation of the axes of the system through any arbitrary angle.

(b) Because of this invariance under translation and rotation of axes, the integrals yielding the motion of the center of mass and those called the integrals of areas follow. Involved here are nine constants of integration — six defining the position of the center of mass at any instant and three defining the orientation of the angular momentum vector. Unfortunately, because a fixed origin and similarly a fixed orientation of axes cannot be defined in space, these nine constants cannot be determined by initial conditions depending upon observation.

(c) A tenth constant, E in Eq. (5–21), results from the integral of energy. Thus we have exhibited 10 constants of integration for the n-body problem. But it is apparent from the equations of motion that we need to find $6n$ constants to solve the problem completely. In the three-body problem, for example, we have only 10 of the 18 constants needed. Many mathematicians have sought other integrals of the equations of motion, hence other constants, to supplement those outlined above. Such efforts have, in general, been unsuccessful. The integrals, such as that of energy, are algebraic relations between the coordinates and velocities. These are sometimes called the *classical* integrals of the three-body problem. In 1887, Bruns* demonstrated that these 10 integrals were the only independent algebraic integrals of the problem. All others could be formed by combinations of these 10. A similar theorem has been proved by Poincaré.† The reader is referred to other sources for an extensive discussion of these theorems,‡ as well as for the underlying mathematical theory for systems of differential equations.§

The conclusion to be drawn is that one cannot, in general, solve for the coordinates and velocity components of the three mass points as functions of the time given their values at some initial epoch. The same is true for the n-body problem. The general n-body problem is unsolvable in closed form, meaning: given the coordinates and velocities of n mass-points moving under their own mutual gravitational attractions, one cannot predict the motion for any arbitrary succeeding time interval. It cannot be predicted in general whether two or more of the masses will collide in any arbitrary finite time interval, or whether some member of the system will escape from it. In succeeding sections, we shall discuss certain special configurations of the masses in the three-body problem which do lead to solutions. These were discovered by Lagrange¶ in 1772.

---

* H. Bruns, "Über die Integrale des Vielkörper-Problems," *Acta Mathematica*, Vol. XI, p. 25, 1887.

† H. Poincaré, *Les Methodes Nouvelle de la Mecanique Céleste*. Paris: Gauthier-Villars, 1892, Chapter 5, p. 250 ff.

‡ E. T. Whittaker, *Analytical Dynamics*, Cambridge: Cambridge University Press, 1917, Chapter 14.

§ W. Kaplan, *Ordinary Differential Equations*, Reading, Mass.: Addison-Wesley Publishing Company, Inc., 1958, Chapter 7, pp. 314–325; Chapter 12, pp. 510–514.

¶ J. L. Lagrange, *Collected Works*. Paris: Gauthier-Villars, 1873, Vol. VI, p. 229.

5–5 Equations of relative motion. The practical impossibility of establishing a fixed coordinate system in space to which the motions of celestial bodies can be referred leads to a consideration of the relative motions of n-1 bodies with respect to the nth. In the solar system, for example, we select the sun as the origin of coordinates and the plane of the ecliptic as the fundamental plane of reference. The motions of the other members of the system, planets, comets, satellites and so forth, can be described relative to the sun. The discussion of this section will be confined to the three-body problem. Generalization to the n-body problem is easily performed.

In Fig. 5–1, let m_1 be chosen as the origin. Then by subtracting Eq. (5–1) from Eqs. (5–2) and (5–3), we find, after some simplification,

$$\ddot{\boldsymbol{\rho}}_{12} = -\frac{k^2(m_1 + m_2)}{\rho_{12}^2}\mathbf{u}_{12} + k^2 m_3\left\{\frac{1}{\rho_{23}^2}\mathbf{u}_{23} - \frac{1}{\rho_{13}^2}\mathbf{u}_{13}\right\}, \quad (5\text{--}22)$$

$$\ddot{\boldsymbol{\rho}}_{13} = -\frac{k^2(m_1 + m_3)}{\rho_{13}^2}\mathbf{u}_{13} - k^2 m_2\left\{\frac{1}{\rho_{23}^2}\mathbf{u}_{23} + \frac{1}{\rho_{12}^2}\mathbf{u}_{12}\right\}. \quad (5\text{--}23)$$

The first of these is the equation of motion of m_2 relative to m_1; the second is the equation of motion of m_3 relative to m_1. The right-hand side of Eq. (5–22), for example, consists of three terms which represent, respectively, (a) the acceleration of m_2 due to the action of m_1, (b) the acceleration of m_2 due to the action of m_3, and (c) the reactive, or negative, acceleration of m_1 due to the presence of m_3. The right-hand terms in Eq. (5–23) can be interpreted similarly. If $m_3 = 0$, it is obvious that Eq. (5–22) describes the motion of m_2 around m_1, as in the two-body problem discussed in Chapter 3. Similarly if $m_2 = 0$, Eq. (5–23) describes the two-body relative motion of m_3 around m_1.

Let m_1 denote the dominant mass of the group of three masses and be situated at the origin of a cartesian coordinate system (Fig. 5–3). Let m denote the body whose motion is to be studied, and let m' be a mass which disturbs the motion of m around m_1. Then the equations of motion for m become

$$\ddot{x} = -\frac{k^2 M x}{r^3} + k^2 m'\left\{\frac{x' - x}{\rho^3} - \frac{x'}{r'^3}\right\}, \quad (5\text{--}24)$$

$$\ddot{y} = -\frac{k^2 M y}{r^3} + k^2 m'\left\{\frac{y' - y}{\rho^3} - \frac{y'}{r'^3}\right\}, \quad (5\text{--}25)$$

$$\ddot{z} = -\frac{k^2 M z}{r^3} + k^2 m'\left\{\frac{z' - z}{\rho^3} - \frac{z'}{r'^3}\right\}, \quad (5\text{--}26)$$

where $M = m_1 + m$.

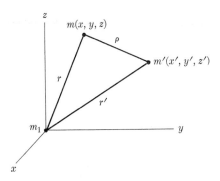

FIG. 5–3. Space orientation in three-body problem.

Because $\rho^2 = (x' - x)^2 + (y' - y)^2 + (z' - z)^2$, we have

$$\frac{x' - x}{\rho^3} = \frac{\partial \rho^{-1}}{\partial x},$$

$$\frac{y' - y}{\rho^3} = \frac{\partial \rho^{-1}}{\partial y},$$

$$\frac{z' - z}{\rho^3} = \frac{\partial \rho^{-1}}{\partial z}.$$

Furthermore, because x, y, and z are independent of x', y', and z', we can write

$$\frac{\partial}{\partial x} \left\{ \frac{xx' + yy' + zz'}{r'^3} \right\} = \frac{x'}{r'^3},$$

$$\frac{\partial}{\partial y} \left\{ \frac{xx' + yy' + zz'}{r'^3} \right\} = \frac{y'}{r'^3},$$

$$\frac{\partial}{\partial z} \left\{ \frac{xx' + yy' + zz'}{r'^3} \right\} = \frac{z'}{r'^3}.$$

Substitution of these expressions into Eqs. (5–24), (5–25), and (5–26) leads to the symmetric forms

$$\ddot{x} = -\frac{k^2 M x}{r^3} + \frac{\partial R}{\partial x}, \tag{5–27}$$

$$\ddot{y} = -\frac{k^2 M y}{r^3} + \frac{\partial R}{\partial y}, \tag{5–28}$$

$$\ddot{z} = -\frac{k^2 M z}{r^3} + \frac{\partial R}{\partial z}, \tag{5–29}$$

where

$$R = k^2 m' \left\{ \frac{1}{\rho} - \frac{xx' + yy' + zz'}{r'^3} \right\}.$$

This function R is called the *disturbing*, or *perturbative, function*. It is obvious that $R = 0$ leads to the simple two-body problem of the relative motion of m around m_1.

If more than one disturbing mass is present, the disturbing function due to all masses is the sum of the disturbing functions for the individual masses. Let

$$R_i = k^2 m_i' \left\{ \frac{1}{\rho_i} - \frac{xx_i' + yy_i' + zz_i'}{r_i'^3} \right\}$$

be the disturbing function for the ith mass which acts on m. Then the equations of motion of m become

$$\ddot{x} = -\frac{k^2 M x}{r^3} + \sum_{i=1}^{n-2} \frac{\partial R_i}{\partial x}, \qquad (5\text{--}30)$$

$$\ddot{y} = -\frac{k^2 M y}{r^3} + \sum_{i=1}^{n-2} \frac{\partial R_i}{\partial y}, \qquad (5\text{--}31)$$

$$\ddot{z} = -\frac{k^2 M z}{r^3} + \sum_{i=1}^{n-2} \frac{\partial R_i}{\partial z}, \qquad (5\text{--}32)$$

where n is the number of masses in the system.

PROBLEMS

1. Let $x = r \cos \theta$, $y = r \sin \theta$ denote polar coordinates in the plane. Show that the equations for perturbative motion in two dimensions become

$$\ddot{r} - r\dot{\theta}^2 + \frac{k^2 M}{r^2} = \frac{\partial R}{\partial r}, \qquad \frac{d}{dt}(r^2 \dot{\theta}) = \frac{\partial R}{\partial \theta};$$

where

$$R = k^2 m' \left\{ \frac{1}{\rho} - \frac{r}{r'^2} \cos(\theta - \theta') \right\}.$$

2. Let m_1, m, and m' in the three-body problem be located permanently at the vertices of an equilateral triangle. Solve the three-body problem in this case. [*Hint:* Use the equations of Problem 1.] How does the period of m around m_1 compare, in this case, with the period m would have if m' were not present?

3. Let m_1, m, and m' be situated permanently along the same straight line. Solve the three-body problem, if possible, in this case.

5–6 Stationary solutions of the three-body problem. In 1772 Lagrange discovered two special solutions of the three-body problem which may be designated *stationary solutions*. The three mass points m_1, m_2, and m_3 are initially assumed to be projected in the same plane. Then, by a stationary

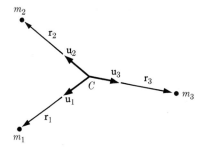

FIG. 5-4. Orientation relative to center of mass in three-body problem.

solution, we mean one in which the geometric configuration of the three masses remains invariant with respect to the time. If the motion of the masses is such that their mutual distances from each other remain unchanged, the configuration simply rotates in its own plane around the center of mass. On the other hand, an expansion or contraction may take place which does not alter the *shape* of the pattern of points.

We consider first the special case in which the three masses revolve in coplanar circular orbits around their center of mass with constant angular speed. Let their position vectors relative to the center of mass C (Fig. 5-4), be $\mathbf{r}_1 = r_1\mathbf{u}_1$, $\mathbf{r}_2 = r_2\mathbf{u}_2$, $\mathbf{r}_3 = r_3\mathbf{u}_3$. For circular motion r_1, r_2, and r_3 are, of course, constant. Here $\mathbf{u}_1$, $\mathbf{u}_2$, and $\mathbf{u}_3$ are unit vectors in the directions of $\mathbf{r}_1$, $\mathbf{r}_2$, and $\mathbf{r}_3$, respectively.

By Eq. (1–11), the total coplanar acceleration of any one of the mass points is given by

$$\mathbf{a} = (\ddot{r} - r\dot{\theta}^2)\mathbf{u}_r + (2\dot{r}\dot{\theta} + r\ddot{\theta})\mathbf{u}_\theta,$$

where $\mathbf{u}_r$ and $\mathbf{u}_\theta$ are unit vectors in the radial and transverse directions, respectively. With the restrictions adopted here in the three-body problem, we have for each mass $\dot{r} = \ddot{r} = 0$, $\dot{\theta} = n$, the constant angular speed of revolution about C, and $\ddot{\theta} = 0$. Therefore the accelerations become

$$\mathbf{a}_i = -r_i n^2 \mathbf{u}_i \qquad (i = 1, 2, 3). \tag{5-33}$$

Using these values in Eqs. (5-1), (5-2), and (5-3), we have

$$-n^2 r_1 \mathbf{u}_1 = k^2 \left\{ \frac{m_2}{\rho_{12}^3} [r_2\mathbf{u}_2 - r_1\mathbf{u}_1] + \frac{m_3}{\rho_{13}^3} [r_3\mathbf{u}_3 - r_1\mathbf{u}_1] \right\}, \tag{5-34}$$

$$-n^2 r_2 \mathbf{u}_2 = k^2 \left\{ \frac{m_3}{\rho_{23}^3} [r_3\mathbf{u}_3 - r_2\mathbf{u}_2] - \frac{m_1}{\rho_{12}^3} [r_2\mathbf{u}_2 - r_1\mathbf{u}_1] \right\}, \tag{5-35}$$

$$-n^2 r_3 \mathbf{u}_3 = k^2 \left\{ -\frac{m_2}{\rho_{23}^3} [r_3\mathbf{u}_3 - r_2\mathbf{u}_2] - \frac{m_1}{\rho_{13}^3} [r_3\mathbf{u}_3 - r_1\mathbf{u}_1] \right\}. \tag{5-36}$$

But the origin has been selected so that

$$m_1 r_1 \mathbf{u}_1 + m_2 r_2 \mathbf{u}_2 + m_3 r_3 \mathbf{u}_3 = 0. \tag{5-37}$$

Therefore, we observe that by multiplying Eq. (5–34) by m_1, Eq. (5–35) by m_2, and adding, we obtain an equation which, upon substitution from Eq. (5–37), is Eq. (5–36). Hence we can use Eq. (5–37) in place of Eq. (5–36) as a third equation in the unit vectors $\mathbf{u}_1$, $\mathbf{u}_2$, and $\mathbf{u}_3$.

We rewrite the system of equations in the form

$$\left(-n^2 + \frac{k^2 m_2}{\rho_{12}^3} + \frac{k^2 m_3}{\rho_{13}^3} \right) r_1 \mathbf{u}_1 - \frac{k^2 m_2}{\rho_{12}^3} r_2 \mathbf{u}_2 - \frac{k^2 m_3}{\rho_{13}^3} r_3 \mathbf{u}_3 = 0, \tag{5-38}$$

$$-\frac{k^2 m_1}{\rho_{12}^3} r_1 \mathbf{u}_1 + \left(-n^2 + \frac{k^2 m_3}{\rho_{23}^3} + \frac{k^2 m_1}{\rho_{12}^3} \right) r_2 \mathbf{u}_2 - \frac{k^2 m_3}{\rho_{23}^3} r_3 \mathbf{u}_3 = 0, \tag{5-39}$$

$$m_1 r_1 \mathbf{u}_1 + m_2 r_2 \mathbf{u}_2 + m_3 r_3 \mathbf{u}_3 = 0. \tag{5-40}$$

These are the conditions which must be fulfilled if the three mass points are to move in a plane in circular orbits around the center of mass with uniform angular speeds, n rad/sec.

Consider now a rectangular coordinate system with the origin at C (Fig. 5–4) and rotating with angular speed n rad/sec in the counterclockwise direction. In this system, the unit vectors $\mathbf{u}_1$, $\mathbf{u}_2$, $\mathbf{u}_3$ are fixed in position. Let the angles in the equations

$$\mathbf{u}_i = \cos \theta_i \mathbf{i} + \sin \theta_i \mathbf{j} \qquad (i = 1, 2, 3),$$

denote their orientations relative to these cartesian axes.

Then by taking the scalar products of $\mathbf{i}$ and Eqs. (5–38), (5–39), and (5–40) we have, after simplification,

$$-n^2 x_1 + \frac{k^2 m_2}{\rho_{12}^3} (x_1 - x_2) + \frac{k^2 m_3}{\rho_{13}^3} (x_1 - x_3) = 0, \tag{5-41}$$

$$-n^2 x_2 + \frac{k^2 m_1}{\rho_{12}^3} (x_2 - x_1) + \frac{k^2 m_3}{\rho_{23}^3} (x_2 - x_3) = 0, \tag{5-42}$$

$$m_1 x_1 + m_2 x_2 + m_3 x_3 = 0, \tag{5-43}$$

where $x_i = r_i \cos \theta_i$ $(i = 1, 2, 3)$.

Similarly, using the scalar products of $\mathbf{j}$ and the same equations, we find

$$-n^2 y_1 + \frac{k^2 m_2}{\rho_{12}^3}(y_1 - y_2) + \frac{k^2 m_3}{\rho_{13}^3}(y_1 - y_3) = 0, \qquad (5\text{–}44)$$

$$-n^2 y_2 + \frac{k^2 m_1}{\rho_{12}^3}(y_2 - y_1) + \frac{k^2 m_3}{\rho_{23}^3}(y_2 - y_3) = 0, \qquad (5\text{–}45)$$

$$m_1 y_1 + m_2 y_2 + m_3 y_3 = 0, \qquad (5\text{–}46)$$

where $y_i = r_i \sin \theta_i$ $(i = 1, 2, 3)$.

Equations (5–41) to (5–46) constitute a system of 6 simultaneous equations in the unknowns $(x_i, y_i)(i = 1, 2, 3)$. We consider here the particular situation in which the masses are located at the vertices of an equilateral triangle. Then $\rho_{12} = \rho_{23} = \rho_{13} = \rho$ at all times. Suppose we adjust the scale of length so that these are all unity for all values of the time. Equations (5–41) to (5–46) may be written then (with $k^2 = 1$ by proper choice of time units)

$$(-n^2 + m_2 + m_3)x_1 - m_2 x_2 - m_3 x_3 = 0,$$
$$-m_1 x_1 + (-n^2 + m_1 + m_3)x_2 - m_3 x_3 = 0, \qquad (5\text{–}47)$$
$$m_1 x_1 + m_2 x_2 + m_3 x_3 = 0;$$

$$(-n^2 + m_2 + m_3)y_1 - m_2 y_2 - m_3 y_3 = 0,$$
$$-m_1 y_1 + (-n^2 + m_1 + m_3)y_2 - m_3 y_3 = 0, \qquad (5\text{–}48)$$
$$m_1 y_1 + m_2 y_2 + m_3 y_3 = 0.$$

These will have a nontrivial solution if

$$\begin{vmatrix} (-n^2 + m_2 + m_3) & -m_2 & -m_3 & 0 & 0 & 0 \\ -m_1 & (-n^2 + m_1 + m_3) & -m_3 & 0 & 0 & 0 \\ m_1 & m_2 & m_3 & 0 & 0 & 0 \\ 0 & 0 & 0 & (-n^2 + m_2 + m_3) & -m_2 & -m_3 \\ 0 & 0 & 0 & -m_1 & (-n^2 + m_1 + m_3) & -m_3 \\ 0 & 0 & 0 & m_1 & m_2 & m_3 \end{vmatrix} = 0. \quad (5\text{–}49)$$

[Obviously the trivial solution $x_i = 0$, $y_i = 0$ $(i = 1, 2, 3)$ is inconsistent with the requirement here that $\rho = 1$.] Let $M = m_1 + m_2 + m_3$ denote the total mass of the system. Then by the usual reduction rules for determinants, we find that Eq. (5–49) reduces to

$$m_3^2(M - n^2)^4 = 0. \qquad (5\text{–}50)$$

This will be satisfied if $n^2 = M$. Had we left k^2 in the equations and also

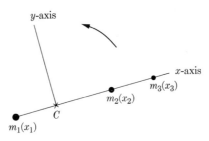

FIG. 5-5. Straight-line solution in three-body problem.

the equal values of $\rho = \rho_{i,j}$ $(i,j = 1, 2, 3; i \neq j)$ this condition would be

$$n^2 = \frac{k^2 M}{\rho^3}. \tag{5-51}$$

Note that Eq. (5-51) is dimensionally consistent and indicates that n is in radians per unit time.

With $n^2 = M$ in Eqs. (5-47) and (5-48), we can choose any two pairs of coordinates (x_i, y_i) arbitrarily, adjust the scale, and determine the third pair in such a way that $\rho = 1$. The equations have a solution, therefore, in this special problem of three-bodies.

A second solution for Eqs. (5-41) to (5-46) can also be found. Suppose that $y_1 = y_2 = y_3 = 0$. All three mass points lie on the x-axis. Then Eqs. (5-44), (5-45), and (5-46) are satisfied. Let the masses be arranged on the x-axis as shown in Fig. 5-5. We denote the distance $x_3 - x_2$ by ρ and arrange the scale so that $x_2 - x_1 = 1$. Then by virtue of the inequalities $x_1 < x_2 < x_3$, Eqs. (5-41), (5-42), and (5-43) become

$$n^2 x_1 + k^2 m_2 + k^2 m_3 (1 + \rho)^{-2} = 0,$$

$$n^2(1 + x_1) - k^2 m_1 + k^2 m_3 \rho^{-2} = 0, \tag{5-52}$$

$$m_1 x_1 + m_2(1 + x_1) + m_3(1 + x_1 + \rho) = 0.$$

From these we eliminate n^2 and x_1 to obtain

$$(m_1 + m_2)\rho^5 + (3m_1 + 2m_2)\rho^4 + (3m_1 + m_2)\rho^3 - (m_2 + 3m_3)\rho^2$$

$$- (2m_2 + 3m_3)\rho - (m_2 + m_3) = 0. \tag{5-53}$$

This is a fifth-degree equation in ρ, originally due to Lagrange,* which has

---

* See, F. Tisserand, *Mécanique Céleste*, Vol. 1, p. 155. Paris: Gauthier-Villars, 1881.

only one real positive root since there is only one change of sign in the coefficients. For the order in which the masses have been arrayed along the x-axis, this has *only one* positive solution for ρ. That is, when ρ is found, we may locate m_3 uniquely, because m_1 and m_2 have already been located arbitrarily to set the scale of distance $(x_2 - x_1 = 1)$. If we interchange the order of location of the masses, we obtain a similar unique solution for each arrangement. The solution for Eq. (5–53) can, in general, be found by numerical or iterative means.

Thus Lagrange found essentially two distinct solutions to the three-body problem, the *equilateral-triangle solution* and the *straight-line solution*, valid for any masses moving in coplanar circular orbits around their center of mass, with uniform angular speed. It is interesting to see the dynamical consequences of this type of motion; or, to put the statement the other way, to see under what dynamical conditions such motions are likely to arise.

It is obvious that, because each mass moves uniformly in a circular path around the center of mass C, the areal velocity in each orbit must be constant. Hence *the resultant force acting on each mass must pass through C.*

Equation (5–33) indicates that the acceleration to which each mass is subjected is $-r_i n^2 \mathbf{u}_i$ $(i = 1, 2, 3)$. Hence the force is $-m_i r_i n^2 \mathbf{u}_i$. We see that the resultant *force on each mass is directly proportional to the distance from C and is directed toward that point.*

It should be clear also in the discussion above that the initial velocity vectors required to produce circular motion of the system are perpendicular to the initial position vectors of the respective masses. Clearly, for each mass m_i the velocity $\mathbf{v}_i = r_i \dot{\mathbf{u}}_i$ so that the velocity is proportional to the distance of m_i from C and is perpendicular to $\mathbf{u}_i$. The motion in the cases discussed above consists of a rotation of the entire system around the center of mass C.

If the initial velocity vectors are not perpendicular to the position vectors of their respective mass points, the configuration which initially may have existed will change with the time. If, however, each vector $\mathbf{v}_i$ $(i = 1,2,3)$ makes the same angle with its corresponding $\mathbf{r}_i$, then an expansion or contraction of the configuration will take place in such a way that the problem is still solvable. The path followed by each mass will be a conic section of eccentricity depending on the initial circumstances of the motion. In this solution, the distances between the bodies vary with the time but always in such a way that their mutual distances apart remain in the same ratio. That is, if ρ_{12}, ρ_{23}, and ρ_{13} denote the distances initially, at time t we would have $\alpha\rho_{12}$, $\alpha\rho_{23}$, and $\alpha\rho_{13}$, where α is the factor of proportionality. This means, of course, that the distances of m_1, m_2, and m_3 from the center of mass at any time are $r_1 = \alpha r_{01}$, $r_2 = \alpha r_{02}$, and $r_3 = \alpha r_{03}$, where r_{0i} $(i = 1, 2, 3)$ are the initial lengths of the position vectors. The *shape* of the configuration remains invariant with time. It is clear that α may be a

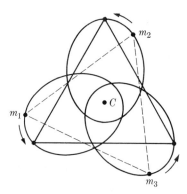

FIG. 5–6. Equilateral-triangle solution in three-body problem.

function of the time. It can be shown* in this case that each mass traverses a conic section with a resultant pattern for the system shown in Fig. 5–6.

The points at the vertices of the equilateral triangle solution of the three-body problem and the points of the straight-line solution are called the *Lagrangian points* of the system. In a coordinate system rotating in its plane around the center of mass with constant angular speed n, these are fixed. A body situated at one of the Lagrangian points and initially at rest there will remain so unless disturbed by external forces. At these points the gravitational and the centrifugal forces just balance each other. We shall discuss this further in connection with the restricted problem of three-bodies in Section 5–7.

PROBLEMS

1. Three masses m_1, m_2, m_3 are placed at rest at the vertices of the equilateral triangle configuration of the three-body problem. Discuss their subsequent motion.

2. Masses $m_1 = 1$, $m_2 = 3$, $m_3 = 5$ are situated along the x-axis in such a way that $x_1 < x_2 < x_3$, as in the straight-line solution of the three-body problem. With $x_2 - x_1 = 1$, find the position of the mass m_3.

3. Suppose that the forces binding m_1, m_2, and m_3 together are not inverse square forces but forces of the form

$$F_{i,j} = m_i m_j \rho_{i,j}^s \ (i, j = 1, 2, 3; i \neq j)$$

acting along the lines joining the masses. Will the equilateral triangle and the straight-line solutions of the three-body problem still hold?

---

* See, for example, F. R. Moulton, *Celestial Mechanics*. 2nd rev. ed. New York: The Macmillan Company, 1914, p. 313 ff.

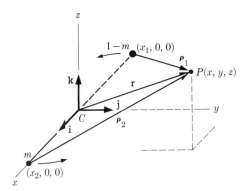

FIG. 5–7. Spatial orientation in restricted three-body problem.

5–7 The restricted three-body problem. Another particular solution of the three-body problem results when one of the three masses is so small in comparison to the other two that it can be neglected as far as its gravitational effects are concerned. This may be called an *infinitesimal* body compared with the two *finite* bodies.

Let two massive bodies having spherical symmetry move about their center of mass in circular orbits. A third mass, the infinitesimal one, moves under the combined gravitational attraction of the two but does not influence their motion. If we ignore the presence of the sun, the lack of sphericity of the earth, and the eccentricity of the moon's orbit, the earth-moon system together with a small artificial satellite constitutes such a system of masses.

Let m denote the smaller of the two finite masses, and $1 - m$ the larger. Thus the unit of mass is so chosen that the sum of the masses is unity. Furthermore, let the unit of time be chosen so that the gravitational constant $k^2 = 1$.

In Fig. 5–7, P denotes the position of the infinitesimal particle and $\mathbf{r}$ its radius vector from the origin at C, the center of mass of m and $1 - m$. Its distances from $1 - m$ and m are denoted by ρ_1 and ρ_2, respectively. The xy-plane is taken to be the orbital plane of motion of the finite masses.

Let $\mathbf{a} = \ddot{\mathbf{r}}$ be the acceleration and $\mathbf{v} = \dot{\mathbf{r}}$ be the velocity of P, as measured in the rotating coordinate system shown, that is, the masses revolving around the z-axis with angular speed n rad/sec. Then in the rotating system the equation of motion of the infinitesimal mass is

$$\mathbf{a} + 2\boldsymbol{\omega} \times \mathbf{v} + \boldsymbol{\omega} \times (\boldsymbol{\omega} \times \mathbf{r}) = -\frac{1 - m}{\rho_1^3}\boldsymbol{\rho}_1 - \frac{m}{\rho_2^3}\boldsymbol{\rho}_2, \qquad (5\text{–}54)$$

where $\boldsymbol{\omega} = n\mathbf{k}$.

Expressing the vectors in Eq. (5–54) in terms of their cartesian components, we have

$$\mathbf{a} = \ddot{x}\mathbf{i} + \ddot{y}\mathbf{j} + \ddot{z}\mathbf{k}, \qquad \mathbf{v} = \dot{x}\mathbf{i} + \dot{y}\mathbf{j} + \dot{z}\mathbf{k},$$

$$\boldsymbol{\omega} \times \mathbf{v} = -n[\dot{y}\mathbf{i} - \dot{x}\mathbf{j}], \qquad \boldsymbol{\omega} \times (\boldsymbol{\omega} \times \mathbf{r}) = -n^2[x\mathbf{i} + y\mathbf{j}].$$

Hence the cartesian equations of motion are

$$\ddot{x} - 2n\dot{y} = n^2 x - \frac{(1 - m)}{\rho_1^3}(x - x_1) - \frac{m}{\rho_2^3}(x - x_2), \quad (5\text{–}55)$$

$$\ddot{y} + 2n\dot{x} = n^2 y - \frac{(1 - m)}{\rho_1^3} y - \frac{m}{\rho_2^3} y, \quad (5\text{–}56)$$

$$\ddot{z} = -\frac{(1 - m)}{\rho_1^3} z - \frac{m}{\rho_2^3} z, \quad (5\text{–}57)$$

where $(x_1, 0)$ and $(x_2, 0)$ are the coordinates of $1 - m$ and m, respectively. These equations have the advantage that, in the rotating coordinate system, the positions of the finite masses do not change with the time.

Now by Kepler's third law, the orbital angular speed n is given by

$$n = \frac{2\pi}{P} = \frac{k\sqrt{m_1 + m_2}}{a^{3/2}}. \quad (5\text{–}58)$$

Let us choose the scale of distance so that $x_2 - x_1 = 1$. Then by Eq. (5–58), together with the assumptions made above relative to k and the masses, we find $n = 1$. Therefore the equations of motion become

$$\ddot{x} - 2\dot{y} = x - \frac{(1 - m)}{\rho_1^3}(x - x_1) - \frac{m}{\rho_2^3}(x - x_2), \quad (5\text{–}59)$$

$$\ddot{y} + 2\dot{x} = y - \frac{(1 - m)}{\rho_1^3} y - \frac{m}{\rho_2^3} y, \quad (5\text{–}60)$$

$$\ddot{z} = -\frac{(1 - m)}{\rho_1^3} z - \frac{m}{\rho_2^3} z. \quad (5\text{–}61)$$

The general problem of determining the motion of the infinitesimal mass is, therefore, one requiring six integrals for its complete solution.

The equations above yield immediately one integral analogous to the energy integral of the three-body problem [Eqs. (5–20), (5–21)]. We define a function

$$U = \tfrac{1}{2}(x^2 + y^2) + \frac{1 - m}{\rho_1} + \frac{m}{\rho_2}. \quad (5\text{–}62)$$

Then

$$\frac{\partial U}{\partial x} = x - \frac{(1-m)}{\rho_1^3}(x - x_1) - \frac{m}{\rho_2^3}(x - x_2),$$

$$\frac{\partial U}{\partial y} = y - \frac{(1-m)}{\rho_1^3}y - \frac{m}{\rho_2^3}y,$$

$$\frac{\partial U}{\partial z} = -\frac{(1-m)}{\rho_1^3}z - \frac{m}{\rho_2^3}z.$$

Equations (5–59), (5–60), and (5–61) then become

$$\ddot{x} - 2\dot{y} = \frac{\partial U}{\partial x},$$

$$\ddot{y} + 2\dot{x} = \frac{\partial U}{\partial y}, \qquad\qquad (5\text{–}63)$$

$$\ddot{z} = \frac{\partial U}{\partial z}.$$

Multiplying these respectively by $2\dot{x}$, $2\dot{y}$, and $2\dot{z}$ and adding, we obtain

$$2\dot{x}\ddot{x} + 2\dot{y}\ddot{y} + 2\dot{z}\ddot{z} = 2\dot{x}\frac{\partial U}{\partial x} + 2\dot{y}\frac{\partial U}{\partial y} + 2\dot{z}\frac{\partial U}{\partial z},$$

or

$$\frac{d}{dt}(\dot{x}^2 + \dot{y}^2 + \dot{z}^2) = 2\frac{dU}{dt}.$$

Integrating, we have

$$v^2 = 2U - C, \qquad\qquad (5\text{–}64)$$

where v is the speed of the infinitesimal mass.

The function U, originally introduced by Jacobi, has the appearance of a potential energy if one includes the energy arising from the rotation of the coordinate system, namely the term $\frac{1}{2}(x^2 + y^2)$. Since Eq. (5–64) involving this function and the constant of integration C constitutes one integral of the equations of motion, there remain five integrals to be found. By further restricting the motion of the infinitesimal mass to the xy- plane, it is possible to reduce the number of constants required to three. Jacobi* has shown that two of these are related to the third. Ultimately, therefore, for a complete solution, there remains to be found one new integral, but, as mentioned earlier, Bruns has demonstrated that no new algebraic integrals

---

* C. G. J. Jacobi, "Vorlesungen über Dynamik," *Collected Works*, Supplement, 1884.

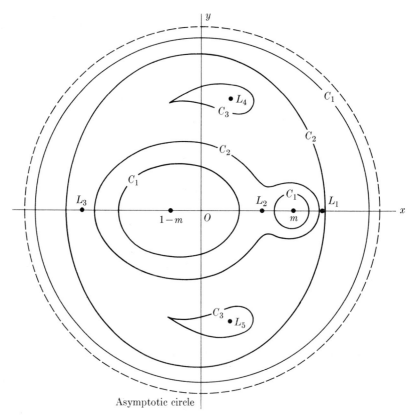

Fig. 5–8. Contours of zero velocity in restricted three-body problem.

in rectangular coordinates exist. The equations of motion in the rotating coordinate system and particularly Eq. (5–64) are very useful in discussing qualitatively the behavior of the infinitesimal particle.

For simplification of discussion, let the infinitesimal mass move in the xy-plane. Then Eq. (5–64) shows that its speed is a function of position in the plane. The constant C depends upon the initial position and velocity of the particle. Clearly there will be curves of zero speed given by $2U - C = 0$ or, in cartesian coordinates, by

$$x^2 + y^2 + \frac{2(1 - m)}{\sqrt{(x - x_1)^2 + y^2}} + \frac{2m}{\sqrt{(x - x_2)^2 + y^2}} = C. \quad (5\text{–}65)$$

Motion of the particle can occur only in those regions of the xy-plane for which $2U - C > 0$. The contour curves [Eq. (5–65)], mark the boundaries of the regions within which motion can take place.

A few of the contour curves are sketched in Fig. 5–8, where we have taken $C_1 > C_2 > C_3$. We shall consider briefly the areas of possible motion as follows:

Case I. When C is very large, $2U - C$ will be positive either if x and y are very large or if ρ_1 or ρ_2 are very small. As C_1 in Fig. (5–8) becomes larger, the oval, outer contour asymptotically approaches the boundary circle. This means that the terms involving

$$\sqrt{(x - x_1)^2 + y^2} \qquad \text{and} \qquad \sqrt{(x - x_2)^2 + y^2}$$

in Eq. (5–65) become vanishingly small.

Likewise for small ρ_1 and ρ_2, and large C, the x^2 and y^2 terms in Eq. (5–65) become insignificant compared with the third and fourth terms. The result is the pair of ovals surrounding $(1-m)$ and m. For this large value of C, motion cannot take place in the region between the ovals and the outer contour. Motion can occur if the particle is within the ovals marked C_1 or outside the nearly circular contour C_1.

Case II. If we allow C to decrease, the ovals around $(1-m)$ and m expand, and the outer contour moves toward the center of the figure. Curves C_2 (Fig. 5–8) illustrate an intermediate situation. The oval contours have merged into a single closed contour around the two masses. The motion of the particle can occur if it lies within this contour or outside the larger contour marked C_2.

Case III. If C is decreased further, the regions of stability, that is, the areas of the plane in which motion can occur, become larger. The enlarged oval pattern around the finite masses merges into that outside the exterior oval, leaving only a small region enclosed by C_3, where motion is impossible.

The points L_1, L_2, L_3, L_4, and L_5 in the diagram are the *Lagrangian points* of the system mentioned in Section 5–6. The first and third of these are points where the inner and the outer systems of ovals merge to a common tangent. The point L_2 is the point where the ovals surrounding finite masses merge. We shall return to a discussion of these later.

In the analysis above, the motion of the infinitesimal mass has been restricted to the xy-plane. If we examine the more general case in which the particle moves in space, an analysis of the contour curves of zero velocity in the xz- and the yz-planes similar to that described above is possible. We shall not dwell upon the details here. In the xz-plane, there exist ovals surrounding $(1 - m)$ and m, together with exterior contours approaching the straight lines $x = \pm C$ asymptotically. In the yz-plane also, the outer contours asymptotically approach the lines $y = \pm C$ for large values of C. In addition, there are closed oval contours surrounding the origin of coordinates.* Actually, therefore, the equation

$$x^2 + y^2 + \frac{2(1-m)}{\sqrt{(x-x_1)^2 + y^2 + z^2}} + \frac{2m}{\sqrt{(x-x_2)^2 + y^2 + z^2}} = C$$

$$(5\text{--}66)$$

defines a surface. The folds and closed parts of this surface intersect the coordinate planes in the manner described above.

We return now to a discussion of the Lagrangian points of the system. The equation of the contour curves for motion in the xy-plane may be written

$$f(x, y) \equiv x^2 + y^2 + \frac{2(1-m)}{\rho_1} + \frac{2m}{\rho_2} = C. \qquad (5\text{--}67)$$

At a Lagrangian point, double tangents appear on these curves. It is shown in the geometry of algebraic curves† that a singular point, or point having two tangents to the curve, will occur where $\partial f/\partial x = 0$, and $\partial f/\partial y = 0$. Applying these conditions, we have, from Eq. (5–67),

$$x - \frac{(1-m)(x-x_1)}{\rho_1^3} - \frac{m(x-x_2)}{\rho_2^3} = 0, \qquad (5\text{--}68)$$

$$y - \frac{(1-m)y}{\rho_1^3} - \frac{my}{\rho_2^3} = 0. \qquad (5\text{--}69)$$

These are observed to be the values of $\partial U/\partial x$ and $\partial U/\partial y$ appearing on the right-hand sides of Eqs. (5–59) and (5–60), respectively. Furthermore, because such a double point lies on the curve $f(x, y) = C$, the velocity components $\dot{x} = \dot{y} = 0$. An examination of Eqs. (5–59), (5–60), and (5–61) then reveals that *at a double point $\ddot{x} = \ddot{y} = 0$*. Also because $z = 0$, we observe that $\ddot{z} = 0$. Hence *there is no acceleration of the particle located at one of these points. If placed there at rest, a particle remains at rest unless acted upon by a force extraneous to the system under consideration.*

The Lagrangian points on the x-axis are given by setting $y = 0$ in the Eqs. (5–68) and (5–69) and solving for the values of x which are the roots of Eq. (5–68). One can show that this equation has one root $x > x_2$, one root $x_1 < x < x_2$, and a third root $x < x_1$. Let us consider these in turn.

---

* Figures for these planes have been sketched in F. R. Moulton, *Celestial Mechanics*, pp. 283–285.
† See, for example, E. Goursat, *A Course in Mathematical Analysis*, translated by E. R. Hedrick, Vol. 1, p. 110 ff. New York: Dover Publications, Inc., 1959.

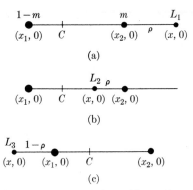

FIG. 5–9. Reference parameter for collinear Lagrangian points.

Case I. $x > x_2$. In Fig. 5–9(a), let

$$x - x_2 = \rho_2 = \rho,$$

$$x - x_1 = \rho_1 = 1 + \rho,$$

$$(1 - m)x_1 + mx_2 = 0.$$

Using the last of these, we find

$$x = 1 - m + \rho.$$

Substitution in Eq. (5–68) yields

$$\rho^5 + (3 - m)\rho^4 + (3 - 2m)\rho^3 - m\rho^2 - 2m\rho - m = 0. \qquad (5\text{–}70)$$

This is obviously Eq. (5–53) with $m_1 = 1 - m$, $m_2 = m$, $m_3 = 0$, and has only one real positive root. This can be found by modern numerical methods such as Graeffe's root squaring process.* Or, because $m < \frac{1}{2}$ by definition, we can first solve Eq. (5–70) with $m = 0$ and then write the solution for $m \neq 0$ as a power series in $m^{1/3}$. The result is

$$\rho = \left(\frac{m}{3}\right)^{1/3} + \frac{1}{3}\left(\frac{m}{3}\right)^{2/3} - \frac{1}{9}\left(\frac{m}{3}\right)^{3/3} + \cdots \qquad (5\text{–}71)$$

Having calculated ρ, we find $\rho_1 = 1 + \rho$, the distance from the mass $(1 - m)$ to the Lagrangian point exterior to x_2.

Case II. $x_1 < x < x_2$. Here we let $\rho_2 = x_2 - x = \rho$, $\rho_1 = x - x_1 = 1 - \rho$, (Fig. 5–9b) and, again from the definition of the center of mass,

---

* See, C. R. Wylie, *Advanced Engineering Mathematics.* 2nd ed. New York: McGraw-Hill Book Company, Inc., 1960, p. 649 ff.

we find $x = (1 - m - \rho)$. The resulting fifth-degree equation in ρ is

$$\rho^5 - (3 - m)\rho^4 + (3 - 2m)\rho^3 - m\rho^2 + 2m\rho - m = 0. \quad (5\text{–}72)$$

The same type of analysis as that in Case I yields

$$\rho = \left(\frac{m}{3}\right)^{1/3} - \frac{1}{3}\left(\frac{m}{3}\right)^{2/3} - \frac{1}{9}\left(\frac{m}{3}\right)^{3/3} - \cdots, \quad (5\text{–}73)$$

and hence $\rho_1 = 1 - \rho$.

   Case III. $x < x_1$. Here we take $1 - \rho$ to be the distance from the larger mass $(1 - m)$ to the point L_3 (Fig. 5–9c). Then $x_1 - x = 1 - \rho$, $x_2 - x = 2 - \rho$, and, from the center of mass equation, $x = -(m + 1) + \rho$. The resulting polynomial equation in ρ becomes

$$\rho^5 - (7 + m)\rho^4 + (19 + 6m)\rho^3 - (24 + 13m)\rho^2$$
$$+ (12 + 14m)\rho - 7m = 0. \quad (5\text{–}74)$$

This equation has the solution

$$\rho = \frac{7}{12}m + \frac{1127}{20{,}736}m^3 + \cdots \quad (5\text{–}75)$$

From this we find

$$\rho_1 = 1 - \rho \qquad \text{and} \qquad \rho_2 = 2 - \rho. \quad (5\text{–}76)$$

   The value of ρ as a function of m for Cases I, II, and III is given in the following table.

m	Case I	Case II	Case III
0.1	0.35264	0.28360	0.05839
0.2	0.45289	0.34327	0.11710
0.3	0.52486	0.38124	0.17647
0.4	0.58306	0.40906	0.23681
0.5	0.63276	0.43086	0.29846

   Case IV. The triangular points. The Lagrangian points away from the x-axis, which we shall denote by L_4 and L_5 (Fig. 5–8), also follow from Eqs. (5–68) and (5–69). Since $y \neq 0$, we can divide Eq. (5–69) by y to obtain

$$1 - \frac{(1 - m)}{\rho_1^3} - \frac{m}{\rho_2^3} = 0. \quad (5\text{–}77)$$

Multiplying this by $x - x_1$, we have

$$(x - x_1) - \frac{(1 - m)}{\rho_1^3} (x - x_1) - \frac{m}{\rho_2^3} (x - x_1) = 0. \quad (5\text{–}78)$$

Multiplying Eq. (5–77) by $x - x_2$, we have

$$(x - x_2) - \frac{(1 - m)}{\rho_1^3} (x - x_2) - \frac{m}{\rho_2^3} (x - x_2) = 0. \quad (5\text{–}79)$$

But from Eq. (5–68)

$$x - \frac{(1 - m)}{\rho_1^3} (x - x_1) - \frac{m}{\rho_2^3} (x - x_2) = 0.$$

Eliminating x from these three equations yields

$$x_2 - \frac{(1 - m)}{\rho_1^3} (x_2 - x_1) = 0, \quad (5\text{–}80)$$

$$x_1 + \frac{m}{\rho_2^3} (x_2 - x_1) = 0. \quad (5\text{–}81)$$

However, $x_2 - x_1 = 1$ and $(1 - m)x_1 + mx_2 = 0$, so that $x_1 = -m$ and $x_2 = 1 - m$. Therefore it follows from Eqs. (5–80) and (5–81) that

$$1 - \frac{1}{\rho_1^3} = 0 \quad \text{and} \quad \frac{1}{\rho_2^3} - 1 = 0. \quad (5\text{–}82)$$

These are satisfied only by $\rho_1 = 1$ and $\rho_2 = 1$. Therefore, L_4 and L_5 (Fig. 5–8) lie at the vertices of equilateral triangles whose common base is the segment (x_1, x_2). The equilateral-triangle solutions are obviously valid regardless of the relative sizes of the two finite masses. This result is in conformity with the stationary solution of the three-body problem discussed in Section 5–6.

PROBLEMS

1. The mass of the moon is $\frac{1}{81}$ that of the earth and the distance from earth to moon is 384,400 km. Consider the moon's orbit to be circular. Where on the line joining earth and moon would one locate a space platform so that it would always remain between the two?

2. The mass of the sun is 2×10^{33} gm, that of the earth is 6×10^{27} gm. Their distance apart is 1.5×10^8 km. On the assumption that the earth's orbit is circular, find the Lagrangian point L_1 (Fig. 5–9a). If the sun's radius is 7×10^5 km and that of the earth is 6.37×10^3 km, determine whether or not L_1 lies within the earth's shadow.

3. The Trojan asteroids are located near the L_4 and L_5 points of the sun-Jupiter system. On the assumption that one of these asteroids is exactly at L_4 or L_5, determine the radius of its orbit. What is the period of its motion? How does this compare with the period of Jupiter? [*Data:* Jupiter's mass = 1/1047 that of the sun; a(Jupiter) = 5.203 A.U.]

4. Show that the function U, Eq. (5–62), can be written

$$U = (1 - m)\left[\frac{\rho_1^2}{2} + \frac{1}{\rho_1}\right] + m\left[\frac{\rho_2^2}{2} + \frac{1}{\rho_2}\right] - \tfrac{1}{2}m(1 - m).$$

Hence, show that $U(\rho_1, \rho_2)$ will have a minimum value $\frac{3}{2} - \frac{1}{2}m(1 - m)$ when $\rho_1 = \rho_2 = 1$. [*Hint:* Use the auxiliary relations $\rho_1^2 = (x - x_1)^2 + y^2$; $\rho_2^2 = (x - x_2)^2 + y^2$; $(1 - m)x_1 + mx_2 = 0$; and $x_2 - x_1 = 1$.]

5–8 Stability of motion near the Lagrangian points. The motion of an infinitesimal particle near one of the Lagrangian points (*L*-points) is said to be *stable* if, when given a very small displacement and small velocity, the particle oscillates for a considerable time around the point in question. If it departs from the point as the time increases, the motion is *unstable*. Expressed mathematically, the stability of motion means bounded displacements and velocities which are bounded functions of the time in the neighborhood of the equilibrium points. This section will be devoted to the mathematical investigation of such stability.

The equations of motion of the infinitesimal mass [Eqs. (5–63)] are

$$\ddot{x} - 2\dot{y} = U_x,$$

$$\ddot{y} + 2\dot{x} = U_y, \qquad (5\text{–}83)$$

$$\ddot{z} = U_z,$$

where the partial derivatives U_x, U_y, and U_z are, respectively,

$$U_x = x - \frac{(1 - m)}{\rho_1^3}(x - x_1) - \frac{m}{\rho_2^3}(x - x_2),$$

$$U_y = y - \frac{(1 - m)y}{\rho_1^3} - \frac{my}{\rho_2^3}, \qquad (5\text{–}84)$$

$$U_z = -\frac{(1 - m)z}{\rho_1^3} - \frac{mz}{\rho_2^3}$$

and

$$\rho_1 = [(x - x_1)^2 + y^2 + z^2]^{1/2},$$

$$\rho_2 = [(x - x_2)^2 + y^2 + z^2]^{1/2}. \qquad (5\text{–}85)$$

Let the coordinates of any one of the L-points be denoted by (x_0, y_0, z_0). We have already seen that these points must occur in the xy-plane so that $z_0 = 0$. Let α, β, γ denote small displacements of the infinitesimal particle from the L-point in question. These are functions of the time and hence there will be velocity and acceleration components $\dot{\alpha}$, $\dot{\beta}$, and $\dot{\gamma}$ and $\ddot{\alpha}$, $\ddot{\beta}$, and $\ddot{\gamma}$, respectively. Then we may write

$$x = x_0 + \alpha, \qquad \dot{x} = \dot{x}_0 + \dot{\alpha}, \qquad \ddot{x} = \ddot{x}_0 + \ddot{\alpha},$$
$$y = y_0 + \beta, \qquad \dot{y} = \dot{y}_0 + \dot{\beta}, \qquad \ddot{y} = \ddot{y}_0 + \ddot{\beta}, \qquad (5\text{–}86)$$
$$z = z_0 + \gamma, \qquad \dot{z} = \dot{z}_0 + \dot{\gamma}, \qquad \ddot{z} = \ddot{z}_0 + \ddot{\gamma}.$$

We assume that the displacements are sufficiently small that the Taylor expansions of U_x, U_y, U_z in Eqs. (5–83) in the region surrounding the L-point can be written

$$U_x = (U_x)_0 + \alpha(U_{xx})_0 + \beta(U_{xy})_0 + \gamma(U_{xz})_0,$$
$$U_y = (U_y)_0 + \alpha(U_{yx})_0 + \beta(U_{yy})_0 + \gamma(U_{yz})_0, \qquad (5\text{–}87)$$
$$U_z = (U_z)_0 + \alpha(U_{zx})_0 + \beta(U_{zy})_0 + \gamma(U_{zz})_0,$$

where the partial derivatives are evaluated at the L-point in question. This assumption amounts to saying that the forces tending to act on the infinitesimal mass when it is displaced, slightly, from the equilibrium position are proportional to the *first power only* of the displacement.

Equations (5–68) and (5–69) show that at the L-point

$$(U_x)_0 = (U_y)_0 = (U_z)_0 = 0.$$

Furthermore,

$$\ddot{x}_0 = \ddot{y}_0 = \ddot{z}_0 = 0$$

and

$$\dot{x}_0 = \dot{y}_0 = \dot{z}_0 = 0$$

at one of these points. Therefore, by Eqs. (5–83), (5–86), and (5–87), we have

$$\ddot{\alpha} - 2\dot{\beta} = \alpha(U_{xx})_0 + \beta(U_{xy})_0 + \gamma(U_{xz})_0,$$
$$\ddot{\beta} + 2\dot{\alpha} = \alpha(U_{yx})_0 + \beta(U_{yy})_0 + \gamma(U_{yz})_0, \qquad (5\text{–}88)$$
$$\ddot{\gamma} = \alpha(U_{zx})_0 + \beta(U_{zy})_0 + \gamma(U_{zz})_0.$$

These are the equations of motion of the infinitesimal mass point in the neighborhood of an L-point when the displacements are small.

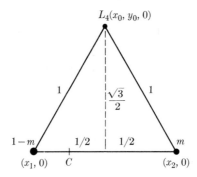

FIG. 5–10. Equilibrium position for motion around the L_4-point.

From Eqs. (5–84), we derive

$$U_{xx} = 1 - \frac{1-m}{\rho_1^3} - \frac{m}{\rho_2^3} + \frac{3(1-m)(x-x_1)^2}{\rho_1^5} + \frac{3m(x-x_2)^2}{\rho_2^5},$$

$$U_{xy} = \frac{3(1-m)(x-x_1)y}{\rho_1^5} + \frac{3m(x-x_2)y}{\rho_2^5},$$

$$U_{xz} = \frac{3(1-m)(x-x_1)z}{\rho_1^5} + \frac{3m(x-x_2)z}{\rho_2^5},$$

$$U_{yy} = 1 - \frac{1-m}{\rho_1^3} - \frac{m}{\rho_2^3} + \frac{3(1-m)y^2}{\rho_1^5} + \frac{3my^2}{\rho_2^5}, \qquad (5\text{–}89)$$

$$U_{yz} = \frac{3(1-m)yz}{\rho_1^5} + \frac{3myz}{\rho_2^5},$$

$$U_{zz} = -\frac{1-m}{\rho_1^3} - \frac{m}{\rho_2^3} + \frac{3(1-m)z^2}{\rho_1^5} + \frac{3mz^2}{\rho_2^5}.$$

We shall apply Eqs. (5–88) and (5–89) to a study of the stability of motion in the neighborhood of the equilateral triangle point L_4 (Fig. 5–10) and in the neighborhood of the straight-line point L_1.

Case I. Motion around the point L_4. In Section 5–7, it was shown that all of the L-points lie in the xy-plane. Therefore, $z_0 = 0$ in each case. Hence for L_4 (Fig. 5–10), we have

$$x_0 - x_1 = \tfrac{1}{2}, \qquad z_0 = 0,$$
$$x_0 - x_2 = -\tfrac{1}{2}, \qquad \rho_1 = \rho_2 = 1.$$
$$y_0 = \sqrt{3}/2,$$

Then the partial derivatives [Eqs. (5–89)] become

$$U_{xx} = \tfrac{3}{4}, \qquad\qquad\qquad U_{yz} = U_{zy} = 0,$$

$$U_{xy} = U_{yx} = \frac{3\sqrt{3}}{2}(\tfrac{1}{2} - m), \qquad U_{yy} = \tfrac{9}{4},$$

$$U_{xz} = U_{zx} = 0, \qquad\qquad\quad U_{zz} = -1.$$

The equations of motion are

$$\ddot{\alpha} - 2\dot{\beta} = \tfrac{3}{4}\alpha + \frac{3\sqrt{3}}{2}(\tfrac{1}{2} - m)\beta, \qquad (5\text{–}90)$$

$$\ddot{\beta} + 2\dot{\alpha} = \frac{3\sqrt{3}}{2}(\tfrac{1}{2} - m)\alpha + \tfrac{9}{4}\beta, \qquad (5\text{–}91)$$

$$\ddot{\gamma} = -\gamma. \qquad (5\text{–}92)$$

Equation (5–92) has the solution

$$\gamma = c_1 \cos t + c_2 \sin t,$$

where c_1 and c_2 are constants of integration. The displacement in the z-direction is periodic with period 2π. This is precisely the period of revolution of the two larger masses around their center of mass. The disturbed motion of the infinitesimal mass is bounded and hence stable in the direction perpendicular to the xy-plane.

To solve Eqs. (5–90) and (5–91), let

$$\alpha = Ae^{\lambda t} \qquad \text{and} \qquad \beta = Be^{\lambda t},$$

where A, B, and λ are parameters to be found. Substitution in the equations of motion and rearrangement yield

$$A[\lambda^2 - \tfrac{3}{4}] + B\left[-2\lambda - \frac{3\sqrt{3}}{2}(\tfrac{1}{2} - m)\right] = 0,$$
$$(5\text{–}93)$$
$$A\left[2\lambda - \frac{3\sqrt{3}}{2}(\tfrac{1}{2} - m)\right] + B[\lambda^2 - \tfrac{9}{4}] = 0.$$

These will have a nontrivial solution for A and B if

$$\begin{vmatrix} \lambda^2 - \tfrac{3}{4} & -2\lambda - \dfrac{3\sqrt{3}}{2}(\tfrac{1}{2} - m) \\[2ex] 2\lambda - \dfrac{3\sqrt{3}}{2}(\tfrac{1}{2} - m) & \lambda^2 - \tfrac{9}{4} \end{vmatrix} = 0, \qquad (5\text{–}94)$$

and this simplifies to

$$4\lambda^4 + 4\lambda^2 + 27m(1 - m) = 0. \qquad (5\text{–}95)$$

The solution of this as a quadratic equation in λ^2 is

$$\lambda^2 = -\tfrac{1}{2} \pm \tfrac{1}{2}\sqrt{1 - 27m(1 - m)}. \qquad (5\text{-}96)$$

It is clear from the nature of the solutions $\alpha = Ae^{\lambda t}$ and $\beta = Be^{\lambda t}$ that these will be periodic and bounded only if λ is pure imaginary. This implies that we must choose m in Eq. (5–96) so that $\lambda^2 < 0$. Hence

$$1 - 27m(1 - m) \geq 0 \qquad (5\text{-}97)$$

if stable motion is to ensue. Solving this equation, we find that $m < 0.0385$ *if λ^2 is to be negative.* The other root of $1 - 27m + 27m^2 = 0$ is greater than $\tfrac{1}{2}$ and is to be excluded according to our original hypothesis that $m < \tfrac{1}{2}$. *Stable motion around the L_4 point will take place if the mass m does not exceed 0.0385.*

The Trojan group of asteroids constitutes an example of the type of motion discussed in the preceding paragraphs. These small bodies, nearly a dozen or more of them, are located near the points L_4 and L_5 of the sun-Jupiter system. They move in closed orbits around one of the equilibrium points while revolving as a group around the sun with the same period as Jupiter. The mass of Jupiter is about 0.001 that of the sun so that the condition for stability expressed by Eq. (5–97) is met. Depending upon the initial small velocity and displacement, the particle will move in elliptic motion around the L-point.

Case II. Motion around the point L_1. In this case (Fig. 5–11)

$$x_0 - x_1 = \rho_1 = 1 + \rho,$$
$$x_0 - x_2 = \rho_2 = \rho,$$
$$y_0 = z_0 = 0.$$

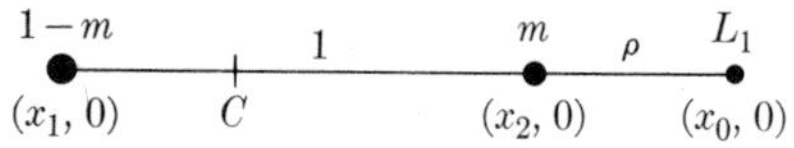

FIG. 5–11. Equilibrium position for motion around the L_1-point.

The partial derivatives, Eqs. (5–89), become

$$U_{xx} = 1 - \frac{(1-m)}{(1+\rho)^3} - \frac{m}{\rho^3} + \frac{3(1-m)}{(1+\rho)^3} + \frac{3m}{\rho^3}$$

$$= 1 + \frac{2(1-m)}{(1+\rho)^3} + \frac{2m}{\rho^3},$$

$$U_{xy} = U_{yx} = U_{xz} = U_{zx} = U_{yz} = U_{zy} = 0,$$

$$U_{yy} = 1 - \frac{(1-m)}{(1+\rho)^3} - \frac{m}{\rho^3},$$

$$U_{zz} = -\frac{(1-m)}{(1+\rho)^3} - \frac{m}{\rho^3}.$$

Substituting these expressions into the Eqs. (5–88), we have, for motion around L_1,

$$\ddot{\alpha} - 2\dot{\beta} = \alpha[1 + 2f], \tag{5-98}$$

$$\ddot{\beta} + 2\dot{\alpha} = \beta[1 - f], \tag{5-99}$$

$$\ddot{\gamma} = -f\gamma, \tag{5-100}$$

where

$$f = \frac{1 - m}{(1 + \rho)^3} + \frac{m}{\rho^3}. \tag{5-101}$$

Equation (5–100) shows immediately that the motion perpendicular to the xy-plane is periodic with frequency $\omega = \sqrt{f}$. Motion in the z-direction is, therefore, bounded with

$$\gamma = c_3 \cos \sqrt{f}\, t + c_4 \sin \sqrt{f}\, t, \tag{5-102}$$

where c_3 and c_4 are constants of integration.

To investigate the motion in the xy-plane, let $\alpha = Ae^{\lambda t}$ and $\beta = Be^{\lambda t}$. Substituting into Eqs. (5–98) and (5–99) and combining terms, we have

$$A[\lambda^2 - (1 + 2f)] + B[-2\lambda] = 0,$$
$$\tag{5-103}$$
$$A[2\lambda] + B[\lambda^2 - (1 - f)] = 0.$$

These will have a nontrivial solution if

$$\begin{vmatrix} \lambda^2 - (1 + 2f) & -2\lambda \\ 2\lambda & \lambda^2 - (1 - f) \end{vmatrix} = 0. \tag{5-104}$$

When simplified, this becomes

$$\lambda^4 + (2 - f)\lambda^2 + (1 + 2f)(1 - f) = 0. \tag{5-105}$$

The student may show directly from the definition of f, together with any $m < \frac{1}{2}$, and the corresponding value of ρ from Eq. (5–71), that

$$(1 + 2f)(1 - f) < 0. \tag{5-106}$$

Therefore the solution

$$\lambda^2 = \frac{-(2 - f) \pm \sqrt{(2 - f)^2 - 4(1 + 2f)(1 - f)}}{2} \tag{5-107}$$

is positive when the plus sign is taken and negative when the minus sign is used. The two real roots of Eq. (5–107) are equal numerically but opposite in sign. The two remaining roots are conjugate imaginary. Let the roots of the characteristic equation [Eq. (5–105)] be

$$\lambda_1 = a, \qquad \lambda_2 = -a, \qquad \lambda_3 = bi, \qquad \lambda_4 = -bi,$$

where

$$a = \left[\frac{-(2-f) + \sqrt{(2-f)^2 - 4(1+f-2f^2)}}{2}\right]^{1/2}, \qquad (5\text{--}108)$$

$$b = \left[\frac{(2-f) + \sqrt{(2-f)^2 - 4(1+f-2f^2)}}{2}\right]^{1/2}. \qquad (5\text{--}109)$$

The solutions of Eqs. (5–98) and (5–99) are then

$$\alpha = A_1 e^{at} + A_2 e^{-at} + A_3 e^{ibt} + A_4 e^{-ibt}, \qquad (5\text{--}110)$$

$$\beta = B_1 e^{at} + B_2 e^{-at} + B_3 e^{ibt} + B_4 e^{-ibt}, \qquad (5\text{--}111)$$

where the B_j are related to the A_j ($j = 1, 2, 3, 4$) through, say, the first of Eqs. (5–103); that is

$$B_j = \left[\frac{\lambda_j^2 - (1+2f)}{2\lambda_j}\right] A_j \qquad (j = 1, 2, 3, 4). \qquad (5\text{--}112)$$

Equations (5–110) and (5–111) show that the presence of the exponential factors e^{at} and e^{-at} means, in general, unbounded motion in the xy-plane. Therefore the L_1 point is an unstable equilibrium point. The same type of analysis will show that the behavior of an infinitesimal mass in the neighborhood of L_2 and L_3 is similar. These Lagrangian points are, *in general*, points of instability.

We shall show, however, that by assigning the appropriate initial conditions for the disturbed motion around L_1, this point can be made a point of stability.

For simplicity, let

$$B_1 = cA_1, \qquad B_2 = -cA_2,$$

$$B_3 = idA_3, \qquad B_4 = -idA_4, \qquad (5\text{--}113)$$

where

$$c = \frac{a^2 - (1+2f)}{2a}, \qquad d = \frac{b^2 + (1+2f)}{2b}. \qquad (5\text{--}114)$$

Then Eqs. (5–110) and (5–111), together with the corresponding velocities, become

$$\begin{aligned}
\alpha &= A_1 e^{at} + A_2 e^{-at} + A_3 e^{ibt} + A_4 e^{-ibt}, \\
\beta &= cA_1 e^{at} - cA_2 e^{-at} + idA_3 e^{ibt} - idA_4 e^{-ibt}, \\
\dot{\alpha} &= aA_1 e^{at} - aA_2 e^{-at} + ibA_3 e^{ibt} - ibA_4 e^{-ibt}, \\
\dot{\beta} &= acA_1 e^{at} + acA_2 e^{-at} - bdA_3 e^{ibt} - bdA_4 e^{-ibt}.
\end{aligned} \qquad (5\text{--}115)$$

Let the initial displacements and velocities be α_0, β_0, $\dot{\alpha}_0$, and $\dot{\beta}_0$. Then for $t = 0$, we have from Eqs. (5–115)

$$\begin{aligned}
\alpha_0 &= A_1 + A_2 + A_3 + A_4, \\
\beta_0 &= c(A_1 - A_2) + id(A_3 - A_4), \\
\dot{\alpha}_0 &= a(A_1 - A_2) + ib(A_3 - A_4), \\
\dot{\beta}_0 &= ac(A_1 + A_2) - bd(A_3 + A_4).
\end{aligned} \qquad (5\text{–}116)$$

If the motion is to be bounded and periodic, we must have $A_1 + A_2 = 0$ and $A_1 - A_2 = 0$. Hence $A_1 = A_2 = 0$. We leave it as a problem for the student to show the relationship among the initial conditions which will guarantee this. With this restriction we find, from the first pair of Eqs. (5–116),

$$A_3 = \frac{\alpha_0}{2} - \frac{i\beta_0}{2d} \quad \text{and} \quad A_4 = \frac{\alpha_0}{2} + \frac{i\beta_0}{2d}.$$

The first two of Eqs. (5–115) then become

$$\alpha = \left(\frac{\alpha_0}{2} - i\frac{\beta_0}{2d}\right)e^{ibt} + \left(\frac{\alpha_0}{2} + i\frac{\beta_0}{2d}\right)e^{-ibt},$$

$$\beta = id\left(\frac{\alpha_0}{2} - i\frac{\beta_0}{2d}\right)e^{ibt} - id\left(\frac{\alpha_0}{2} + i\frac{\beta_0}{2d}\right)e^{-ibt},$$

which, by means of the well-known Euler relations, can be simplified to

$$\begin{aligned}
\alpha &= \alpha_0 \cos bt + \frac{\beta_0}{d} \sin bt, \\
\beta &= \beta_0 \cos bt - d\alpha_0 \sin bt.
\end{aligned} \qquad (5\text{–}117)$$

These are the parametric equations of the path of the infinitesimal mass around L_1. The parameter t may be eliminated from these equations by solving for $\cos bt$ and $\sin bt$, then by squaring the results and adding. The result is

$$\frac{\alpha^2}{(d^2\alpha_0^2 + \beta_0^2)/d^2} + \frac{\beta^2}{d^2\alpha_0^2 + \beta_0^2} = 1. \qquad (5\text{–}118)$$

This is an ellipse with center at L_1 and axes parallel to the x- and y-axes of the rotating coordinate system. Let the student show that $d^2 > 1$, and hence that the major axis of this ellipse is parallel to the y-axis. He may also show that the eccentricity of the ellipse is given by $e^2 = 1 - (1/d^2)$. Hence the shape of the curve depends only on the relative mass distribution through the constant d and not upon the initial circumstances of the disturbed motion.

There is reason to suppose that the *counterglow*, or *gegenschein*, observed as a hazy patch of light in the sky 180° from the sun and near the ecliptic, is due to numerous small dust particles trapped near the L_1-point of the sun-earth system. Even if the constants A_1 and A_2 in Eqs. (5–116) are not zero but are very small in comparison with A_3 and A_4, such particles would linger for long periods near L_1 before departing indefinitely far from it. The initial conditions under which the meteoric particles find themselves near the L_1-point are crucial in this explanation of the gegenschein.

Problems

1. The mass of the earth is $1/333{,}420$ that of the sun. What is the period of oscillation of a small particle perpendicular to the ecliptic plane at the L_1-point of the sun-earth system?

2. What is the period of an infinitesimal particle near the L_1-point in Problem 1 if oscillation occurs parallel to the xy-plane? What is the eccentricity of the orbit of the particle?

3. The mass of Jupiter is $1/1047$ that of the sun. Calculate the frequencies of oscillation of an infinitesimal mass in its motion parallel to the xy-plane in the neighborhood of the L_4-point of the sun-Jupiter system.

4. Find the relation between the constants α_0, β_0, $\dot{\alpha}_0$, and $\dot{\beta}_0$ of Eqs. (5–116) which will insure that $A_1 = 0$ and $A_2 = 0$.

5. The equations for perturbed two-dimensional motion in polar coordinates (see Problem 1, Section 5–5) are

$$\ddot{r} - r\dot{\theta}^2 + \frac{k^2 M}{r^2} = \frac{\partial R}{\partial r},$$

$$\frac{d}{dt}(r^2\dot{\theta}) = \frac{\partial R}{\partial \theta},$$

$$R = k^2 m' \left\{ \frac{1}{\rho} - \frac{r}{r'^2} \cos(\theta - \theta') \right\}.$$

Discuss the stability of motion of a Trojan asteroid around the L_4-point by performing the following steps:

(a) Let $r = r_0 + q_1$ and $\theta = n + \dot{q}_2$, where q_1, q_2, $\dot{q}_1$, and $\dot{q}_2$ are small so that squares and products can be neglected; find the required Taylor expansions for $(\partial R/\partial r)$, $(\partial R/\partial \theta)$ in the neighborhood of L_4; show that the equations of disturbed motion are

$$\ddot{q}_1 - 2nr_0\dot{q}_2 = \left[n^2 + \frac{2k^2 M}{r_0^3} + \left(\frac{\partial^2 R}{\partial r^2} \right)_0 \right] q_1 + \left(\frac{\partial^2 R}{\partial r\,\partial\theta} \right)_0 q_2,$$

$$r_0^2 \ddot{q}_2 + 2nr_0\dot{q}_1 = \left(\frac{\partial^2 R}{\partial r\,\partial\theta} \right)_0 q_1 + \left(\frac{\partial^2 R}{\partial\theta^2} \right)_0 q_2,$$

where $M = m_1 + m$, and m is *very* small compared with m_1.

(b) Evaluate the derivatives at $r_0 = r_0' = \rho = a$ and $(\theta - \theta') = 60°$.

(c) By setting $n^2 a^3 = k^2(m_1 + m') \cong k^2(M + m')$ and ignoring terms in m'/M of degree > 1, show that the equations of perturbed motion become

$$\ddot{q}_1 - 2na\dot{q}_2 = \left[3n^2 - \frac{9n^2}{4}\left(\frac{m'}{M}\right)\right]q_1 + \left[\frac{3\sqrt{3}\,n^2 a}{4}\left(\frac{m'}{M}\right)\right]q_2,$$

$$a^2\ddot{q}_2 + 2na\dot{q}_1 = \left[\frac{3\sqrt{3}\,n^2 a}{4}\left(\frac{m'}{M}\right)\right]q_1 + \left[\frac{9n^2 a^2}{4}\left(\frac{m'}{M}\right)\right]q_2.$$

(d) Let $q_1 = Ae^{\lambda t}$, $q_2 = Be^{\lambda t}$ and show that the characteristic equation for λ is

$$\lambda^4 + n^2\lambda^2 + \frac{27n^4}{4}\left(\frac{m'}{M}\right)\left(1 - \frac{m'}{M}\right) = 0.$$

(e) Again ignoring powers of $(m'/M) > 1$, show that the values of λ are

$$\pm in\sqrt{\tfrac{27}{4}(m'/M)} \quad \text{and} \quad \pm in[1 - \tfrac{27}{8}(m'/M)],$$

where $i^2 = -1$.

(f) With $2\pi/n = 11.9$ yr for Jupiter, show that the periods of disturbed motion for the Trojan asteroid are approximately

$$148 \text{ yr} \qquad \text{and} \qquad 11.9 \text{ yr}.$$

The longer of these is in the transverse (q_2) direction and the shorter is in the radial (q_1). These motions are known as the long and short period *librations*.

CHAPTER 6

THEORY OF PERTURBATIONS

The three-body problem discussed in the last chapter is indicative of the complexity arising when more than two mutually gravitating masses are involved. In the present chapter we shall treat in more detail the basic mathematical description of the perturbation problem together with applications to some common astronomical systems.

Consider for a moment the planetary system. The dominant mass is the sun. Each planet moves in nearly Keplerian two-body motion around it. This is a good first approximation. But the other planets all exert gravitational influences tending to disturb this motion. Here the effect is to change slowly the elements of the Keplerian orbit. That is, a, e, i, ω, Ω, T are slowly changing functions of the time. When the rates of change of these elements are known, the future orbital characteristics of the planet can be predicted. In this situation, as in all the problems so far studied, the distances between bodies are so large compared with the sizes of the objects that the latter can be considered point masses.

Another class of problems arises from the perturbations in the motion of a satellite close to a planet. The lack of sphericity, or the oblateness, of the planet causes large perturbations from the simple two-body orbit. The motions of artificial earth satellites are examples. Here the line of nodes and the perigee point move very rapidly under the noncentral force field arising from the oblateness of the earth.

Still other perturbations arise because of the drag of the atmosphere on a satellite close to the earth's surface.

6–1 Variation of parameters. The student is assumed to be familiar with the standard method for solving second-order differential equations known as the *method of variation of parameters.* * In the application here, due to Lagrange, we assume that the cartesian coordinates defining the position of a planet (or other object) are

$$x = x(t, c_1, c_2, c_3, c_4, c_5, c_6),$$
$$y = y(t, c_1, c_2, c_3, c_4, c_5, c_6),$$
$$z = z(t, c_1, c_2, c_3, c_4, c_5, c_6),$$

---

* See, for example, M. Morris and O. E. Brown, *Differential Equations.* 3rd ed. New York: Prentice-Hall, Inc., 1952, p. 90 ff.

or, in vector form with $\mathbf{r} = x\mathbf{i} + y\mathbf{j} + z\mathbf{k}$,

$$\mathbf{r} = \mathbf{r}(t, c_1, c_2, c_3, c_4, c_5, c_6), \tag{6-1}$$

where $\mathbf{i}$, $\mathbf{j}$, and $\mathbf{k}$ are unit vectors along the x-, y-, and z-axes, respectively.

In Eq. (6–1) the quantities c_k ($k = 1, 2, \ldots, 6$) are constants if the orbit is Keplerian (i.e., in two-body motion) but are slowly varying functions of the time under the disturbing influence of other masses in the system. It is clear that the c_k are identical, in the Keplerian case, to a, e, i, ω, Ω, T or to combinations of these elements. Our problem is to find the time rates of change of the c_k.

Consider the set of elements c_k at any *fixed instant*. These define an orbit called the *osculating orbit* at the point in question. The planet, say, at this instant has the *same coordinates* and, by definition, the *same velocity components* in the unperturbed and in the perturbed orbit. Stated otherwise, the planet has the position and is moving instantaneously as it would in purely two-body motion. Obviously one could compute a set of elements to define an osculating orbit at any point of the actual orbit.

The equations describing the motion of a mass m around a central mass m_1 under the perturbing influence of a mass m' have been derived in Section 5–5, Eqs. (5–27), (5–28), and (5–29). In vector form they are

$$\ddot{\mathbf{r}} + \frac{\mu \mathbf{r}}{r^3} = \nabla R, \tag{6-2}$$

where

$$R = k^2 m' \left\{ \frac{1}{\rho} - \frac{xx' + yy' + zz'}{r'^3} \right\}, \qquad \nabla R = \frac{\partial R}{\partial x}\mathbf{i} + \frac{\partial R}{\partial y}\mathbf{j} + \frac{\partial R}{\partial z}\mathbf{k},$$

$$\mu = k^2(m_1 + m). \tag{6-3}$$

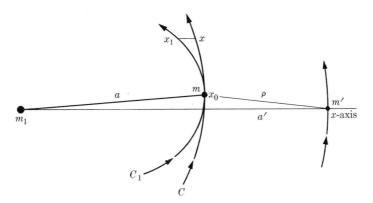

FIG. 6–1. Illustration of perturbation in one dimension.

Before undertaking the general discussion of Eq. (6–2), we shall consider a simple order of magnitude calculation. Suppose that the masses m and m' are moving in circular orbits of radii a and $a'(a' > a)$ around the central mass m_1 (Fig. 6–1) and consider only the x-component of motion. If m' were not present, the mass m in a short interval of time τ would move along the osculating orbit C_1 so that x_0 changes to x_1. Actually, however, because of the presence of m', the mass m moves along C so that x_0 changes to x in the same time τ. Here C is the *true* orbit.

We assume for simplicity that the time interval is small enough so that the values of x and x_1 can be written with sufficient accuracy as

$$x = x_0 + \left(\frac{dx}{dt}\right)_0 \tau + \left(\frac{d^2x}{dt^2}\right)_0 \frac{\tau^2}{2} + \cdots ,$$

$$x_1 = x_0 + \left(\frac{\partial x}{\partial t}\right)_0 \tau + \left(\frac{\partial^2 x}{\partial t^2}\right)_0 \frac{\tau^2}{2} + \cdots , \tag{6-4}$$

where the subscripts denote the evaluation of the derivatives at the osculating point x_0. The deviation or perturbation due to the presence of m' is, therefore,

$$x - x_1 \equiv \delta x = \left[\left(\frac{dx}{dt}\right)_0 - \left(\frac{\partial x}{\partial t}\right)_0\right]\tau + \left[\left(\frac{d^2x}{dt^2}\right)_0 - \left(\frac{\partial^2 x}{\partial t^2}\right)_0\right]\frac{\tau^2}{2}. \tag{6-5}$$

The distinction between the total derivatives and the partial derivatives should be clear. The former refer to the true orbit and take into account the changes in the orbital elements. That is,

$$\frac{dx}{dt} = \frac{\partial x}{\partial t} + \sum_{k=1}^{6} \frac{\partial x}{\partial c_k} \dot{c}_k. \tag{6-6}$$

The partial derivatives, on the other hand, refer to the osculating orbit for which the c_k are constants. By the definition of the osculating orbit, the velocity in it at x_0 and that in the true orbit are the same. Therefore $(dx/dt)_0 - (\partial x/\partial t)_0 = 0$.

Furthermore, we have, by Eq. (6–2),

$$\left(\frac{d^2x}{dt^2}\right)_0 + \frac{\mu x_0}{r_0^3} = \left(\frac{\partial R}{\partial x}\right)_0$$

and, for the osculating orbit,

$$\left(\frac{\partial^2 x}{\partial t^2}\right)_0 + \frac{\mu x_0}{r_0^3} = 0.$$

Therefore,

$$\left(\frac{d^2x}{dt^2}\right)_0 - \left(\frac{\partial^2 x}{\partial t^2}\right)_0 = \left(\frac{\partial R}{\partial x}\right)_0 .$$

The perturbation [Eq. (6–5)] is then, in general,

$$\delta x = \tfrac{1}{2}\tau^2 \left(\frac{\partial R}{\partial x}\right)_0 = \tfrac{1}{2}\tau^2 k^2 m' \left[\frac{x' - x}{\rho^3} - \frac{x'}{r'^3}\right]_0,$$

by application of Eq. (6–3).

For our purposes, we assume that the masses are aligned approximately so that $x' - x \cong a' - a$, and we ignore the perturbations in the y- and z-directions. Furthermore for convenience, we express the time interval τ in units of the period P of m around m_1. By Kepler's third law, we know that the period is given approximately by

$$P^2 = \frac{4\pi^2 a^3}{k^2 m_1}, \qquad \text{if } m_1 \gg m.$$

Introducing these changes, we have for the perturbation

$$\delta x = 2\pi^2 a^3 \left(\frac{m'}{m_1}\right) \left(\frac{\tau}{P}\right)^2 \left[\frac{1}{(a' - a)^2} - \frac{1}{a'^2}\right]. \qquad (6\text{–}7)$$

As an illustration, consider the perturbation produced by Jupiter on an asteroid which has a period one-half that of Jupiter's period. By Kepler's third law, the asteroid would be at a mean distance $a = 3.3$ A.U. In Eq. (6–7), then, we use $a' = 5.2$ and $m'/m_1 = 0.001$ to find $\delta x \cong 0.16 \,(\tau/P)^2$ A.U. If, for simplicity, we assume that the effective contact for the perturbation lasts for 0.1 period of the asteroid, the deviation becomes $\delta x = 0.0016$ A.U. $= 240,000$ km, which is a sizeable displacement. We emphasize again that this calculation merely indicates the order of magnitude of the perturbative effects produced by a giant planet such as Jupiter. Perturbations of this kind account for the gaps in the ring of asteroid orbits lying between the orbits of Mars and Jupiter. These are known as the Kirkwood gaps after the astronomer who discovered them. Another example of a similar phenomenon is the Cassini division in the rings of Saturn, which is due to perturbative effects caused by the satellite Mimas.

We return now to a general discussion of the perturbation equation, [Eq. (6–2)]. From Eq. (6–1) with the c_k ($k = 1, 2, 3, \ldots$) functions of the time, we write

$$\dot{\mathbf{r}} = \frac{\partial \mathbf{r}}{\partial t} + \sum_{k=1}^{6} \frac{\partial \mathbf{r}}{\partial c_k} \dot{c}_k. \qquad (6\text{–}8)$$

The $\dot{c}_k$ are defined in such a way that

$$\sum_{k=1}^{6} \frac{\partial \mathbf{r}}{\partial c_k} \dot{c}_k = 0. \qquad (6\text{–}9)$$

As mentioned in the simplified example, this means that the velocity in the osculating orbit, namely

$$\frac{\partial \mathbf{r}}{\partial t} = \frac{\partial x}{\partial t}\mathbf{i} + \frac{\partial y}{\partial t}\mathbf{j} + \frac{\partial z}{\partial t}\mathbf{k},$$

is the same as that in the true orbit ($\dot{\mathbf{r}} = \dot{x}\mathbf{i} + \dot{y}\mathbf{j} + \dot{z}\mathbf{k}$).

Invoking Eq. (6–9) and differentiating Eq. (6–8) with respect to t, we obtain

$$\ddot{\mathbf{r}} = \frac{\partial^2 \mathbf{r}}{\partial t^2} + \sum_{k=1}^{6} \frac{\partial^2 \mathbf{r}}{\partial t\, \partial c_k} \dot{c}_k. \qquad (6\text{–}10)$$

Substitution of Eq. (6–10) into Eq. (6–2) yields

$$\frac{\partial^2 \mathbf{r}}{\partial t^2} + \frac{\mu \mathbf{r}}{r^3} + \sum_{k=1}^{6} \frac{\partial^2 \mathbf{r}}{\partial t\, \partial c_k} \dot{c}_k = \nabla R. \qquad (6\text{–}11)$$

For the osculating orbit, however, $R = 0$ and the c_k are constants so that

$$\frac{\partial^2 \mathbf{r}}{\partial t^2} + \frac{\mu \mathbf{r}}{r^3} = 0. \qquad (6\text{–}12)$$

Hence Eq. (6–11) reduces to

$$\sum_{k=1}^{6} \frac{\partial^2 \mathbf{r}}{\partial t\, \partial c_k} \dot{c}_k = \nabla R. \qquad (6\text{–}13)$$

The time derivatives of the orbital elements can be found by solving Eqs. (6–9) and (6–13) simultaneously for the $\dot{c}_k$. Before proceeding, however, we can simplify Eq. (6–13) somewhat by noting that

$$\frac{\partial^2 \mathbf{r}}{\partial t\, \partial c_k} = \frac{\partial}{\partial c_k}\left(\frac{\partial \mathbf{r}}{\partial t}\right) = \frac{\partial \dot{\mathbf{r}}}{\partial c_k}. \qquad (6\text{–}14)$$

This follows from the definition [Eq. (6–9)] that $\dot{\mathbf{r}} = \partial \mathbf{r}/\partial t$ at the osculating orbit. Hence Eq. (6–13) can be written

$$\sum_{k=1}^{6} \frac{\partial \dot{\mathbf{r}}}{\partial c_k} \dot{c}_k = \nabla R. \qquad (6\text{–}15)$$

The solution of Eqs. (6–9) and (6–15) for the $\dot{c}_k$ can be performed more readily by a rearrangement which introduces new functions of the parameters c_k called *Lagrange's brackets*. We take the scalar product of Eq. (6–15) by $\partial \mathbf{r}/\partial c_j$, the scalar product of Eq. (6–9) by $\partial \dot{\mathbf{r}}/\partial c_j$, and subtract to obtain

$$\sum_{k=1}^{6} \left[\frac{\partial \mathbf{r}}{\partial c_j} \cdot \frac{\partial \dot{\mathbf{r}}}{\partial c_k} - \frac{\partial \mathbf{r}}{\partial c_k} \cdot \frac{\partial \dot{\mathbf{r}}}{\partial c_j}\right] \dot{c}_k = \nabla R \cdot \frac{\partial \mathbf{r}}{\partial c_j} \qquad (j = 1, 2, \ldots, 6). \quad (6\text{–}16)$$

The quantity in brackets in Eq. (6–16) is Lagrange's bracket and will be denoted by $[c_j, c_k]$. In terms of its cartesian components,

$$[c_j, c_k] = \frac{\partial(x, \dot{x})}{\partial(c_j, c_k)} + \frac{\partial(y, \dot{y})}{\partial(c_j, c_k)} + \frac{\partial(z, \dot{z})}{\partial(c_j, c_k)}, \tag{6–17}$$

where

$$\frac{\partial(x, \dot{x})}{\partial(c_j, c_k)} \equiv \begin{vmatrix} \dfrac{\partial x}{\partial c_j} & \dfrac{\partial x}{\partial c_k} \\[2mm] \dfrac{\partial \dot{x}}{\partial c_j} & \dfrac{\partial \dot{x}}{\partial c_k} \end{vmatrix}, \tag{6–18}$$

and there are similar expressions for y and z. The functional determinant appearing in Eq. (6–18) is the Jacobian of x and $\dot{x}$ with respect to c_j and c_k.

The right-hand side of Eq. (6–16) is the partial derivative of R with respect to c_j. Hence Eq. (6–16) can be written very simply as

$$\sum_{k=1}^{6} [c_j, c_k]\dot{c}_k = \frac{\partial R}{\partial c_j} \qquad (j = 1, 2, \ldots, 6). \tag{6–19}$$

These six equations are to be solved for $\dot{c}_k$.

As a simple illustration of this method, let us consider the one-dimensional linear oscillator whose differential equation of motion is

$$\ddot{x} + x = R(t). \tag{6–20}$$

We know that the solution of this equation when $R = 0$ is $x = c_1 \sin t + c_2 \cos t$. Now we allow c_1 and c_2 to be functions of the time and write

$$\dot{x} = (c_1 \cos t - c_2 \sin t) + (\dot{c}_1 \sin t + \dot{c}_2 \cos t).$$

The first parenthesis is $\partial x/\partial t$ and the second is the analogue of the summation on the right-hand side of Eq. (6–8). Then by Eq. (6–9), we set

$$\dot{c}_1 \sin t + \dot{c}_2 \cos t = 0. \tag{6–21}$$

Differentiating once more, we find

$$\ddot{x} = (-c_1 \sin t - c_2 \cos t) + (\dot{c}_1 \cos t - \dot{c}_2 \sin t). \tag{6–22}$$

As the student will observe, the first parenthesis in Eq. (6–22) is $\partial^2 x/\partial t^2$ and the second is

$$\dot{c}_1 \frac{\partial^2 x}{\partial t\, \partial c_1} + \dot{c}_2 \frac{\partial^2 x}{\partial t\, \partial c_2},$$

which is the analogue of the summation on the right-hand side of Eq. (6–10). Substitution of Eq. (6–22) into Eq. (6–20) yields

$$\dot{c}_1 \cos t - \dot{c}_2 \sin t = R(t).$$

Thus we have to solve, simultaneously,

$$\dot{c}_1 \sin t + \dot{c}_2 \cos t = 0,$$

$$\dot{c}_1 \cos t - \dot{c}_2 \sin t = R(t), \qquad (6\text{-}23)$$

for $\dot{c}_1$ and $\dot{c}_2$. Observe that

$$\frac{\partial}{\partial c_1}\left(\frac{\partial x}{\partial t}\right) = \frac{\partial \dot{x}}{\partial c_1} = \cos t,$$

$$\frac{\partial}{\partial c_2}\left(\frac{\partial x}{\partial t}\right) = \frac{\partial \dot{x}}{\partial c_2} = -\sin t,$$

which, for this example, are analogous to Eq. (6–14). Furthermore

$$\frac{\partial x}{\partial c_1} = \sin t; \qquad \frac{\partial x}{\partial c_2} = \cos t.$$

Thus, for comparison with Eqs. (6–9) and (6–15), Eqs. (6–23) can be written as

$$\dot{c}_1 \frac{\partial \dot{x}}{\partial c_1} + \dot{c}_2 \frac{\partial \dot{x}}{\partial c_2} = R(t),$$

$$\dot{c}_1 \frac{\partial x}{\partial c_1} + \dot{c}_2 \frac{\partial x}{\partial c_2} = 0. \qquad (6\text{-}24)$$

Multiplying the first of these expressions by $\partial x/\partial c_j$ and the second by $\partial \dot{x}/\partial c_j (j = 1, 2)$ and subtracting, we obtain

$$\dot{c}_1 \left[\frac{\partial x}{\partial c_j} \frac{\partial \dot{x}}{\partial c_1} - \frac{\partial x}{\partial c_1} \frac{\partial \dot{x}}{\partial c_j} \right] + \dot{c}_2 \left[\frac{\partial x}{\partial c_j} \frac{\partial \dot{x}}{\partial c_2} - \frac{\partial x}{\partial c_2} \frac{\partial \dot{x}}{\partial c_j} \right] = R \frac{\partial x}{\partial c_j} \qquad (j = 1, 2)$$

$$(6\text{-}25)$$

or, introducing Lagrange's brackets,

$$[c_j, c_1]\dot{c}_1 + [c_j, c_2]\dot{c}_2 = R \frac{\partial x}{\partial c_j} \qquad (j = 1, 2). \qquad (6\text{-}26)$$

This is analogous to Eq. (6–16). Now the student may show that

$$[c_1, c_1] = [c_2, c_2] = 0,$$
$$[c_1, c_2] = -1,$$
$$[c_2, c_1] = 1,$$

and hence that Eq. (6–26) for $j = 1, 2$ reduces to

$$\dot{c}_2 = -R \sin t, \qquad \dot{c}_1 = R \cos t. \qquad (6\text{-}27)$$

The functions $c_1(t)$ and $c_2(t)$ follow directly by integration when $R(t)$ is given.

PROBLEMS

1. Using an order of magnitude calculation such as that exhibited in Eq. (6–7), find the perturbation in the motion of Venus due to the presence of the earth. The data follows.

	Earth	Venus
Mass (solar units)	$(333,420)^{-1}$	$(408,000)^{-1}$
Mean distance (A.U.)	1.000	0.723
Period (days)	365.3	224.7

Assume that the contact lasts for 0.1 of the period of Venus.

2. The mean distance of the satellite Mimas from the center of Saturn is 1.86×10^5 km. Its period is 0.942 days; its mass is 6.68×10^{-8} that of Saturn. Calculate the approximate perturbation due to Mimas for a particle located in the Cassini division 1.18×10^5 km from the center of Saturn. What is the period of this particle in units of the period of Mimas? Assume that the time of greatest perturbative action is 0.1 the period of the small particle.

6–2 Properties of the Lagrange brackets. By the definition of $[c_j, c_k]$ given in Eq. (6–16), together with Eqs. (6–17) and (6–18), we note that

$$[c_j, c_j] = 0, \qquad [c_k, c_j] = -[c_j, c_k]. \tag{6–28}$$

Another property, and a very important one, is

$$\frac{\partial}{\partial t} [c_j, c_k] = 0, \tag{6–29}$$

which implies that the $[c_j, c_k]$ are independent of the time explicitly. This is useful because the brackets may be computed for any convenient epoch, say at perihelion, and they remain invariant with respect to the time thereafter.

The property stated in Eq. (6–29) may be proved in the following way. For convenience let us denote any one bracket by $[p, q]$ and one of the Jacobians [Eq. (6–18)] by $J[(x, \dot{x})/(p, q)]$. Then we have

$$\frac{\partial J}{\partial t} = \frac{\partial}{\partial t} \left\{ \frac{\partial x}{\partial p} \frac{\partial \dot{x}}{\partial q} - \frac{\partial x}{\partial q} \frac{\partial \dot{x}}{\partial p} \right\}$$

$$= \frac{\partial^2 x}{\partial t \, \partial p} \frac{\partial \dot{x}}{\partial q} - \frac{\partial^2 x}{\partial t \, \partial q} \frac{\partial \dot{x}}{\partial p} + \frac{\partial^2 \dot{x}}{\partial t \, \partial q} \frac{\partial x}{\partial p} - \frac{\partial^2 \dot{x}}{\partial t \, \partial p} \frac{\partial x}{\partial q}. \tag{6–30}$$

But, $\partial x/\partial t = \dot{x}$ by the definition of the osculating orbit; therefore, the first two terms become

$$\frac{\partial \dot{x}}{\partial p} \frac{\partial \dot{x}}{\partial q} - \frac{\partial \dot{x}}{\partial q} \frac{\partial \dot{x}}{\partial p} = 0.$$

The last two can be written

$$\frac{\partial}{\partial q}\left(\frac{\partial \dot{x}}{\partial t}\right)\frac{\partial x}{\partial p} - \frac{\partial}{\partial p}\left(\frac{\partial \dot{x}}{\partial t}\right)\frac{\partial x}{\partial q}.$$

Now by the equations of motion for the osculating orbit

$$\frac{\partial \dot{x}}{\partial t} \equiv \frac{\partial^2 x}{\partial t^2} = -\frac{\mu x}{r^3} = \frac{\partial V}{\partial x},$$

where $V = \mu/r$. We may, therefore, write Eq. (6–30) in the form

$$\frac{\partial J}{\partial t} = \frac{\partial}{\partial q}\left(\frac{\partial V}{\partial x}\right)\frac{\partial x}{\partial p} - \frac{\partial}{\partial p}\left(\frac{\partial V}{\partial x}\right)\frac{\partial x}{\partial q}. \tag{6–31}$$

Similar expressions can be written with y and z substituted for x. The function $V(x, y, z)$ is continuous and has continuous derivatives at all points except the origin. Hence we may change the order of differentiation and, adding in the terms in y and z, write

$$\frac{\partial J}{\partial t} = \frac{\partial [p, q]}{\partial t} = \left\{\frac{\partial V_q}{\partial x}\frac{\partial x}{\partial p} + \frac{\partial V_q}{\partial y}\frac{\partial y}{\partial p} + \frac{\partial V_q}{\partial z}\frac{\partial z}{\partial p}\right\}$$
$$- \left\{\frac{\partial V_p}{\partial x}\frac{\partial x}{\partial q} + \frac{\partial V_p}{\partial y}\frac{\partial y}{\partial q} + \frac{\partial V_p}{\partial z}\frac{\partial z}{\partial q}\right\},$$

where $V_p \equiv \partial V/\partial p$ and $V_q \equiv \partial V/\partial q$. It is clear that the first group of terms is $\partial V_q/\partial p$ and the second is $\partial V_p/\partial q$. Furthermore these second partial derivatives are equal. Therefore

$$\frac{\partial [p, q]}{\partial t} = \frac{\partial V_q}{\partial p} - \frac{\partial V_p}{\partial q} = 0, \tag{6–32}$$

and we have shown that the Lagrange bracket is independent of the time explicitly.

PROBLEMS

1. If $x_0, y_0, z_0, \dot{x}_0, \dot{y}_0,$ and $\dot{z}_0$ are the coordinates and velocity components of the moving mass m at $t = t_0$, show from the definition of the Lagrange bracket that brackets of the form $[x_0, y_0]$, $[x_0, \dot{y}_0]$, and $[z_0, \dot{x}_0]$, etc., all vanish and that $[x_0, \dot{x}_0] = [y_0, \dot{y}_0] = [z_0, \dot{z}_0] = 1$. Write the equations corresponding to Eqs. (6–19) for this case.

2. For two functions $x(t, c_1, c_2, c_3)$ and $y(t, c_1, c_2, c_3)$ which are continuously differentiable, the Lagrange bracket is, by definition,

$$[c_i, c_j] = \begin{vmatrix} \dfrac{\partial x}{\partial c_i} & \dfrac{\partial x}{\partial c_j} \\ \dfrac{\partial y}{\partial c_i} & \dfrac{\partial y}{\partial c_j} \end{vmatrix}.$$

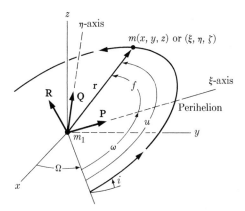

FIG. 6–2. Unit vectors for evaluation of Lagrange's brackets.

Show that

$$\frac{\partial[c_i, c_j]}{\partial c_k} + \frac{\partial[c_j, c_k]}{\partial c_i} + \frac{\partial[c_k, c_i]}{\partial c_j} \equiv 0,$$

for any combination i, j, k.

6–3 Evaluation of Lagrange's brackets. The Lagrange brackets $[c_j, c_k]$ defined in Section 6–1 must be evaluated in terms of the orbital elements in order that Eqs. (6–19) may be solved for the $\dot{c}_k$ ($k = 1, 2, \ldots, 6$). We shall illustrate the procedure here and quote the complete set of values, referring the student to other sources for further details.*

In Fig. 6–2, let **P** be a unit vector in the direction of perihelion, let **Q** be a similar unit vector in the direction $f = 90°$, and let **R** be a unit vector perpendicular to the orbital plane. The latter is directed in the sense **R** = **P** × **Q**. Then we have, by inspection,

$$\mathbf{P} = (\cos \omega \cos \Omega - \sin \omega \sin \Omega \cos i)\mathbf{i}$$
$$+ (\cos \omega \sin \Omega + \sin \omega \cos \Omega \cos i)\mathbf{j} + (\sin \omega \sin i)\mathbf{k}, \qquad (6\text{–}33)$$

$$\mathbf{Q} = (-\sin \omega \cos \Omega - \cos \omega \sin \Omega \cos i)\mathbf{i}$$
$$+ (-\sin \omega \sin \Omega + \cos \omega \cos \Omega \cos i)\mathbf{j} + (\cos \omega \sin i)\mathbf{k}, \qquad (6\text{–}34)$$

$$\mathbf{R} = (\sin \Omega \sin i)\mathbf{i} + (-\cos \Omega \sin i)\mathbf{j} + (\cos i)\mathbf{k}, \qquad (6\text{–}35)$$

where **i**, **j**, **k** are unit vectors along x, y, z, respectively.

Clearly these unit vectors depend only upon the orbital elements Ω, ω, i which orient the orbit in space and not upon a, e, T which define its shape

---

* See W. M. Smart, *Celestial Mechanics*. New York: Longmans, Green and Co., Inc., 1953, p. 63 ff.

and the position of the body in the orbital plane. The elements c_k, therefore, fall naturally into two groups of three each. For convenience, we shall denote the group a, e, T by α_1, α_2, α_3, and the group Ω, ω, i by β_1, β_2, β_3. The Lagrangian brackets correspondingly fall into three categories: $[\alpha_r, \alpha_s]$, $[\alpha_r, \beta_s]$, and $[\beta_r, \beta_s]$, where $r \neq s; r, s = 1, 2, 3$. We shall evaluate only the first of these as an illustration of the procedure.

To do this, we simplify Eqs. (6–33), (6–34), and (6–35) to

$$\mathbf{P} = P_1\mathbf{i} + P_2\mathbf{j} + P_3\mathbf{k},$$
$$\mathbf{Q} = Q_1\mathbf{i} + Q_2\mathbf{j} + Q_3\mathbf{k}, \qquad (6\text{–}36)$$
$$\mathbf{R} = R_1\mathbf{i} + R_2\mathbf{j} + R_3\mathbf{k},$$

where the various components of $\mathbf{P}$, $\mathbf{Q}$, and $\mathbf{R}$ are the direction cosines of the respective vectors relative to the x-, y-, and z-axes.

The radius vector at any instant, then, can be expressed by

$$\mathbf{r} = x\mathbf{i} + y\mathbf{j} + z\mathbf{k} = \xi\mathbf{P} + \eta\mathbf{Q}, \qquad (6\text{–}37)$$

where ξ and η are cartesian coordinates in the orbital plane. From Eq. (6–37), the velocity can be written as

$$\dot{\mathbf{r}} = \dot{x}\mathbf{i} + \dot{y}\mathbf{j} + \dot{z}\mathbf{k} = \dot{\xi}\mathbf{P} + \dot{\eta}\mathbf{Q} + \xi\dot{\mathbf{P}} + \eta\dot{\mathbf{Q}}.$$

But by the definition of the osculating orbit, $\dot{\mathbf{r}} = \partial\mathbf{r}/\partial t$ and hence

$$\xi\dot{\mathbf{P}} + \eta\dot{\mathbf{Q}} = 0,$$

so that

$$\dot{\mathbf{r}} = \dot{\xi}\mathbf{P} + \dot{\eta}\mathbf{Q}. \qquad (6\text{–}38)$$

It is clear from Eqs. (6–37) and (6–38) that x, $\dot{x}$, y, $\dot{y}$, z, and $\dot{z}$ can be expressed in terms of the new coordinates ξ, η and the new velocity components $\dot{\xi}$, $\dot{\eta}$, whenever desired.

From the definition [Eq. (6–17)] the Lagrangian bracket $[\alpha_r, \alpha_s]$ is

$$\frac{\partial(x, \dot{x})}{\partial(\alpha_r, \alpha_s)} + \frac{\partial(y, \dot{y})}{\partial(\alpha_r, \alpha_s)} + \frac{\partial(z, \dot{z})}{\partial(\alpha_r, \alpha_s)} =$$

$$\begin{vmatrix} \dfrac{\partial x}{\partial \alpha_r} & \dfrac{\partial x}{\partial \alpha_s} \\[2mm] \dfrac{\partial \dot{x}}{\partial \alpha_r} & \dfrac{\partial \dot{x}}{\partial \alpha_s} \end{vmatrix} + \begin{vmatrix} \dfrac{\partial y}{\partial \alpha_r} & \dfrac{\partial y}{\partial \alpha_s} \\[2mm] \dfrac{\partial \dot{y}}{\partial \alpha_r} & \dfrac{\partial \dot{y}}{\partial \alpha_s} \end{vmatrix} + \begin{vmatrix} \dfrac{\partial z}{\partial \alpha_r} & \dfrac{\partial z}{\partial \alpha_s} \\[2mm] \dfrac{\partial \dot{z}}{\partial \alpha_r} & \dfrac{\partial \dot{z}}{\partial \alpha_s} \end{vmatrix} . \qquad (6\text{–}39)$$

But in place of $(\partial x/\partial \alpha_r)$, $(\partial \dot{x}/\partial \alpha_r)$, we may write, by Eqs. (6–37) and (6–38),

$$\frac{\partial x}{\partial \alpha_r} = \frac{\partial x}{\partial \xi}\frac{\partial \xi}{\partial \alpha_r} + \frac{\partial x}{\partial \eta}\frac{\partial \eta}{\partial \alpha_r}, \qquad \frac{\partial \dot{x}}{\partial \alpha_r} = \frac{\partial \dot{x}}{\partial \dot{\xi}}\frac{\partial \dot{\xi}}{\partial \alpha_r} + \frac{\partial \dot{x}}{\partial \dot{\eta}}\frac{\partial \dot{\eta}}{\partial \alpha_r},$$

together with corresponding terms in y and z. Furthermore,

$$\frac{\partial x}{\partial \xi} = P_1 \quad \text{and} \quad \frac{\partial \dot{x}}{\partial \dot{\xi}} = P_1,$$

$$\frac{\partial x}{\partial \eta} = Q_1 \quad \text{and} \quad \frac{\partial \dot{x}}{\partial \dot{\eta}} = Q_1,$$

with similar terms for y and z. Substituting into Eq. (6–39), we have

$$\begin{vmatrix} \left(P_1\frac{\partial \xi}{\partial \alpha_r} + Q_1\frac{\partial \eta}{\partial \alpha_r}\right) & \left(P_1\frac{\partial \xi}{\partial \alpha_s} + Q_1\frac{\partial \eta}{\partial \alpha_s}\right) \\ \left(P_1\frac{\partial \dot{\xi}}{\partial \alpha_r} + Q_1\frac{\partial \dot{\eta}}{\partial \alpha_r}\right) & \left(P_1\frac{\partial \dot{\xi}}{\partial \alpha_s} + Q_1\frac{\partial \dot{\eta}}{\partial \alpha_s}\right) \end{vmatrix}$$

for the first determinant and similar expressions for the second and third determinants.

The direction cosines, however, have the properties

$$P_1^2 + P_2^2 + P_3^2 = 1,$$
$$Q_1^2 + Q_2^2 + Q_3^2 = 1,$$
$$P_1Q_1 + P_2Q_2 + P_3Q_3 = 0.$$

Therefore, when the determinants are evaluated and the terms collected, we find

$$[\alpha_r, \alpha_s] = \begin{vmatrix} \frac{\partial \xi}{\partial \alpha_r} & \frac{\partial \xi}{\partial \alpha_s} \\ \frac{\partial \dot{\xi}}{\partial \alpha_r} & \frac{\partial \dot{\xi}}{\partial \alpha_s} \end{vmatrix} + \begin{vmatrix} \frac{\partial \eta}{\partial \alpha_r} & \frac{\partial \eta}{\partial \alpha_s} \\ \frac{\partial \dot{\eta}}{\partial \alpha_r} & \frac{\partial \dot{\eta}}{\partial \alpha_s} \end{vmatrix} = \frac{\partial(\xi, \dot{\xi})}{\partial(\alpha_r, \alpha_s)} + \frac{\partial(\eta, \dot{\eta})}{\partial(\alpha_r, \alpha_s)}. \quad (6\text{–}40)$$

To evaulate these Jacobians, we invoke the time invariant property of the bracket, proved in Section 6–2, and perform the evaluation at perihelion. We have shown that the bracket is constant for all t. In particular, we assume such a value of t that the mean anomaly $M = n(t - T)$ is small and hence that the eccentric anomaly $E \approx 0$. Then we may write, to terms of order 3,

$$\sin E = E - \frac{E^3}{3!} + \cdots,$$

and, by Kepler's equation [Eq. (3–40)],

$$E - e\sin E = n(t - T),$$
$$E - eE + \frac{eE^3}{3!} = n(t - T).$$

Neglecting the term eE^3 in comparison with eE, we have

$$E = \frac{n(t - T)}{1 - e}, \tag{6-41}$$

and hence

$$\sin E \cong \frac{n(t - T)}{1 - e}, \tag{6-42}$$

$$\cos E \cong 1 - \frac{n^2(t - T)^2}{2(1 - e)^2}. \tag{6-43}$$

By the definitions of ξ, η (Fig. 6–2), and by Eqs. (3–35) and (3–36),

$$\xi = r \cos f = a \cos E - ae,$$
$$\eta = r \sin f = a \sin E \sqrt{1 - e^2}. \tag{6-44}$$

Thus, from Eqs. (6–42) and (6–43),

$$\xi = a\left[1 - \frac{n^2(t - T)^2}{2(1 - e)^2}\right] - ae, \tag{6-45}$$

$$\eta = \frac{na \sqrt{1 - e^2} \, (t - T)}{1 - e} = na \sqrt{(1 + e)/(1 - e)}(t - T). \tag{6-46}$$

From these we obtain

$$\dot{\xi} = -\frac{n^2 a}{(1 - e)^2} (t - T),$$
$$\dot{\eta} = na \sqrt{(1 + e)/(1 - e)}, \tag{6-47}$$

where we bear in mind that, by Kepler's third law,

$$n^2 a^3 = \mu.$$

When taking partial derivatives of ξ, η, $\dot{\xi}$, and $\dot{\eta}$ with respect to a, one must first express n in Eqs. (6–45) to (6–47) in terms of a.

We are now in a position to evaluate the Jacobians in Eq. (6–40). Let, $[\alpha_r, \alpha_s] = [a, e]$, for example. Then by Eq. (6–45)

$$\frac{\partial \xi}{\partial a} = \left[1 - \frac{n^2(t - T)^2}{2(1 - e)^2}\right] + a\left[-\frac{n(\partial n/\partial a)(t - T)^2}{(1 - e)^2}\right] - e,$$

and, at $t = T$, this becomes

$$\left(\frac{\partial \xi}{\partial a}\right)_T = 1 - e.$$

In a similar way,

$$\left(\frac{\partial \xi}{\partial a}\right)_T = \frac{\partial}{\partial a}\left\{-\frac{\mu(t-T)}{a^2(1-e)^2}\right\}_T = \left[\frac{2\mu(t-T)}{a^3(1-e)^2}\right]_T = 0,$$

$$\left(\frac{\partial \xi}{\partial e}\right)_T = \left[-\frac{n^2a(t-T)^2}{(1-e)^3} - a\right]_T = -a,$$

$$\left(\frac{\partial \dot{\xi}}{\partial e}\right)_T = \left[-\frac{2n^2a(t-T)}{(1-e)^3}\right]_T = 0.$$

Then the Jacobian

$$\frac{\partial(\xi, \dot{\xi})}{\partial(a, e)} = 0. \tag{6–48}$$

Let the student show that

$$\left(\frac{\partial \eta}{\partial a}\right)_T = 0, \qquad \left(\frac{\partial \dot{\eta}}{\partial a}\right)_T = -\frac{n}{2}\sqrt{(1+e)/(1-e)},$$

$$\left(\frac{\partial \eta}{\partial e}\right)_T = 0, \qquad \left(\frac{\partial \dot{\eta}}{\partial e}\right)_T = \frac{na}{(1-e)\sqrt{1-e^2}};$$

and thus

$$\frac{\partial(\eta, \dot{\eta})}{\partial(a, e)} = 0. \tag{6–49}$$

The Jacobians [Eqs. (6–48) and (6–49)], used in Eq. (6–40), obviously yield $[a, e] = 0$.

In a similar way, one may evaluate all of the Lagrangian brackets needed to solve the perturbation equations, [Eqs. (6–19)]. To summarize, we find nonvanishing brackets

$$[\Omega, a] = \frac{na \cos i \sqrt{1-e^2}}{2},$$

$$[\omega, a] = \frac{na \sqrt{1-e^2}}{2},$$

$$[e, \Omega] = \frac{na^2 e \cos i}{\sqrt{1-e^2}}, \tag{6–50}$$

$$[e, \omega] = \frac{na^2 e}{\sqrt{1-e^2}},$$

$$[i, \Omega] = -na^2 \sin i \sqrt{1-e^2},$$

$$[a, T] = \frac{n^2 a}{2},$$

and all the others are zero. If one uses the element $\sigma = -nT$ in place of T, the bracket

$$[\sigma, a] = \frac{na}{2}. \tag{6-51}$$

The first four brackets in Eqs. (6–50) are of the type $[\alpha_r, \beta_s]$, the fifth is of type $[\beta_r, \beta_s]$, and the last is of the type $[\alpha_r, \alpha_s]$.

PROBLEMS

Given

$$x = \xi P_1 + \eta Q_1, \qquad y = \xi P_2 + \eta Q_2, \qquad z = \xi P_3 + \eta Q_3,$$

and similar relations for $\dot{x}$, $\dot{y}$, $\dot{z}$, show that

$$[\beta_r, \beta_s] = (\xi\dot{\eta} - \eta\dot{\xi})\left[\frac{\partial(P_1, Q_1)}{\partial(\beta_r, \beta_s)} + \frac{\partial(P_2, Q_2)}{\partial(\beta_r, \beta_s)} + \frac{\partial(P_3, Q_3)}{\partial(\beta_r, \beta_s)}\right].$$

Show also that $\xi\dot{\eta} - \eta\dot{\xi} = na^2\sqrt{1 - e^2}$. Finally, obtain

$$[\Omega, \omega] = 0,$$
$$[\Omega, i] = -na^2 \sin i\sqrt{1 - e^2},$$
$$[i, \omega] = 0.$$

[*Hint:* Use Eqs. (6–33), (6–34), and (6–35) to evaluate the partial derivatives of P_j, Q_j, R_j with respect to β_r, β_s.]

6–4 Solution of the perturbation equations. Having evaluated the Lagrangian brackets, we may now complete the solution of Eqs. (6–19) for the time derivatives of the orbital elements. Substituting from Eqs. (6–50) into Eqs. (6–19) and making use of the property $[c_j, c_k] = -[c_k, c_j]$, we find

$$\tfrac{1}{2}na\dot{a} = \frac{\partial R}{\partial \sigma}, \tag{6-52}$$

$$(\tfrac{1}{2}na\sqrt{1 - e^2})\dot{a} - \left(\frac{na^2 e}{\sqrt{1 - e^2}}\right)\dot{e} = \frac{\partial R}{\partial \omega}, \tag{6-53}$$

$$(\tfrac{1}{2}na\cos i\sqrt{1 - e^2})\dot{a} - \left(\frac{na^2 e\cos i}{\sqrt{1 - e^2}}\right)\dot{e} - (na^2 \sin i\sqrt{1 - e^2})\frac{di}{dt} = \frac{\partial R}{\partial \Omega}, \tag{6-54}$$

$$(na^2 \sin i\sqrt{1 - e^2})\dot{\Omega} = \frac{\partial R}{\partial i}, \tag{6-55}$$

$$(-\tfrac{1}{2}na\cos i\sqrt{1 - e^2})\dot{\Omega} - (\tfrac{1}{2}na\sqrt{1 - e^2})\dot{\omega} - (\tfrac{1}{2}na)\dot{\sigma} = \frac{\partial R}{\partial a}, \tag{6-56}$$

$$\left(\frac{na^2 e\cos i}{\sqrt{1 - e^2}}\right)\dot{\Omega} + \left(\frac{na^2 e}{\sqrt{1 - e^2}}\right)\dot{\omega} = \frac{\partial R}{\partial e}. \tag{6-57}$$

The simultaneous solution of these for the time derivatives yields

$$\dot{a} = \frac{2}{na} \frac{\partial R}{\partial \sigma}, \tag{6-58}$$

$$\dot{e} = \left(\frac{1-e^2}{na^2 e}\right) \frac{\partial R}{\partial \sigma} - \left(\frac{\sqrt{1-e^2}}{na^2 e}\right) \frac{\partial R}{\partial \omega}, \tag{6-59}$$

$$\dot{\sigma} = \left(-\frac{1-e^2}{na^2 e}\right) \frac{\partial R}{\partial e} - \frac{2}{na} \frac{\partial R}{\partial a}, \tag{6-60}$$

$$\dot{\Omega} = \left(\frac{1}{na^2 \sin i \sqrt{1-e^2}}\right) \frac{\partial R}{\partial i}, \tag{6-61}$$

$$\dot{\omega} = \left(\frac{-\cos i}{na^2 \sin i \sqrt{1-e^2}}\right) \frac{\partial R}{\partial i} + \left(\frac{\sqrt{1-e^2}}{na^2 e}\right) \frac{\partial R}{\partial e}, \tag{6-62}$$

$$\frac{di}{dt} = \left(\frac{\cos i}{na^2 \sin i \sqrt{1-e^2}}\right) \frac{\partial R}{\partial \omega} - \left(\frac{1}{na^2 \sin i \sqrt{1-e^2}}\right) \frac{\partial R}{\partial \Omega}. \tag{6-63}$$

In using Eq. (6–60) it may be convenient to introduce the mean anomaly $M = n(t - T) = nt + \sigma$ in lieu of σ itself. This implies that the perturbation function can be written in the form $R(a, e, i, \omega, \Omega, M)$. This is quite possible because the cartesian coordinates in which R was defined originally are functions of the time and of T which in turn can be expressed in terms of M.

To make this conversion, we note that

$$\dot{M} = n + \dot{n}t + \dot{\sigma} = n + \frac{dn}{da} \dot{a}t + \dot{\sigma}, \tag{6-64}$$

and $\dot{\sigma}$ is given by Eq. (6–60). In using the latter equation we need $\partial R/\partial a$. However, R depends upon a both explicitly and also through M, because $n = \mu^{1/2} a^{-3/2}$ (Kepler's third law), and hence

$$M = \mu^{1/2} a^{-3/2} t + \sigma.$$

Therefore,

$$\frac{\partial R}{\partial a} = \left(\frac{\partial R}{\partial a}\right)_M + \frac{\partial R}{\partial M} \frac{\partial M}{\partial a} = \left(\frac{\partial R}{\partial a}\right)_M + \left(-\frac{3n}{2a} t\right) \frac{\partial R}{\partial M}, \tag{6-65}$$

where $(\partial R/\partial a)_M$ denotes the derivative taken *explicitly* with respect to a. Clearly $\partial R/\partial e$ is not affected in this way.

With Eq. (6–65) and $dn/da = -3n/2a$ substituted in Eq. (6–64), we have

$$\dot{M} = n - \frac{3n\dot{a}t}{2a} - \left(\frac{1-e^2}{na^2 e}\right) \frac{\partial R}{\partial e} - \frac{2}{na} \left(\frac{\partial R}{\partial a}\right)_M + \frac{3t}{a^2} \frac{\partial R}{\partial M}. \tag{6-66}$$

But from Eq. (6–58),

$$\dot{a} = \frac{2}{na} \frac{\partial R}{\partial \sigma} = \frac{2}{na} \frac{\partial R}{\partial M}.$$

Upon substituting this relation into the second term of Eq. (6–66), we find that this cancels the last term. Therefore

$$\dot{M} = n - \left(\frac{1 - e^2}{na^2 e}\right) \frac{\partial R}{\partial e} - \frac{2}{na} \left(\frac{\partial R}{\partial a}\right)_M, \qquad (6\text{–}67)$$

and

$$\dot{a} = \frac{2}{na} \frac{\partial R}{\partial M}. \qquad (6\text{–}68)$$

These two relations replace Eqs. (6–60) and (6–58), respectively, when the mean anomaly is used in place of σ as the sixth parameter of the orbit.

In order to apply Eqs. (6–58) to (6–68), it is clear that

$$R(x, y, z, x', y', z')$$

must be expressed in terms of the elements desired. We shall not elaborate upon the method* here, but in a later section we will illustrate the ideas by considering the earth-moon system as perturbed by the sun.

There are many applications of Eqs. (6–58) through (6–68) in which the perturbing forces are directed along the radius vector, transverse to it, and perpendicular to the plane of the orbit. There are other applications in which the perturbing force components are tangent to the orbit, normal to the orbit, and perpendicular to the orbital plane. For example, an artificial satellite moving close to the earth experiences a drag due to the earth's atmosphere. This is a perturbing force tangent to the orbit in the direction opposite to the velocity vector. We shall conclude this section by exhibiting the equations appropriate for the two force systems described. In the following discussion, we shall mean *force per unit mass* wherever the word force is used.

Case I. Radial, transverse, and orthogonal components. Let $\mathbf{u}_r$, $\mathbf{u}_\theta$, $\mathbf{u}_A$ be a right-handed triad of unit vectors with $\mathbf{u}_r$ along r, $\mathbf{u}_\theta$ perpendicular to r in the orbital plane and making an angle less than 90° with the velocity $\mathbf{v}$, $\mathbf{u}_A$ perpendicular to the orbital plane in the sense

$$\mathbf{u}_A = \mathbf{u}_r \times \mathbf{u}_\theta.$$

Let $u = \omega + f$ be the angle from the line of nodes to the radius vector. Then the force under consideration is

$$\mathbf{F} = R'\mathbf{u}_r + S'\mathbf{u}_\theta + W'\mathbf{u}_A, \qquad (6\text{–}69)$$

---

* See, for example, W. M. Smart, *op. cit.*, Chapters 5 and 6.

where the unit vectors in terms of the cartesian coordinate system are

$$\mathbf{u}_r = (\cos \Omega \cos u - \sin \Omega \sin u \cos i)\mathbf{i}$$
$$+ (\sin \Omega \cos u + \cos \Omega \sin u \cos i)\mathbf{j} + (\sin u \sin i)\mathbf{k}, \qquad (6\text{–}70)$$

$$\mathbf{u}_\theta = (-\cos \Omega \sin u - \sin \Omega \cos u \cos i)\mathbf{i}$$
$$+ (-\sin \Omega \sin u + \cos \Omega \cos u \cos i)\mathbf{j} + (\cos u \sin i)\mathbf{k},$$

$$\mathbf{u}_A = (\sin \Omega \sin i)\mathbf{i} + (-\cos \Omega \sin i)\mathbf{j} + (\cos i)\mathbf{k}.$$

It should be clear from the discussion in Section 6–1 that the partial derivatives $(\partial R/\partial x)$, $(\partial R/\partial y)$, and $(\partial R/\partial z)$ in Eqs. (6–2) and (6–3) are the components of the acceleration when the latter is due to the perturbation function R. In vector form, this acceleration is

$$\nabla R \equiv \frac{\partial R}{\partial x}\mathbf{i} + \frac{\partial R}{\partial y}\mathbf{j} + \frac{\partial R}{\partial z}\mathbf{k}.$$

The force components due to R enter the perturbation equations [Eqs. (6–58) through (6–68)] only through the partial derivatives $(\partial R/\partial a)$, $(\partial R/\partial e)$, etc. The transformation to the new force $\mathbf{F}$ is readily made. It has already been shown that, if c_j represents any one of the elements,

$$\frac{\partial R}{\partial c_j} = \nabla R \cdot \frac{\partial \mathbf{r}}{\partial c_j} \qquad (j = 1, 2, 3, \ldots, 6), \qquad (6\text{–}71)$$

where $\mathbf{r} = x\mathbf{i} + y\mathbf{j} + z\mathbf{k}$.

For our purposes, therefore, we need only evaluate

$$\frac{\partial R}{\partial c_j} = \mathbf{F} \cdot \frac{\partial \mathbf{r}}{\partial c_j} \qquad (6\text{–}72)$$

in terms of the force components R', S', and W' and use these partial derivatives in Eqs. (6–58) through (6–68). To take one calculation as an example, we shall consider $\partial R/\partial a$. From Eq. (6–37) we have $\mathbf{r} = \xi\mathbf{P} + \eta\mathbf{Q}$, and hence

$$\frac{\partial \mathbf{r}}{\partial a} = \mathbf{P}\frac{\partial \xi}{\partial a} + \mathbf{Q}\frac{\partial \eta}{\partial a},$$

where $\mathbf{P}$ and $\mathbf{Q}$ are unit vectors as shown in Fig. 6–2. Then Eq. (6–72) yields

$$\frac{\partial R}{\partial a} = \mathbf{F} \cdot \mathbf{P}\frac{\partial \xi}{\partial a} + \mathbf{F} \cdot \mathbf{Q}\frac{\partial \eta}{\partial a}, \qquad (6\text{–}73)$$

where, by Eqs. (6–44),

$$\frac{\partial \xi}{\partial a} = \cos E - e = \frac{\xi}{a}, \qquad \frac{\partial \eta}{\partial a} = \sin E \sqrt{1 - e^2} = \frac{\eta}{a}. \qquad (6\text{–}74)$$

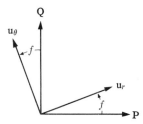

FIG. 6–3. Relationship between unit vectors for Case I.

Now, by Eq. (6–69),

$$\mathbf{F} = R'\mathbf{u}_r + S'\mathbf{u}_\theta + W'\mathbf{u}_A.$$

Therefore, we find (Fig. 6–3)

$$\mathbf{F} \cdot \mathbf{P} = R' \cos f - S' \sin f, \qquad \mathbf{F} \cdot \mathbf{Q} = R' \sin f + S' \cos f.$$

Furthermore,

$$\xi = r \cos f, \qquad \eta = r \sin f,$$

and hence

$$\mathbf{F} \cdot \mathbf{P} = \frac{1}{r}\{R'\xi - S'\eta\}, \qquad \mathbf{F} \cdot \mathbf{Q} = \frac{1}{r}\{R'\eta + S'\xi\}. \qquad (6\text{–}75)$$

With Eqs. (6–75) and (6–74) substituted in Eq. (6–73), we have

$$\frac{\partial R}{\partial a} = R'\frac{r}{a}.$$

This is the partial derivative required for the force system that we postulated.

In a similar way, the other derivatives can be found. We list them here for reference.

$$\frac{\partial R}{\partial a} = R'\frac{r}{a},$$

$$\frac{\partial R}{\partial e} = -R'a \cos f + S'a \sin f \left[1 + \frac{r}{a(1 - e^2)}\right],$$

$$\frac{\partial R}{\partial \sigma} = \frac{R'ea \sin f}{\sqrt{1 - e^2}} + \frac{S'a^2 \sqrt{1 - e^2}}{r},$$

$$\frac{\partial R}{\partial \Omega} = S'r \cos i - W'r \sin i \cos u,$$

$$\frac{\partial R}{\partial \omega} = S'r,$$

$$\frac{\partial R}{\partial i} = W'r \sin u.$$

$$(6\text{–}76)$$

With these substituted into Eqs. (6–58) through (6–63), we find, for the perturbation rates,

$$\dot{a} = \frac{2e \sin f}{n \sqrt{1 - e^2}} R' + \frac{2a \sqrt{1 - e^2}}{rn} S', \tag{6-77}$$

$$\dot{e} = \frac{\sin f \sqrt{1 - e^2}}{na} R' + \frac{\sqrt{1 - e^2}}{a^2 ne} \left[\frac{a^2(1 - e^2) - r^2}{r} \right] S', \tag{6-78}$$

$$\dot{\sigma} = \left[\frac{(1 - e^2) \cos f}{ane} - \frac{2r}{na^2} \right] R' - \frac{(1 - e^2) \sin f}{ane} \left[1 + \frac{r}{a(1 - e^2)} \right] S', \tag{6-79}$$

$$\dot{\Omega} = \frac{r \sin u}{a^2 n \sin i \sqrt{1 - e^2}} W', \tag{6-80}$$

$$\dot{\omega} = \frac{-\cos f \sqrt{1 - e^2}}{ane} R' + \frac{\sin f \sqrt{1 - e^2}}{ane} \left[1 + \frac{r}{a(1 - e^2)} \right] S'$$
$$- \frac{r \sin u \cot i}{a^2 n \sqrt{1 - e^2}} W', \tag{6-81}$$

$$\frac{di}{dt} = \frac{r \cos u}{a^2 n \sqrt{1 - e^2}} W'. \tag{6-82}$$

Equations (6–67) and (6–68) may be transformed in a similar way if needed. Equations (6–80) and (6–82) show clearly that the spatial orientation of the orbit given by Ω and i will change only when a perturbing force having a W'-component is acting.

Case II. Tangential, normal, and orthogonal components. It is convenient here to express the radial and transverse components of Case I in terms of the desired tangential and normal components. Let

$$\mathbf{G} = T' \mathbf{u}_T + N' \mathbf{u}_N + W' \mathbf{u}_A \tag{6-83}$$

define the force. Here $\mathbf{u}_T$, $\mathbf{u}_N$, $\mathbf{u}_A$ are unit vectors, respectively, along the tangent in the direction of motion, along the normal to the orbit directed toward its concave side, and perpendicular to the orbit in the sense $\mathbf{u}_A = \mathbf{u}_T \times \mathbf{u}_N$. Obviously W' here is the same as W' in Case I. We need only concern ourselves with the transformation from R', S' to T', N'.

The component of $\mathbf{G}$ in the radial direction is

$$R' \equiv \mathbf{G} \cdot \mathbf{u}_r = T'(\mathbf{u}_T \cdot \mathbf{u}_r) + N'(\mathbf{u}_N \cdot \mathbf{u}_r) \tag{6-84}$$

and in the transverse direction it is

$$S' \equiv \mathbf{G} \cdot \mathbf{u}_\theta = T'(\mathbf{u}_T \cdot \mathbf{u}_\theta) + N'(\mathbf{u}_N \cdot \mathbf{u}_\theta). \tag{6-85}$$

The scalar products are easily evaluated by remembering that $\mathbf{u}_T$ and $\mathbf{u}_N$ are along and perpendicular to the velocity vector. In other words, we may write

$$\mathbf{v} = \dot{r}\mathbf{u}_r + r\dot{f}\mathbf{u}_\theta = v\mathbf{u}_T.$$

From this we find, by taking scalar products,

$$\frac{\dot{r}}{v} = \mathbf{u}_r \cdot \mathbf{u}_T = \mathbf{u}_\theta \cdot \mathbf{u}_N,$$

$$\frac{r\dot{f}}{v} = \mathbf{u}_\theta \cdot \mathbf{u}_T = -\mathbf{u}_r \cdot \mathbf{u}_N.$$

(6–86)

The second part of these expressions follows from the geometry of the unit vectors.

The discussion of elliptic motion in Chapter 2 yielded the equations

$$r = \frac{a(1 - e^2)}{1 + e \cos f},$$

$$r^2 \dot{f} = h = \sqrt{k^2 M a(1 - e^2)}.$$

(6–87)

Evaluation of $\dot{r}$ from the first of these equations and the elimination of $\dot{f}$ by means of the second yields

$$\dot{r} = \frac{k \sqrt{M} e \sin f}{\sqrt{a(1 - e^2)}},$$

$$r\dot{f} = \frac{k \sqrt{M} (1 + e \cos f)}{\sqrt{a(1 - e^2)}},$$

$$v = \frac{k \sqrt{M} (1 + e^2 + 2e \cos f)^{1/2}}{\sqrt{a(1 - e^2)}}.$$

Therefore the scalar products [Eqs. (6–86)] become

$$\mathbf{u}_r \cdot \mathbf{u}_T = \mathbf{u}_\theta \cdot \mathbf{u}_N = \frac{e \sin f}{(1 + e^2 + 2e \cos f)^{1/2}},$$

$$\mathbf{u}_\theta \cdot \mathbf{u}_T = -\mathbf{u}_r \cdot \mathbf{u}_N = \frac{1 + e \cos f}{(1 + e^2 + 2e \cos f)^{1/2}}.$$

(6–88)

Substituting Eqs. (6–88) into Eqs. (6–84) and (6–85), we have

$$R' = \frac{e \sin f}{(1 + e^2 + 2e \cos f)^{1/2}} T' - \frac{1 + e \cos f}{(1 + e^2 + 2e \cos f)^{1/2}} N',$$

$$S' = \frac{1 + e \cos f}{(1 + e^2 + 2e \cos f)^{1/2}} T' + \frac{e \sin f}{(1 + e^2 + 2e \cos f)^{1/2}} N'.$$

(6–89)

With these equations, given T' and N', one may substitute for R' and S' in Eqs. (6–77) through (6–82) to obtain the perturbations due to a force which has been resolved into tangential, normal, and orthogonal components. An application of these equations will be deferred to a later section.

PROBLEMS

1. Let the perturbing force $\mathbf{F} = X\mathbf{i} + Y\mathbf{j} + Z\mathbf{k}$ be that defined by Eq. (6–69). Show that

$$X = R'(\cos \Omega \cos u - \sin \Omega \sin u \cos i)$$
$$- S'(\cos \Omega \sin u + \sin \Omega \cos u \cos i) + W'(\sin \Omega \sin i),$$

$$Y = R'(\sin \Omega \cos u + \cos \Omega \sin u \cos i)$$
$$- S'(\sin \Omega \sin u - \cos \Omega \cos u \cos i) - W'(\cos \Omega \sin i),$$

$$Z = R'(\sin u \sin i) + S'(\cos u \sin i) + W'(\cos i).$$

2. Suppose that a low-thrust rocket is attached to a space vehicle moving in an elliptic orbit around the earth. For our purpose, the latter will be considered spherical. Discuss (a) the perturbations that will occur if the rocket thrust is directed along the velocity vector, (b) what happens if the thrust is radially outward along $\mathbf{r}$, and (c) what happens if the thrust is directed transverse to $\mathbf{r}$ but in the direction opposite the motion.

3. If the perturbing force is a resistive force and equal to $\mathbf{F} = -cv\mathbf{v}$, where c is a positive constant, write the radial and transverse components. Which orbital elements are influenced by this force and what are their time rates of change? Describe what happens to the shape and position of the orbit.

6–5 Expansion of the perturbation function. In order to obtain the time rates of change of the orbital elements from Eqs. (6–58) to (6–68),

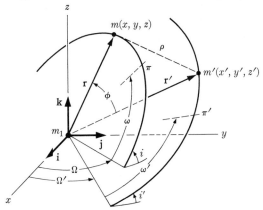

FIG. 6–4. Orbital geometry for expansion of perturbation function.

the disturbing function R is customarily expressed as an infinite series in which the orbital elements appear either in the coefficients or in the arguments of trigonometric functions. In this section we shall outline the method of expansion, referring the student to other sources for many of the details.

In Fig. 6–4, let m and m' be the perturbed and the perturbing masses, respectively. Let r and r' be their distances from the central mass m_1, and let $r' > r$ at all times. In the following discussion, it will be readily apparent how to modify the analysis for the case in which $r' < r$. The letters π and π' denote the perihelion points of the two orbits.

The perturbation function [Eq. (6–3)] can be written

$$
\begin{aligned}
R &= k^2 m' \left[\frac{1}{\rho} - \frac{xx' + yy' + zz'}{r'^3} \right] \\
&= k^2 m' \left[(r^2 + r'^2 - 2rr' \cos \phi)^{-1/2} - \frac{rr' \cos \phi}{r'^3} \right] \\
&= k^2 m' \left[\frac{1}{r'} \left\{ 1 + \left(\frac{r}{r'} \right)^2 - 2 \left(\frac{r}{r'} \right) \cos \phi \right\}^{-1/2} - \frac{rr' \cos \phi}{r'^3} \right] \\
&= \frac{k^2 m'}{r'} \left[\left\{ 1 + \left(\frac{r}{r'} \right)^2 - 2 \left(\frac{r}{r'} \right) \cos \phi \right\}^{-1/2} - \left(\frac{r}{r'} \right) \cos \phi \right], \quad (6\text{--}90)
\end{aligned}
$$

where ϕ is the angle between the radius vectors.

Expanding the first term in the bracket by the binomial theorem, we have

$$
\begin{aligned}
\left[1 + \left(\frac{r}{r'} \right)^2 - 2 \left(\frac{r}{r'} \right) \cos \phi \right]^{-1/2} &= \\
1 + \left(\frac{r}{r'} \right) \cos \phi &+ \left(\frac{r}{r'} \right)^2 \left(-\tfrac{1}{2} + \tfrac{3}{2} \cos^2 \phi \right) \\
&+ \left(\frac{r}{r'} \right)^3 \left(-\tfrac{3}{2} \cos \phi + \tfrac{5}{2} \cos^3 \phi \right) \\
&+ \left(\frac{r}{r'} \right)^4 \left(\tfrac{3}{8} - \tfrac{15}{4} \cos^2 \phi + \tfrac{35}{8} \cos^4 \phi \right) + \cdots \quad (6\text{--}91)
\end{aligned}
$$

The groups of trigonometric functions in Eq. (6–91) are the *Legendre polynomials of the first kind*,* $P_n (\cos \phi)$. We list the polynomials here for

---

* For a tabulation of these polynomials, together with numerical values, see E. Jahnke and F. Emde, *Tables of Functions*. New York: Dover Publications, Inc., 1943, p. 107 ff. The properties of the polynomials are discussed, for example, in R. V. Churchill, *Fourier Series and Boundary Value Problems*. New York: McGraw-Hill Book Co., Inc., 1941, Chapter 9.

future reference.

$$P_0 \,(\cos \phi) = 1,$$
$$P_1 \,(\cos \phi) = \cos \phi,$$
$$P_2 \,(\cos \phi) = \tfrac{1}{2}[3 \cos^2 \phi - 1],$$
$$P_3 \,(\cos \phi) = \tfrac{1}{2}[5 \cos^3 \phi - 3 \cos \phi],$$
$$P_4 \,(\cos \phi) = \tfrac{1}{8}[35 \cos^4 \phi - 30 \cos^2 \phi + 3],$$
$$P_5 \,(\cos \phi) = \tfrac{1}{8}[63 \cos^5 \phi - 70 \cos^3 \phi + 15 \cos \phi].$$

They may also be expressed in the form

$$P_0 \,(\cos \phi) = 1,$$
$$P_1 \,(\cos \phi) = \cos \phi,$$
$$P_2 \,(\cos \phi) = \tfrac{1}{4}[3 \cos 2\phi + 1],$$
$$P_3 \,(\cos \phi) = \tfrac{1}{8}[5 \cos 3\phi + 3 \cos \phi],$$
$$P_4 \,(\cos \phi) = \tfrac{1}{64}[35 \cos 4\phi + 20 \cos 2\phi + 9],$$

and so forth. The latter functions are called the *Legendre coefficients*. It may be shown* that they are uniformly bounded, that is

$$|P_n \,(\cos \phi)| \le 1 \qquad n = 0, 1, 2, \ldots .$$

Hence the series

$$\sum_{n=0}^{\infty} \left(\frac{r}{r'}\right)^n P_n \,(\cos \phi)$$

is convergent, since we have chosen $(r/r') < 1$. By combining Eq. (6–90) with Eq. (6–91), it is clear that

$$R = \frac{k^2 m'}{r'} \left\{ 1 + \left(\frac{r}{r'}\right)^2 P_2 + \left(\frac{r}{r'}\right)^3 P_3 + \left(\frac{r}{r'}\right)^4 P_4 + \cdots \right\}. \qquad (6\text{–}92)$$

To express R in terms of the orbital elements requires an examination of the nature of the ratios $(r/r')^n$ and of the polynomials $P_n \,(\cos \phi)$. For illustration we shall confine our attention to the term $(r/r')^2 P_2 \,(\cos \phi)$, treating the factors in this product separately.

I. The factor $(r/r')^2$. In Eq. (3–44), we have seen how the eccentric anomaly E can be expanded into a series of trigonometric functions of the mean anomaly M. In an analogous way it may be shown† that, to terms

---

* *Ibid.*

† The details concerning these expansions can be found in D. Brouwer and G. M. Clemence, *Methods of Celestial Mechanics*, New York: Academic Press, 1961, Chapter 2, or in W. M. Smart, *op. cit.*, Chapter 3.

of order 2 in e,

$$\frac{r}{a} = 1 + \tfrac{1}{2}e^2 - e \cos M - \tfrac{1}{2}e^2 \cos 2M, \tag{6-93}$$

$$\frac{a}{r} = 1 + e \cos M + e^2 \cos 2M, \tag{6-94}$$

$$\cos E = -\tfrac{1}{2}e + (1 - \tfrac{3}{8}e^2) \cos M + \tfrac{1}{2}e \cos 2M + \tfrac{3}{8}e^2 \cos 3M, \tag{6-95}$$

$$\sin E = (1 - \tfrac{1}{8}e^2) \sin M + \tfrac{1}{2}e \sin 2M + \tfrac{3}{8}e^2 \sin 3M. \tag{6-96}$$

We may write, using Eqs. (6–93) and (6–94),

$$\frac{r}{r'} \equiv \left(\frac{r}{a}\right)\left(\frac{a'}{r'}\right)\left(\frac{a}{a'}\right)$$

$$= \frac{a}{a'} [1 + \tfrac{1}{2}e^2 - e \cos M - \tfrac{1}{2}e^2 \cos 2M][1 + e' \cos M' + e'^2 \cos 2M']. \tag{6-97}$$

Squaring this yields, to terms of order e^2,

$$\left(\frac{r}{r'}\right)^2 = \left(\frac{a}{a'}\right)^2 [1 + e^2 + e^2 \cos^2 M - 2e \cos M - e^2 \cos 2M$$

$$+ e'^2 \cos^2 M' + 2e' \cos M' - 4ee' \cos M \cos M'$$

$$+ 2e'^2 \cos 2M']. \tag{6-98}$$

But terms such as $\cos^2 M$ and $\cos M \cos M'$ can be always transformed by trigonometric identities into functions of the multiple angle or of sums and differences of angles. Thus,

$$\cos^2 M = \tfrac{1}{2}(1 + \cos 2M)$$

and

$$\cos M \cos M' = \tfrac{1}{2}[\cos (M + M') + \cos (M - M')].$$

Hence Eq. (6–98) can be written

$$\left(\frac{r}{r'}\right)^2 = \left(\frac{a}{a'}\right)^2 [1 + \tfrac{3}{2}e^2 + \tfrac{1}{2}e'^2 - 2e \cos M + 2e' \cos M' - \tfrac{1}{2}e^2 \cos 2M$$

$$+ \tfrac{5}{2}e'^2 \cos 2M' - 2ee' \cos (M + M')$$

$$- 2ee' \cos (M - M')]. \tag{6-99}$$

Thus it is clear that $(r/r')^2$ is the sum of terms of the form

$$A_{pq} \cos (pM + qM'),$$

where p and q are positive or negative integers or zero, and the coefficients A_{pq} are functions of the elements a, a', e, and e'.

II. The factor P_2 (cos ϕ). The polynomial

$$P_2 (\cos \phi) = -\tfrac{1}{2} + \tfrac{3}{2} \cos^2 \phi.$$

Hence we seek first the form of cos ϕ in terms of the orbital elements.
By reference to Eqs. (6–37) and (6–44), and to Fig. (6–2), it is clear that

$$\mathbf{r} = \xi\mathbf{P} + \eta\mathbf{Q} = a \{(\cos E - e)\mathbf{P} + (\sqrt{1 - e^2} \sin E)\mathbf{Q}\}, \quad (6\text{–}100)$$

where $\mathbf{P}$ and $\mathbf{Q}$ are unit vectors whose components as functions of Ω, ω, i
are given by Eqs. (6–33) and (6–34). An equation similar to Eq. (6–100)
relates $\mathbf{r}'$ to the appropriate unit vectors $\mathbf{P}'$ and $\mathbf{Q}'$.
  Now we may write

$$\cos \phi = \frac{\mathbf{r} \cdot \mathbf{r}'}{rr'} = \frac{(\xi\mathbf{P} + \eta\mathbf{Q}) \cdot (\xi'\mathbf{P}' + \eta'\mathbf{Q}')}{rr'}$$

$$= \frac{\xi\xi'\mathbf{P} \cdot \mathbf{P}' + \eta\xi'\mathbf{Q} \cdot \mathbf{P}' + \xi\eta'\mathbf{P} \cdot \mathbf{Q}' + \eta\eta'\mathbf{Q} \cdot \mathbf{Q}'}{rr'}. \quad (6\text{–}101)$$

Consider a typical term such as $\xi\xi'\mathbf{P} \cdot \mathbf{P}'/rr'$. Since

$$\xi = a (\cos E - e) \qquad \text{and} \qquad \xi' = a' (\cos E' - e'),$$

we obtain, by using Eq. (6–95),

$$\frac{\xi\xi'}{rr'} = \left(\frac{a}{r}\right)\left(\frac{a'}{r'}\right) \{-\tfrac{3}{2}e + (1 - \tfrac{3}{8}e^2) \cos M + \tfrac{1}{2}e \cos 2M + \tfrac{3}{8}e^2 \cos 3M\}$$

$$\times \{-\tfrac{3}{2}e' + (1 - \tfrac{3}{8}e'^2) \cos M' + \tfrac{1}{2}e' \cos 2M' + \tfrac{3}{8}e'^2 \cos 3M'\}. \quad (6\text{–}102)$$

A typical product of terms from the two braces is of the form

$$\cos pM \cos qM',$$

and we have discussed above the conversion of such a term into the form

$$\tfrac{1}{2}\{\cos (pM + qM') + \cos (pM - qM')\}.$$

Furthermore, products of these typical terms by the series expansions for
(a/r) and (a'/r') can be reduced in a similar manner. We conclude that the
product $\xi\xi'/rr'$ takes the form

$$B_{pq} \cos (pM + qM'),$$

where p and q are positive or negative integers or zero, and the coefficients
B_{pq} are functions of a, a', e, and e'.

The product $\mathbf{P} \cdot \mathbf{P}'$ can be written $\mathbf{P} \cdot \mathbf{P}' = P_1 P_1' + P_2 P_2' + P_3 P_3'$, where the components are

$$P_1 = \cos \Omega \cos \omega - \sin \Omega \sin \omega \cos i,$$
$$P_2 = \sin \Omega \cos \omega + \cos \Omega \sin \omega \cos i,$$
$$P_3 = \sin \omega \sin i,$$

with similar expressions for P_1', P_2', P_3'. For convenience, we write $\cos i = 1 - 2 \sin^2 (i/2)$. In most applications i is a small quantity so that $\sin (i/2) \simeq i/2 = \gamma$. Hence $\cos i = 1 - 2\gamma^2$, and we have

$$P_1 = \cos (\Omega + \omega) + 2\gamma^2 \sin \omega \sin \Omega;$$

and, by using

$$2 \sin \omega \sin \Omega = -[\cos (\Omega + \omega) - \cos (\Omega - \omega)],$$

we find

$$P_1 = (1 - \gamma^2) \cos (\Omega + \omega) + \gamma^2 \cos (\Omega - \omega). \qquad (6\text{--}103)$$

Similarly,

$$P_1' = (1 - \gamma'^2) \cos (\Omega' + \omega') + \gamma'^2 \cos (\Omega' - \omega'). \qquad (6\text{--}104)$$

The other components of $\mathbf{P}$ and of $\mathbf{Q}$ can be expressed similarly. We are interested here only in the general form of the product $\mathbf{P} \cdot \mathbf{P}'$ as typified by the term $P_1 P_1'$.

It is clear from Eqs. (6–103) and (6–104) that the product $P_1 P_1'$ will consist of terms of the form $\cos (\Omega + \omega) \cos (\Omega' + \omega')$ which can be reduced to sums such as

$$\tfrac{1}{2} [\cos (\Omega + \omega + \Omega' + \omega') + \cos (\Omega + \omega - \Omega' - \omega')].$$

Hence all products arising from $\mathbf{P} \cdot \mathbf{P}'$ and the other scalar products in Eq. (6–101) take the form $C_j \cos [j_1 \Omega + j_2 \Omega' + j_3 \omega + j_4 \omega')]$, where the j_i $(i = 1, 2, 3, 4)$ are positive or negative integers or zero, and the C_j are functions of γ and γ'.

From this outlined analysis of the term $\xi \xi' P_1 P_1' / rr'$, we may conclude that $\cos \phi$ can be expressed as a sum of products of cosine terms with arguments which are functions of M, M', Ω, Ω', ω, ω'. Further, $\cos^2 \phi$, and higher powers of $\cos \phi$, can thereby be expressed as products of such functions and ultimately reduced by trigonometric identities to sums of cosines of multiple angles. In the final analysis, therefore, the results described above yield for the perturbation function the form

$$R = k^2 m' \sum_p C_p(a, a', e, e', \gamma, \gamma')$$

$$\times \cos [p_1 M + p_2 M' + p_3 \Omega + p_4 \Omega' + p_5 \omega + p_6 \omega'], \qquad (6\text{--}105)$$

where the p_i $(i = 1, 2, 3, \ldots, 6)$ are integers, positive or negative or zero.

The expression for R [Eq. (6–105)] can now be used in Eqs. (6–58) to (6–63) to obtain the perturbations in the orbital elements. Let $M = nt + \sigma$ and $M' = n't + \sigma'$ so that

$$p_1 M + p_2 M' = (p_1 n + p_2 n')t + p_1 \sigma + p_2 \sigma'. \qquad (6\text{–}106)$$

Let the angular argument in R be denoted by

$$\theta = (p_1 n + p_2 n')t + p_1 \sigma + p_2 \sigma' + p_3 \Omega + p_4 \Omega' + p_5 \omega + p_6 \omega'. \qquad (6\text{–}107)$$

The orbital elements of the perturbing body m' will be considered constant so that Eq. (6–107) may be written

$$\theta = (p_1 n + p_2 n')t + p_1 \sigma + p_3 \Omega + p_5 \omega + \theta_0, \qquad (6\text{–}108)$$

where θ_0 contains all of the contributions due to combinations of p_2, p_4, and p_6 with σ', Ω', and ω'. With these designations, we have

$$R = k^2 m' \sum_p C_p \cos[(p_1 n + p_2 n')t + p_1 \sigma + p_3 \Omega + p_5 \omega + \theta_0], \qquad (6\text{–}109)$$

where the summation refers to all p_i ($i = 1, 2, 3, \ldots, 6$).
Then

$$\frac{\partial R}{\partial \sigma} = -k^2 m' \sum_p C_p p_1 \sin \theta \qquad (p_1 \neq 0), \qquad (6\text{–}110)$$

$$\frac{\partial R}{\partial \sigma} = 0 \qquad (p_1 = 0),$$

$$\frac{\partial R}{\partial \Omega} = -k^2 m' \sum_p C_p p_3 \sin \theta, \qquad (6\text{–}111)$$

$$\frac{\partial R}{\partial \omega} = -k^2 m' \sum_p C_p p_5 \sin \theta, \qquad (6\text{–}112)$$

$$\frac{\partial R}{\partial e} = k^2 m' \sum_p \frac{\partial C_p}{\partial e} \cos \theta, \qquad (6\text{–}113)$$

$$\frac{\partial R}{\partial i} = \tfrac{1}{2} k^2 m' \cos\left(\frac{i}{2}\right) \sum_p \frac{\partial C_p}{\partial \gamma} \cos \theta, \qquad (6\text{–}114)$$

$$\frac{\partial R}{\partial a} = k^2 m' \sum_p \frac{\partial C_p}{\partial a} \cos \theta - k^2 m' \sum_p C_p \left(p_1 t \frac{\partial n}{\partial a}\right) \sin \theta, \qquad (6\text{–}115)$$

where $\partial n / \partial a = -3n/2a$.
Consider now an equation such as Eq. (6–61) which is

$$\dot{\Omega} = \left(\frac{1}{na^2 \sin i \sqrt{1 - e^2}}\right) \frac{\partial R}{\partial i}.$$

Upon substituting Eq. (6–114) in this, we have

$$\dot{\Omega} = \frac{k^2 m' \cos\left(\dfrac{i}{2}\right)}{2na^2 \sin i \sqrt{1 - e^2}} \sum_p \frac{\partial C_p}{\partial \gamma}$$

$$\times \cos\left[(p_1 n + p_2 n')t + p_1 \sigma + p_3 \Omega + p_5 \omega + \theta_0\right]. \quad (6\text{–}116)$$

Usually the mass m' is small, compared with that of the sun. Hence we assume as a first approximation that the orbital elements on the right-hand side of Eq. (6–116) are constants, the osculating elements. The derivative, $\dot{\Omega}$, then becomes a periodic function of t alone, if p_1 and p_2 are not both zero. If p_1 and p_2 are both zero, $\dot{\Omega}$ is a constant, say A. We may therefore consider $\dot{\Omega}$ to be separated, that is

$$\dot{\Omega} = A + \sum_p B_p \cos\left[(p_1 n + p_2 n')t + \theta_1\right], \quad (6\text{–}117)$$

where $\theta_1 = p_1\sigma_0 + p_3\Omega_0 + p_5\omega_0 + \theta_0$ and the subscript zero denotes the fixed elements. Integrating Eq. (6–117), we find

$$\Omega = \Omega_0 + At + \sum_p \frac{B_p}{(p_1 n + p_2 n')} \sin\left[(p_1 n + p_2 n')t + \theta_1\right], \quad (6\text{–}118)$$

where p_1 and p_2 are not zero simultaneously.

The linear part of the change in Ω, namely At, is known as a *secular perturbation* term. Also it is quite apparent from Eq. (6–117) that secular terms would arise if the combination $p_1 n + p_2 n' = 0$. This requires, however, a commensurability in the periods of the perturbed and the perturbing planets. For, if P and P' are these periods, we have

$$\frac{P'}{P} = \frac{n}{n'} = -\frac{p_2}{p_1}, \quad (6\text{–}119)$$

and p_1 and p_2 are integers. This would be a highly improbable situation in the solar system.

The nature of the periodic perturbations in an element such as Ω depends on the magnitude of B_p and on $p_1 n + p_2 n'$. In the solar system, B_p is not large. If $p_1 n + p_2 n'$ as a whole is large for a given pair of values (p_1, p_2), then it is evident that Ω will have for these values of p_1, p_2 periodic terms of small amplitude and short period. These are called *short-period in-equalities*. On the other hand if, for a pair of values (p_1, p_2), the frequency $p_1 n + p_2 n'$ is very small, the corresponding perturbation in Ω will have a relatively large amplitude and a very long period. These are called the *long-period inequalities* in the element.

It should be clear from an inspection of Eqs. (6–58) to (6–63) and Eqs. (6–110) to (6–115) that all of the elements except a will exhibit secular as well as periodic changes when an analysis to the first order in m', such as that for Ω, is made. For the semimajor axis, however,

$$\dot{a} = \frac{-2k^2 m'}{na} \sum_p C_p p_1 \sin \theta \qquad (p_1 \neq 0), \qquad (6\text{–}120)$$

$$\dot{a} \equiv 0 \qquad\qquad (p_1 = 0).$$

If we take p_1 and p_2 simultaneously equal to zero, we observe immediately that $\dot{a} \equiv 0$ and hence that no secular perturbation can result. There will be a periodic inequality given by $\delta(a)$, where

$$\delta(a) = \frac{2k^2 m'}{na_0} \sum_p C_p \left(\frac{p_1}{p_1 n + p_2 n'} \right) \cos \theta, \qquad (6\text{–}121)$$

and

$$a = a_0 + \delta(a).$$

We see that the length of the semimajor axis oscillates about the mean value a_0 with a period

$$P = \frac{2\pi}{p_1 n + p_2 n'}.$$

The analysis outlined here for the elements Ω and a can, of course, be applied to the other orbital elements as well. The resulting expressions for the perturbed elements contain only the first power of the perturbing mass m'. If we were to take the revised values of the elements, such as $\Omega = \Omega_0 + At$ plus periodic terms, and resubstitute in Eqs. (6–58) to (6–63), we would obtain a second approximation containing new periodic terms in t^2, and all would contain m'^2. Thus higher order approximations result.

Changes in the elements over long periods of time obviously are important in deciding whether or not the planetary system is stable. We have seen that the semimajor axis, at least in the first-order theory, undergoes no secular change. If it did, the orbit of the planet concerned would expand or contract indefinitely. In a similar way, if the eccentricity e were to change progressively for a sufficiently long time, a close approach to another planet might result in disruption of the system. These vital questions have been under discussion for well over two hundred years. For example, in 1776, Lagrange* showed that, when all powers of e were included in the analysis to the first order in m', the semimajor axis underwent no secular change. Poisson†, in 1809, showed that the same result

---

* J. L. Lagrange, *Memoirs of the Berlin Academy*, 1776.
† S. D. Poisson, *Journal de l'Ecole Polytechnique*, Vol. XV, 1809.

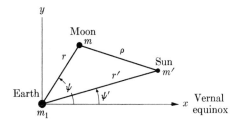

FIG. 6-5. The earth-moon system.

held when terms in m'^2 were introduced. On the other hand, Haretu*
showed, in 1885, that a secular term in the perturbation of the semimajor
axis does occur if third-order terms in m' are included. A recent summary
by Hagihara† gives many references to the literature concerning the
stability of the solar system.

PROBLEMS

1. Analyze the perturbations in e by the methods outlined above.

2. Jupiter has a period $P_J = 11.86$ yr.; Saturn has a period $P_S = 29.46$ yr.
Calculate the values of n'_J and n_S and their ratio. Find the periods of terms in
the disturbing function representing the influence of Jupiter on Saturn which
have $p_1/p_2 = -2, -5/2, -72/29$. Are the amplitudes of these terms large or
small?

6-6 The earth-moon system. As one illustration of the theory of
perturbations, we shall discuss briefly the motion of the moon around the
earth under the disturbing influence of the sun. The complete theory is
very complex. This is due principally to the relatively large mass of the
moon in comparison with that of the earth and with the proximity of the
moon to the earth. Here the primary mass m_1 is the earth; m, the perturbed
mass, is the moon; and m' is the mass of the sun.

The orbit of the moon is inclined about 5° to the plane of the ecliptic.
For illustrative purposes, we shall make the approximation that this is
negligible; i.e., the sun, earth, and moon are in the same plane. Furthermore we shall neglect the eccentricity of the earth's orbit around the sun.
The inclusion of $e = 0.06$ for the earth's orbit will have only a second-
order effect on the analysis. The problem then is reduced to a two-dimensional one.

Let ψ be the celestial longitude of the moon (Fig. 6-5), and let ψ' be
the longitude of the sun. By reference to Eq. (6-92), we see that, with

---

* S. C. Haretu, *Ann. Observatoire Paris*, Mem., Vol. 19, 1885.

† Y. Hagihara, *Stability in Celestial Mechanics*, Tokyo, 1957.

$\phi = \psi - \psi'$, the perturbation function becomes

$$R = \frac{k^2 m'}{a'} \left\{ 1 + \left(\frac{r}{a'}\right)^2 P_2 \left[\cos (\psi - \psi') \right] + \cdots \right\}, \qquad (6\text{-}122)$$

where a' is the radius of the earth's orbit, assumed circular. For our purposes R will be truncated at terms of the second order in (r/a').

From the list of Legendre coefficients in Section 6–5, we have

$$P_2 \left[\cos (\psi - \psi') \right] = \tfrac{1}{4} + \tfrac{3}{4} \cos 2(\psi - \psi'),$$

and since

$$\left(\frac{r}{a'}\right)^2 = \left(\frac{a}{a'}\right)^2 \left(\frac{r}{a}\right)^2,$$

R may be written

$$R = \frac{k^2 m'}{a'} \left\{ 1 + \frac{1}{4} \left(\frac{a}{a'}\right)^2 \left(\frac{r}{a}\right)^2 + \frac{3}{4} \left(\frac{a}{a'}\right)^2 \left(\frac{r}{a}\right)^2 \cos 2(\psi - \psi') \right\}. \quad (6\text{-}123)$$

We must now express R in terms of the elements of the moon's orbit. Neglecting the terms in Eq. (6–99) containing e', which we have assumed to be zero, we have

$$\left(\frac{r}{a'}\right)^2 = \left(\frac{a}{a'}\right)^2 \left\{ 1 + \frac{3e^2}{2} - 2e \cos M - \tfrac{1}{2}e^2 \cos 2M \right\} \quad (6\text{-}124)$$

to terms of second order in e.

Because we have assumed the moon, sun, and earth to be in the same plane, we can write

$$\psi = \Omega + \omega + f,$$

where f is the true anomaly of the moon. Then

$$\left(\frac{r}{a}\right)^2 \cos 2(\psi - \psi') = \left(\frac{r}{a}\right)^2 \cos \{2f + 2(\Omega + \omega - \psi')\}, \quad (6\text{-}125)$$

which can be expanded into

$$2 \left(\frac{r}{a}\right)^2 \cos^2 f \cos 2(\Omega + \omega - \psi') - \left(\frac{r}{a}\right)^2 \cos 2(\Omega + \omega - \psi')$$

$$-2 \left[\left(\frac{r}{a}\right) \sin f \right]\left[\left(\frac{r}{a}\right) \cos f \right] \sin 2(\Omega + \omega - \psi'). \quad (6\text{-}126)$$

Now, by Eqs. (6–44), (6–95), and (6–96),

$$(r/a) \cos f \qquad \text{and} \qquad (r/a) \sin f$$

can be expanded as functions of M. Thus,

$$\frac{r}{a} \cos f = (1 - \tfrac{3}{8}e^2) \cos M + \tfrac{1}{2}e \cos 2M + \tfrac{3}{8}e^2 \cos 3M - \tfrac{3}{2}e, \quad (6\text{-}127)$$

$$\frac{r}{a} \sin f = (1 - \tfrac{5}{8}e^2) \sin M + \tfrac{1}{2}e \sin 2M + \tfrac{3}{8}e^2 \sin 3M. \quad (6\text{-}128)$$

Substituting from Eqs. (6–127) and (6–128) into Eq. (6–126) and subsequently using Eq. (6–126) together with Eq. (6–124) in Eq. (6–123), we find, for the disturbing function, the series

$$
\begin{aligned}
R = \frac{k^2 m' a^2}{a'^3} \{ & \tfrac{1}{4} + \tfrac{3}{8}e^2 - \tfrac{1}{2}e \cos M - \tfrac{1}{8}e^2 \cos 2M \\
& + \tfrac{15}{8}e^2 \cos [2(\Omega + \omega - \psi')] && \text{(A)} \\
& - \tfrac{9}{4}e \cos [2(\Omega + \omega - \psi') + M] \\
& + \tfrac{3}{4} \cos [2(\Omega + \omega - \psi') + 2M] && \text{(B)} \\
& - \tfrac{15}{8}e^2 \cos [2(\Omega + \omega - \psi') + 2M] \\
& + \tfrac{3}{4}e \cos [2(\Omega + \omega - \psi') + 3M] \\
& + \tfrac{3}{4}e^2 \cos [2(\Omega + \omega - \psi') + 4M] \}. && (6\text{-}129)
\end{aligned}
$$

In the above expansion we have ignored terms of higher order than two in e. Furthermore, we have ignored the moon's mass in writing the disturbing function. Appropriate modifications in R to include the effects of the moon's mass can be made.* A more refined expansion for R containing terms with e' and γ as coefficients is given in the reference cited.

The complexity of the simplified perturbing function Eq. (6–129) indicates the difficulty in describing precisely the moon's motion. Terms in R such as $3k^2 m' a^2 e^2 / 8 a'^3$ give rise to secular variations in the orbital elements. Those terms involving only $\cos M$ and $\cos 2M$ are elliptic terms, which are similar to terms arising from a series representation of motion in a Keplerian orbit. The remaining terms in R depend on the relative positions of moon and sun, and hence are strictly perturbative terms. Many of these have names. We mention only two: the *evection* and the *variation*. In Eq. (6–129) these are designated by (A) and (B), respectively.

To illustrate the effect of a typical term in R on the orbital elements and on the moon's longitude, we shall sketch the method of analysis for the evection. Let the evection term be denoted by

$$A = \tfrac{15}{8}n'^2 a^2 e^2 \cos 2(\Omega + \omega - \psi'),$$

where $n'^2 = k^2 m' / a'^3$. Then the differential equations for the orbital

---

* See, for example, D. Brouwer and G. M. Clemence, *op. cit.*, p. 310 ff.

elements [Eqs. (6–58) to (6–68)] become

$$\dot{a} = \frac{2}{na} \frac{\partial A}{\partial M} = 0,$$

$$\dot{e} = \frac{15}{4} \frac{n'^2 e}{n} \sin 2(\Omega + \omega - \psi'), \qquad (6\text{–}130)$$

$$\dot{M} = n - \frac{15}{4} \frac{n'^2}{n} (1 + e^2) \cos 2(\Omega + \omega - \psi'), \qquad (6\text{–}131)$$

$$\dot{\omega} = \frac{d(\Omega + \omega)}{dt} = \frac{15}{4} \left(1 - \frac{1}{2} e^2\right) \frac{n'^2}{n} \cos 2(\Omega + \omega - \psi'), \quad (6\text{–}132)$$

$$\dot{\Omega} = 0,$$

$$\frac{di}{dt} = 0.$$

The last two equations follow from the fact that we have assumed $i = 0$ in the discussion above. It is obvious also that there is no perturbation in the semimajor axis due to the evection term in R.

Integration of Eqs. (6–130), (6–131), and (6–132) yields

$$e = e_0 + \frac{15}{8} \left(\frac{n'}{n}\right) e_0 \cos 2(\Omega_0 + \omega_0 - \psi'),$$

$$M = M_0 + \frac{15}{8} \left(\frac{n'}{n}\right) (1 + e_0^2) \sin 2(\Omega_0 + \omega_0 - \psi'),$$

$$\Omega + \omega = (\Omega + \omega)_0 + \frac{15}{8} \left(1 - \frac{1}{2} e_0^2\right) \left(\frac{n'}{n}\right) \sin 2(\Omega_0 + \omega_0 - \psi'),$$

where the subscripts refer to the osculating orbit of reference. In performing the integrations we bear in mind that $\psi' = \Omega' + \omega' + n'(t - t_0)$, where n', Ω', and ω' refer to the sun's *apparent* motion around the earth. The perturbations are, therefore,

$$\delta(e) = \frac{15}{8} \left(\frac{n'}{n}\right) e_0 \cos 2(\Omega_0 + \omega_0 - \psi'), \qquad (6\text{–}133)$$

$$\delta(M) = \frac{15}{8} \left(\frac{n'}{n}\right) (1 + e_0^2) \sin 2(\Omega_0 + \omega_0 - \psi'), \qquad (6\text{–}134)$$

$$\delta(\Omega + \omega) = \frac{15}{8} \left(\frac{n'}{n}\right) \left(1 - \frac{1}{2} e_0^2\right) \sin 2(\Omega_0 + \omega_0 - \psi'). \qquad (6\text{–}135)$$

The perturbation of first order in longitude, $\delta(\psi)$, can be found from the relations $\psi = \Omega + \omega + f$ and $f = M + 2e \sin M$. We have

$$\delta(\psi) = \delta(\Omega + \omega) + (1 + 2e \cos M) \delta(M) + 2 \sin M \, \delta(e),$$

and hence, using Eqs. (6–133), (6–134) and (6–135), we obtain

$$\delta(\psi) = \frac{15}{4}\left(\frac{n'}{n}\right) e_0 \sin\left[2(\Omega_0 + \omega_0 - \psi') + M\right]. \qquad (6\text{–}136)$$

The period of this perturbation in longitude due to the evection term in R is about one month, and it has an amplitude of about one degree.

If the effects of the eccentricity of the earth's orbit and the inclination of the moon's orbit are included in the analysis, other perturbations arise. These are notably the perturbations in Ω and hence, through Eq. (6–135), in ω. The inclusion of i in the disturbing function and subsequently of $\partial R/\partial i$ in Eq. (6–61) leads to

$$\dot{\Omega} = -\frac{3}{4}\frac{n'^2}{n}\frac{i}{\sin i} \cong -\frac{3}{4}\frac{n'^2}{n},$$

since i is small. Therefore

$$\delta(\Omega) = -\frac{3}{4}\frac{n'^2}{n}(t - t_0) = -\frac{3}{4}\frac{n'}{n}n'\,\delta t, \qquad (6\text{–}137)$$

where $n' = 2\pi/P_e$, and P_e is the period of the earth's orbital motion around the sun. Since $n = 2\pi/P_m$ for the moon, Eq. (6–137) can be written

$$\frac{\delta(\Omega)}{2\pi} = -\frac{3}{4}\left(\frac{P_m}{P_e}\right)\frac{\delta t}{P_e} = -0.056\,\frac{\delta t}{P_e}, \qquad (6\text{–}138)$$

and we find that Ω changes by 2π rad when $\delta t = 6580$ days or approximately 18 yr. The minus sign indicates that the node of the moon's orbit regresses, that is, moves toward the west along the ecliptic, completing a revolution in about 18 yr. While this effect would appear periodic, it should be emphasized that it is a secular perturbation in the sense that it is a change in Ω which is a linear function of the time.

This brief and oversimplified discussion of the moon's motion indicates the complexity of the analysis required. Several hundred periodic terms are necessary to describe the motion, as the exhaustive work by E. W. Brown* shows. The principal secular effects, however, are that: (a) *the line of nodes regresses at an average rate of one revolution in* 18.6 *yr, and* (b) *the line of apsides* (the major axis of the orbit) *advances* ($\dot{\omega} > 0$) *at an average rate of one revolution in* 8.9 *yr.*

---

* E. W. Brown, *An Introductory Treatise on the Lunar Theory.* Cambridge: Cambridge University Press, 1896. Also, *Memoirs of the Roy. Astron. Soc.* **54**, 1900; **57**, 1905; **59**, 1908.

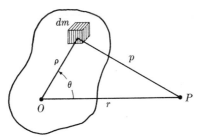

FIG. 6-6. Potential at exterior point due to irregular mass.

PROBLEMS

1. The disturbing function for the moon contains the *variation*

$$B = \frac{3k^2 m'a^2}{4a'^3} \cos{[2(\Omega + \omega - \psi') + 2M]}.$$

Calculate the first-order perturbations in the orbital elements and in the longitude ψ arising from this term.

2. Determine the first-order changes in the elements of the moon's orbit which are due to the secular terms in R, namely,

$$C = \frac{k^2 m'a^2}{a'^3} [\tfrac{1}{4} + \tfrac{3}{8}e^2].$$

3. The radius vector of the moon is given approximately by

$$r = a(1 - e \cos M).$$

Estimate the first-order change in r due to the evection term in R.

6-7 Potential due to an oblate spheroid. The application of the theory of perturbations to the motion of an earth satellite in close proximity to the earth requires an expression for the potential due to an oblate spheroid. Let a unit mass be placed at a point P (Fig. 6-6) a distance r from the center of mass of a bounded distribution of matter of total mass M. Let dm be an element of the mass at a distance ρ from O. Then the potential at P due to dm is

$$dU = \frac{-k^2 \, dm}{(\rho^2 + r^2 - 2r\rho \cos \theta)^{1/2}}.$$

The total potential at P is, therefore,

$$U = -k^2 \int_M \frac{dm}{(\rho^2 + r^2 - 2r\rho \cos \theta)^{1/2}}. \qquad (6\text{-}139)$$

In the integration, r is held fixed. Expanding the function

$$(\rho^2 + r^2 - 2r\rho \cos \theta)^{-1/2},$$

we have

$$(\rho^2 + r^2 - 2r\rho \cos \theta)^{-1/2} = \frac{1}{r}\left[1 - 2\frac{\rho}{r}\cos\theta + \left(\frac{\rho}{r}\right)^2\right]^{-1/2}$$

$$= \frac{1}{r}\left\{1 + \left(\frac{\rho}{r}\right)\cos\theta + \left(\frac{\rho}{r}\right)^2 (-\tfrac{1}{2} + \tfrac{3}{2}\cos^2\theta) + \cdots\right\}, \quad (6\text{-}140)$$

in which powers greater than 2 in ρ/r will not be needed in the following analysis. The expression in its more complete form, however, is necessary when precise studies of the shape of the earth, for instance, are being carried out. For the sake of completeness, therefore, we mention here the general expansion in terms of Legendre polynomials of the first kind. These polynomials are listed in Section 6–5.

In terms of the Legendre polynomials, we have

$$(\rho^2 + r^2 - 2r\rho \cos \theta)^{-1/2} = \frac{1}{r}\sum_{n=1}^{\infty}\left(\frac{\rho}{r}\right)^n P_n (\cos \theta). \quad (6\text{-}141)$$

The function on the left in Eq. (6–141) is called the generating function of the polynomials; the polynomials are sometimes called *zonal harmonics*.

By using Eq. (6–140), we can write

$$U = -\frac{k^2}{r}\int_M \left\{1 + \left(\frac{\rho}{r}\right)\cos\theta + \left(\frac{\rho}{r}\right)^2 (-\tfrac{1}{2} + \tfrac{3}{2}\cos^2\theta)\right\} dm,$$

and expanding, we have

$$U = -\frac{k^2}{r}\int_M dm - \frac{k^2}{r^2}\int_M \rho \cos\theta\, dm + \frac{k^2}{2r^3}\int_M \rho^2\, dm$$

$$-\frac{3k^2}{2r^3}\int_M \rho^2 \cos^2\theta\, dm. \quad (6\text{-}142)$$

The physical interpretation of these integrals is almost obvious. The first is the total mass, the second is the first moment about an axis through O perpendicular to OP, and is zero because the origin was chosen as the center of mass, and the third is the moment of inertia about the origin. The last integral can be written

$$\int_M (\rho^2 - \rho^2 \sin^2 \theta)\, dm = I_0 - I,$$

where I_0 is the moment of inertia about the origin and I is that about the line OP.

The potential is then

$$U = -\frac{k^2 M}{r} - \frac{k^2}{2r^3}(2I_0 - 3I). \quad (6\text{-}143)$$

The student will recognize the first term as the potential due to a homogeneous solid sphere. The second term arises from the departure of the mass M from spherical shape.

If I_1, I_2, and I_3 are the principal moments of inertia of the mass M, we may write $2I_0 = I_1 + I_2 + I_3$ and have finally

$$U = -\frac{k^2 M}{r}\left\{1 + \frac{1}{2Mr^2}\left[I_1 + I_2 + I_3 - 3I\right]\right\}, \qquad (6\text{–}144)$$

or, if by symmetry $I_1 = I_2 \neq I_3$, as would be the case for an oblate spheroid such as the earth,

$$U = -\frac{k^2 M}{r}\left\{1 + \frac{1}{2Mr^2}\left[2I_e + I_3 - 3I\right]\right\}, \qquad (6\text{–}145)$$

where I_e is the moment of inertia about any axis in the equatorial plane, and I_3 is the moment of inertia about the axis of rotation. It should be clear that, although these are constant quantities, I varies with the position of P (Fig. 6–6) in space.

Equation (6–145) has been derived on the assumption that ρ/r is small. Actually the approximation is very good for a planet, such as the earth, where I_e and I_3 do not differ greatly. Note that, if these were equal as for a sphere, the bracket $2I_e + I_3 - 3I$ would vanish, and the potential U is that already exhibited in Eq. (1–30).

Let the body of mass M be an oblate spheroid with axial moment of inertia I_3 and equatorial moment of inertia I_e. Let I_1, I_2, I_3 be its principal moments of inertia, and let the principal axes be denoted by the unit vectors $\mathbf{u}_1$, $\mathbf{u}_2$, $\mathbf{u}_3$ (Fig. 6–7). Then the moment of inertia about any line

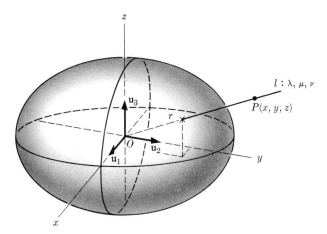

FIG. 6–7. Unit vectors for the calculation of moment of inertia.

whose direction cosines are λ, μ, ν is

$$I = I_1\lambda^2 + I_2\mu^2 + I_3\nu^2 = I_e(\lambda^2 + \mu^2) + I_3\nu^2.$$

But $\lambda = x/r$, $\mu = y/r$, $\nu = z/r$, where $r = (x^2 + y^2 + z^2)^{1/2}$ and (x, y, z) is any point on the line. Therefore,

$$I = \frac{I_e(x^2 + y^2) + I_3 z^2}{r^2},$$

which may be written

$$I = I_e + (I_3 - I_e)\frac{z^2}{r^2}. \tag{6-146}$$

Using this value for I in Eq. (6-145), we obtain the potential

$$U = -\frac{k^2 M}{r} - \frac{k^2(I_3 - I_e)}{2r^3} + \frac{3k^2(I_3 - I_e)}{2r^5}z^2. \tag{6-147}$$

The force field resulting from this is $-\nabla U$, where

$$\nabla U = \left[\frac{k^2 M}{r^2} + \frac{3k^2(I_3 - I_e)}{2r^4}\right]\mathbf{u}_r + \nabla\left[\frac{3k^2(I_3 - I_e)}{2}\frac{z^2}{r^5}\right]$$

$$= \left[\frac{k^2 M}{r^2} + \frac{3k^2(I_3 - I_e)}{2r^4} - \frac{15k^2(I_3 - I_e)}{2r^6}z^2\right]\mathbf{u}_r$$

$$+ \frac{3k^2(I_3 - I_e)z}{r^5}\mathbf{u}_3. \tag{6-148}$$

The reader will recognize the first term of this expression as the radial inverse-square force per unit mass which would arise if the body were spherical. The second and third terms constitute a radial perturbative acceleration. The last term is a perturbative acceleration perpendicular to the equatorial xy-plane of the oblate spheroid. The force acting on a mass at P is *not a central force*. Qualitatively it is apparent that perturbations will arise due to a force per unit mass

$$\mathbf{F} = -\left\{\frac{3k^2(I_3 - I_e)}{2r^4}\left(1 - \frac{5z^2}{r^2}\right)\mathbf{u}_r + \frac{3k^2(I_3 - I_e)z}{r^5}\mathbf{u}_3\right\}. \tag{6-149}$$

When $z = 0$ and the point P is in the equatorial plane, this force is purely radial. Generally, however, the z-component will also have its influence.

In the preceding analysis, we have considered the potential and force arising *at an external point* only. If we should want the potential for a point *on the earth's surface*, for instance, the centripetal acceleration due to the earth's rotation would have to be taken into account. At the equator where this is a maximum it amounts to about 0.3% of the gravitational component. The potential at the surface of the earth, including the rotational contribution, is

$$U = -\frac{k^2 M}{r}\left\{1 + \frac{1}{2Mr^2}[2I_e + I_3 - 3I]\right\} - \tfrac{1}{2}\omega^2(x^2 + y^2), \quad (6\text{--}150)$$

where ω is the angular velocity of rotation of the earth, 7.292×10^{-5} rad/sec.

6–8 Perturbations due to an oblate planet. During the past few years important studies have necessarily been made of the motion of a man-made satellite moving relatively close to the earth. The perturbations of such a satellite are due primarily to departures of the earth's figure from that of a homogeneous sphere and to the resisting drag of the earth's atmosphere. In the present section we shall assume that air drag is negligible. Furthermore, we shall assume that the satellite is close enough to the earth so that perturbations due to the sun and moon are small compared with those due to the oblateness of the earth. It has been shown by Spitzer* that such will be true for satellite orbits at distances of the order of 500 km to 1000 km, or less, above the earth. We shall, therefore, confine our attention here to perturbations arising from the oblateness of the earth.

Before entering upon a detailed discussion, let us consider a few qualitative results which are derivable from the equations of the preceding sections. The earth is considered an oblate spheroid, that is, it has axial symmetry. It has an axial moment of inertia I_3 and a moment of inertia I_e about any axis in the equatorial plane. We shall restrict our discussion here to a potential function, such as that in Eq. (6–141), in which powers greater than 2 in ρ/r are ignored.

Equation (6–149), then, shows that the perturbing acceleration is

$$\mathbf{F} = -\frac{3k^2(I_3 - I_e)}{2r^4}\left(1 - \frac{5z^2}{r^2}\right)\mathbf{u}_r - \frac{3k^2(I_3 - I_e)}{r^5}z\mathbf{u}_3,$$

where, now, the xy-plane is that of the earth's equator, $\mathbf{u}_r$ is a unit vector directed along OP (Fig. 6–8) and $\mathbf{u}_3$ is a unit vector directed toward the north pole of the earth.

Let r_e be the equatorial radius of the earth and let a be the semimajor axis of the satellite orbit. Also we have, by Kepler's third law, approximately,

$$n^2 a^3 = k^2 M_e,$$

where M_e is the mass of the earth, since the satellite's mass is negligible

---

* L. Spitzer, Jr., "Perturbations of a Satellite Orbit," *J. Brit. Interplanetary Soc.* **9**, 131, 1950.

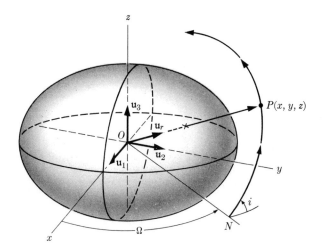

FIG. 6–8. Motion of a satellite about an oblate planet.

in this application. Finally, let

$$J = \frac{3(I_3 - I_e)}{2M_e r_e^2} = 1.624 \times 10^{-3}$$

be introduced as a dimensionless constant. Then, *if we measure the radius vector and semimajor axis in units of* r_e, the perturbing acceleration can be written

$$\mathbf{F} = -\frac{Jn^2 a^3 r_e}{r^4} \left\{ \left(1 - \frac{5z^2}{r^2} \right) \mathbf{u}_r + \frac{2z}{r} \mathbf{u}_3 \right\}. \qquad (6\text{–}151)$$

It is clear that this is *not* a central force *unless the satellite orbit is in the xy-plane.* To obtain a qualitative picture of the effect of such a force, consider the *torque field* created by $\mathbf{F}$, namely,

$$\mathbf{N} = \mathbf{r} \times \mathbf{F} = -2Jn^2 a^3 r_e \left(\mathbf{r} \times \frac{z}{r^5} \mathbf{u}_3 \right). \qquad (6\text{–}152)$$

This expression may be written

$$\mathbf{N} = -\frac{2Jn^2 a^3 r_e z}{r^5} (y\mathbf{u}_1 - x\mathbf{u}_2), \qquad (6\text{–}153)$$

where $\mathbf{u}_1$ and $\mathbf{u}_2$ are unit vectors along the x-axis and the y-axis, respectively. This vector is parallel to the xy-plane and vanishes in that plane. Furthermore, $\mathbf{N}$ is always perpendicular to the plane passing through the satellite and containing the z-axis.

Imagine the satellite fixed rigidly to the plane of its orbit. Then its behavior, together with the "attached" plane is much like that of a gyro-scope wheel when subjected to a torque. The torque $\mathbf{N}$ in this case tries to force the plane of the orbit into the plane of the equator. However, instead of accomplishing this, the torque results in a precession or twisting of the orbital plane. The line of nodes, ON (Fig. 6–8) moves toward OX. Thus the longitude of the node decreases due to the perturbative action of the earth's oblateness.

Other perturbative effects, such as those in ω, a, e, i, σ, are not so ap-parent in this qualitative picture. To obtain the rates of change of these elements we resolve $\mathbf{F}$ into components R', S', and W', as defined in Case I, Section 6–4. These are

$$ R' = \mathbf{F} \cdot \mathbf{u}_r = - \frac{Jn^2 a^3 r_e}{r^4} [1 - 3 \sin^2 u \sin^2 i], \qquad (6\text{--}154) $$

$$ S' = \mathbf{F} \cdot \mathbf{u}_\theta = - \frac{2Jn^2 a^3 r_e}{r^4} \sin^2 i \sin 2u, \qquad (6\text{--}155) $$

$$ W' = \mathbf{F} \cdot \mathbf{u}_A = - \frac{2Jn^2 a^3 r_e}{r^4} \sin u \sin 2i, \qquad (6\text{--}156) $$

where $u = \omega + f$. These expressions substituted into Eqs. (6–77) through (6–82) yield the time rates of change of the osculating orbital elements. Here we shall investigate only the most pronounced of these *secular* perturbations; the motion of the node, $\dot{\Omega}$, and the motion of perigee, $\dot{\omega}$. A summary of the *periodic* perturbations will follow later.

From Eq. (6–80), we find, for the time rate of change of the longitude of the node,

$$ \dot{\Omega} = \frac{r \sin u W'}{a^2 n \sqrt{1 - e^2} \sin i} = - \frac{2Jna \cos i \sin^2 u}{r^3 \sqrt{1 - e^2}}. \qquad (6\text{--}157) $$

At any given instant t_0, or *epoch*, the osculating elements a, e, i, etc. are presumed known. Over a short time interval, Δt, from the epoch, these elements may be considered constants and Eq. (6–157) may be integrated numerically, if desired, to yield $\Delta \Omega$ for the time interval concerned. Simi-larly from Eqs. (6–77), (6–78), ... the variations Δa, Δe, Δi, ... can be com-puted. When applied to the original elements, these increments yield new values for them at the time $t_0 + \Delta t$. The calculation can be repeated successively for new increments and hence a new set of values for the elements obtained. Thus, step by step, the elements, and hence the position of the satellite, can be determined for any instant.

Let us consider here only the change in Ω during one revolution of the satellite from perigee to perigee, *on the assumption that all the elements except Ω remain constant during this interval*. Equation (6–157) can then be integrated by writing

$$\dot{\Omega} = \frac{d\Omega}{df}\dot{f} = \frac{h}{r^2}\frac{d\Omega}{df} = \frac{na^2\sqrt{1-e^2}}{r^2}\frac{d\Omega}{df},$$

and hence

$$\frac{d\Omega}{df} = -\frac{2J\cos i}{a(1-e^2)}\frac{\sin^2(\omega+f)}{r}.$$

Using

$$\frac{1}{r} = \frac{1+e\cos f}{a(1-e^2)},$$

we obtain by integration

$$\Delta\Omega = -\frac{2\pi J\cos i}{a^2(1-e^2)^2},$$

where $\Delta\Omega$ is the change in Ω in one period. If P is the period, we may write this as

$$\frac{\Delta\Omega}{P} = -\frac{Jn\cos i}{a^2(1-e^2)^2}. \tag{6–158}$$

This is the *average rate of regression of the node per period*. When the inclination of the orbit is small, this motion of the node is large. When the orbit is a polar orbit, $\Delta\Omega/P$ vanishes.

In a similar way one can evaluate the motion of perigee from Eqs. (6–81), (6–154), (6–155), and (6–156). The integrations are rather cumbersome, but the result is

$$\frac{\Delta\omega}{P} = \frac{Jn(2 - \frac{5}{2}\sin^2 i)}{a^2(1-e^2)^2}. \tag{6–159}$$

Here it is obvious that perigee advances or regresses depending upon the inclination of the orbit. If $\sin^2 i > 0.8$ ($i > 63°.4$), the value of ω decreases with the time. If $i < 63°.4$, the value of ω increases with the time. It has been assumed here that the motion of the satellite in its orbit is direct.

More complete discussions of the motion of a close earth satellite have appeared in the literature during the past three years.* We shall outline here the analysis by Kozai. His method of analysis is similar to the one we have used in discussing the motion of the moon in Section 6–6.

Under the assumptions of no air drag and an axially symmetric earth, the potential at distance r from the earth's center and at latitude δ can

---

* A few of these contributions are: Y. Kozai, *Astron. J.* **64**, 367, 1959. J. A. O'Keefe, A. Eckels, R. K. Squires, *Astron. J.* **64**, 245, 1959. B. Garfinkel, *Astron. J.* **63**, 88, 1959; **64**, 353, 1959. T. E. Sterne, *Astron. J.* **63**, 28, 1958. D. Brouwer, *Astron. J.* **64**, 378, 1959.

be written

$$U = - \frac{k^2 M_e}{r} \left\{ 1 + \frac{A_2}{r^2} \left(\tfrac{1}{3} - \sin^2 \delta\right) + \frac{A_3}{r^3} \left(\tfrac{5}{3}\sin^2 \delta - \tfrac{3}{2}\right) \sin \delta \right.$$

$$\left. + \frac{A_4}{r^4} \left(\tfrac{3}{35} + \tfrac{1}{7}\sin^2 \delta - \tfrac{1}{4}\sin^2 2\delta\right) + \cdots \right\}, \qquad (6\text{–}160)$$

where M_e is the mass of the earth and A_j ($j = 2, 3, 4 \ldots$) are coefficients involving the shape of the earth. *In our previous analysis* $A_2 \equiv J r_e^2$.

The terms involving A_2 and A_4 are due to the earth's oblateness. The term containing A_3 arises because of asymmetry with respect to the equatorial plane. The quantities in parentheses are related to the Legendre polynomials referred to in Section 6–5.

With $\sin \delta = \sin i \sin u$, where $u = \omega + f$, the disturbing function deduced from Eq. (6–160) is

$$R = \mu \left\{ \frac{A_2}{a^3} \left(\frac{a}{r}\right)^3 [\tfrac{1}{3} - \tfrac{1}{2}\sin^2 i + \tfrac{1}{2}\sin^2 i \cos 2u] \right.$$

$$+ \frac{A_3}{a^4} \left(\frac{a}{r}\right)^4 [(\tfrac{15}{8}\sin^2 i - \tfrac{3}{2}) \sin u - \tfrac{5}{8}\sin^2 i \sin 3u] \sin i$$

$$+ \frac{A_4}{a^5} \left(\frac{a}{r}\right)^5 [\tfrac{3}{35} - \tfrac{3}{7}\sin^2 i + \tfrac{3}{8}\sin^4 i + \sin^2 i \left(\tfrac{3}{7} - \tfrac{1}{2}\sin^2 i\right) \cos 2u$$

$$\left. + \tfrac{1}{8}\sin^4 i \cos 4u] \right\} \cdot \qquad (6\text{–}161)$$

Instead of the true anomaly f which appears in Eq. (6–161) through $u = \omega + f$, we may use the mean anomaly $M = n(t - T)$, which is a linear function of the time in the unperturbed elliptic motion. The conversion from f to M can be made from the relation

$$\frac{df}{dM} = \left(\frac{a}{r}\right)^2 (1 - e^2)^{1/2}, \qquad (6\text{–}162)$$

which follows from Kepler's second law, namely,

$$\frac{df}{dt} = \frac{df}{dM}\frac{dM}{dt} = \frac{df}{dM} n = \frac{h}{r^2} = \frac{na^2(1 - e^2)^{1/2}}{r^2} \cdot$$

In previous sections, we have seen that (a/r) and f can be expressed as series in trigonometric functions of M with coefficients involving powers of e. Substitution for f and (a/r) in Eq. 6–161 results in a disturbing function which is periodic in both ω and M. The terms arising in R can then be classified as (a) secular terms, depending on neither ω nor M, (b) long-period terms, depending on ω but not on M, and (c) short-period terms, depending on M.

In applying Eq. 6–161 the terms, such as $(a/r)^3$, $(a/r)^3 \sin 2f$, etc., are replaced by their average values over one cycle of the orbital motion. The following formulae derived from Tisserand,* are useful in this connection:

$$\overline{\left(\frac{a}{r}\right)^3} = \frac{1}{2\pi} \int_0^\pi \left(\frac{a}{r}\right)^3 dM = (1 - e^2)^{-3/2},$$

$$\overline{\left(\frac{a}{r}\right)^3 \sin 2f} = \overline{\left(\frac{a}{r}\right)^3 \cos 2f} = 0,$$

$$\overline{\left(\frac{a}{r}\right)^4 \cos f} = e(1 - e^2)^{-5/2},$$

$$\overline{\left(\frac{a}{r}\right)^4 \sin f} = \overline{\left(\frac{a}{r}\right)^4 \cos 3f} = \overline{\left(\frac{a}{r}\right)^4 \sin 3f} = 0, \qquad (6\text{–}163)$$

$$\overline{\left(\frac{a}{r}\right)^5} = (1 - e^2)^{-7/2} \left(1 + \frac{3e^2}{2}\right),$$

$$\overline{\left(\frac{a}{r}\right)^5 \cos 2f} = \frac{3e^2}{4} (1 - e^2)^{-7/2},$$

$$\overline{\left(\frac{a}{r}\right)^5 \sin 2f} = \overline{\left(\frac{a}{r}\right)^5 \cos 4f} = \overline{\left(\frac{a}{r}\right)^5 \sin 4f} = 0.$$

Use of these relations in Eq. (6–161) results in the following breakdown of the perturbation function R:

$$R_1 = \frac{\mu A_2}{a^3} (\tfrac{1}{3} - \tfrac{1}{2} \sin^2 i)(1 - e^2)^{-3/2}, \qquad (6\text{–}164)$$

$$R_2 = \frac{\mu A_4}{a^5} (\tfrac{3}{35} - \tfrac{3}{7} \sin^2 i + \tfrac{3}{8} \sin^4 i)(1 + \tfrac{3}{2}e^2)(1 - e^2)^{-7/2}, \qquad (6\text{–}165)$$

$$R_3 = \mu \left\{ \frac{3A_3}{2a^4} \sin i \, (\tfrac{5}{4} \sin^2 i - 1)(1 - e^2)^{-5/2} e \sin \omega \right.$$
$$\left. + \frac{A_4}{a^5} \sin^2 i \, (\tfrac{9}{28} - \tfrac{3}{8} \sin^2 i)(1 - e^2)^{-7/2} e^2 \cos 2\omega \right\}, \qquad (6\text{–}166)$$

$$R_4 = \mu \frac{A_2}{a^3} \left(\frac{a}{r}\right)^3 \left\{ (\tfrac{1}{3} - \tfrac{1}{2} \sin^2 i) \left[1 - \left(\frac{r}{a}\right)^3 (1 - e^2)^{-3/2}\right] \right.$$
$$\left. + \tfrac{1}{2} \sin^2 i \cos 2u \right\}, \qquad (6\text{–}167)$$

---

* F. Tisserand, *Traité de Mécanique Céleste*, Vol. 1, Chapter 16. Paris: Gauthier Villars, 1896.

where $\mu = k^2 M_e$, the power of the force center. Here R_1 is the first-order secular term and corresponds to the order of approximation that we adopted in the discussion at the beginning of this section. R_2 is the second-order secular term. We ignored this in the approximation made earlier. R_3 is the long-period part of the disturbing function. R_4 is the short-period part of the disturbing function. By comparing R_4 with Eqs. (6–154), (6–155), and (6–156), it will be clear that the short-period terms are included in the latter equations through the periodic functions of u.

We have already written the time derivatives of the orbital elements in terms of the partial derivatives of R. These are given in Section 6–4, Eqs. (6–59), (6–61), (6–62), (6–63), (6–67), and (6–68). Using $R = R_1$ in these equations, we have for the first-order secular perturbations

$$\bar{\omega} = \omega_0 + \frac{A_2 \bar{n} t}{a^2 (1 - e^2)^2} (2 - \tfrac{5}{2} \sin^2 i), \tag{6–168}$$

$$\bar{\Omega} = \Omega_0 - \frac{A_2 \bar{n} t \cos i}{a^2 (1 - e^2)^2}, \tag{6–169}$$

$$\overline{M} = M_0 + \bar{n} t, \tag{6–170}$$

$$\bar{n} = n_0 + \frac{A_2 n_0}{a^2 (1 - e^2)^{3/2}} (1 - \tfrac{3}{2} \sin^2 i). \tag{6–171}$$

Here ω_0, Ω_0, and M_0 are mean values at the epoch, that is, the values at the initial time t_0 with the periodic perturbations subtracted. Let the student show that these relations for the changes in Ω and ω are identical, over a period, with Eqs. (6–158) and (6–159).

Short-period first-order perturbations can be found by using $R = R_4$ in the perturbation equations. We assume the elements a, n, e, i, and ω to be constants in the right-hand sides of the perturbation equations [Eqs. (6–58) to (6–68)] and integrate to find the changes in the elements. To do this, we can change the independent variable from t to f, as before, through Kepler's second law $\dot{f} = h/r^2$, that is,

$$dt = \frac{r^2 \, df}{na^2 \sqrt{1 - e^2}}.$$

For example, from Eq. (6–63), the change in the inclination becomes

$$\frac{di}{dt} = \frac{\cos i}{na^2 \sin i \sqrt{1 - e^2}} \frac{\partial R}{\partial \omega},$$

$$\frac{di}{df} = \frac{\cos i}{n^2 a^2 \sin i \, (1 - e^2)} \left(\frac{r}{a}\right)^2 \frac{\partial R}{\partial w},$$

and, for any interval beginning at perigee,

$$\Delta i = \frac{\cos i}{n^2 a^2 \sin i (1 - e^2)} \int_0^f \left(\frac{r}{a}\right)^2 \frac{\partial R}{\partial \omega} \, df.$$

In this way the short-period perturbations can be calculated. We refer the reader to the paper by Kozai for the details and results of these calculations. Here we list the *mean values* of these short period changes taken with respect to the mean anomaly. They are

$$\overline{\Delta e} = \frac{A_2 \sin^2 i}{a^2 (1 - e^2)^2} \left(\frac{1 - e^2}{6e}\right) \cos 2\omega \, \overline{\cos 2f}, \tag{6-172}$$

$$\overline{\Delta \omega} = \frac{A_2}{a^2 (1 - e^2)^2} \left\{ \sin^2 i \left(\frac{1}{8} + \frac{1 - e^2}{6e^2} \overline{\cos 2f}\right) + \frac{1}{6} \cos^2 i \, \overline{\cos 2f} \right\} \sin 2\omega, \tag{6-173}$$

$$\overline{\Delta i} = - \frac{A_2 \sin 2i}{12 a^2 (1 - e^2)^2} \cos 2\omega \, \overline{\cos 2f}, \tag{6-174}$$

$$\overline{\Delta \Omega} = - \frac{A_2 \cos i}{6 a^2 (1 - e^2)^2} \sin 2\omega \, \overline{\cos 2f}, \tag{6-175}$$

$$\overline{\Delta M} = - \frac{A_2 \sin^2 i}{a^2 (1 - e^2)^{3/2}} \left\{ \frac{1}{8} + \frac{2 + e^2}{12 e^2} \overline{\cos 2f} \right\} \sin 2\omega, \tag{6-176}$$

where the mean value

$$\overline{\cos 2f} = \frac{e^2 (1 + 2 \sqrt{1 - e^2})}{(1 + \sqrt{1 - e^2})^2}. \tag{6-177}$$

The mean value of the short-period perturbation in a vanishes.

Long-period perturbations are discussed in the paper by Kozai. The expressions for the time rates of change are complicated and will not be quoted here. It is proved that there are no long-period perturbations of the first order in the semimajor axis.

PROBLEMS

1. For Satellite 1958 $\beta 2$ (Vanguard I) the orbital data are:

$$P = 134.04 \text{ min}, \quad \omega = 162°.7,$$
$$e = 0.190, \quad a = 8676 \text{ km},$$
$$i = 34°.25, \quad T = 7.5188 \text{ January 1960}.$$
$$\Omega = 318°.8,$$

Calculate the rates of change of the ascending node and the argument of perigee, that is, $\dot{\Omega}$ and $\dot{\omega}$.

2. (a) Show from Eq. (6–166) that, to terms of third order in e, the part of R involving A_3 can be written

$$\frac{3\mu A_3}{2a^4} [\tfrac{5}{4} \sin^2 i - 1](1 + \tfrac{5}{2}e^2)e \sin i \sin \omega.$$

(b) Given

$$\dot{\Omega} = - \frac{A_2 n \cos i}{a^2(1 - e^2)^2},$$

show that the periodic perturbation in the orbital eccentricity can be written

$$\delta e = \frac{3A_3}{4A_2 a} \sin i \sin \omega.$$

(c) Suppose that δe is found by observation to vary sinusoidally with ω. Can you draw any conclusions about the shape of the earth from this fact?

6–9 Perturbations due to atmospheric drag. In this section we shall consider briefly the perturbative effects of the air resistance on a small satellite moving in the earth's atmosphere. We shall assume that the satellite moves in an elliptical orbit, and we shall neglect the perturbative effects due to the earth's oblateness.

The resisting force per unit mass acting on a spherical body is given* approximately by the formula

$$F = \frac{C_D A \rho V^2}{2m}, \tag{6–178}$$

where

C_D is the drag coefficient,
A is the cross-sectional area of the body,
m is the mass of the body,
V is its speed,
$\rho = \rho(r)$ is the atmospheric density at distance r
  from the center of the earth.

The coefficient C_D has a value of about 2 for a sphere which is small compared with the mean free path of the gas molecules and for which the molecules either adhere to its surface or are totally reflected.

The resisting force F is tangential to the orbit, and hence Eqs. (6–89) yield

$$R' = \frac{e \sin f}{(1 + e^2 + 2e \cos f)^{1/2}} [-b\rho V^2], \tag{6–179}$$

$$S' = \frac{1 + e \cos f}{(1 + e^2 + 2e \cos f)^{1/2}} [-b\rho V^2], \tag{6–180}$$

$$W' = 0,$$

* T. E. Sterne, "An Atmospheric Model, and Some Remarks on the Inference of Density from the Orbit of a Close Earth Satellite," *Astron. J.* **63**, 81, 1958.

where $b = C_D A/2m$. Then by Eqs. (6–77) to (6–82) and by appropriate modifications to incorporate M instead of σ in the analysis, we have

$$\frac{da}{dt} = \frac{-2b\rho V^2 (1 + e^2 + 2e \cos f)^{1/2}}{n(1 - e^2)^{1/2}}, \qquad (6\text{--}181)$$

$$\frac{de}{dt} = \frac{-2b\rho V^2 (1 - e^2)^{1/2}(e + \cos f)}{na(1 + e^2 + 2e \cos f)^{1/2}}, \qquad (6\text{--}182)$$

$$\frac{d\omega}{dt} = \frac{-2b\rho V^2 (1 - e^2)^{1/2} \sin f}{nae(1 + e^2 + 2e \cos f)^{1/2}}, \qquad (6\text{--}183)$$

$$\frac{dM}{dt} = n + \frac{2b\rho V^2 (1 - e^2) \sin f}{nae(1 + e \cos f)} \left[\frac{1 + e^2 + e \cos f}{(1 + e^2 + 2e \cos f)^{1/2}} \right], \quad (6\text{--}184)$$

$$\frac{di}{dt} = 0, $$

$$\frac{d\Omega}{dt} = 0. $$

The presence of the factor $\sin f$ in Eqs. (6–183) and (6–184) implies that the rates of change of ω and M are periodic. We shall not consider these further. Equations (6–181) and (6–182) indicate, however, that a and e change secularly with the time. These we shall examine in more detail.

To facilitate the integration of Eqs. (6–181) and (6–182), we introduce the eccentric anomaly E as the variable of integration. Thus,

$$r = a(1 - e \cos E) = \frac{a(1 - e^2)}{1 + e \cos f}, \qquad (6\text{--}185)$$

$$h^2 = \mu a(1 - e^2), \qquad (6\text{--}186)$$

$$M = n(t - T) = E - e \sin E, \qquad (6\text{--}187)$$

$$V^2 = \frac{h^2}{a^2(1 - e^2)^2} [1 + e^2 + 2e \cos f]. \qquad (6\text{--}188)$$

The last equation can be found by noting that $V^2 = \dot{r}^2 + r^2 \dot{f}^2$ and by using Eqs. (6–185) and (6–186).

Substituting the above equations into Eqs. (6–181) and (6–182), we obtain

$$\frac{da}{dE} = -2b\rho a^2 \left\{ \frac{(1 + e \cos E)^3}{1 - e \cos E} \right\}^{1/2}, \qquad (6\text{--}189)$$

$$\frac{de}{dE} = -2b\rho a \left\{ \frac{1 + e \cos E}{1 - e \cos E} \right\}^{1/2} (1 - e^2) \cos E. \qquad (6\text{--}190)$$

Integration over one period in E yields

$$\Delta a = -4ba^2 \int_0^\pi \rho(r) \frac{(1 + e \cos E)^{3/2}}{(1 - e \cos E)^{1/2}} \, dE, \tag{6–191}$$

$$\Delta e = -4ba(1 - e^2) \int_0^\pi \rho(r) \left[\frac{1 + e \cos E}{1 - e \cos E}\right]^{1/2} \cos E \, dE. \tag{6–192}$$

Let a_e be the radius of the earth and ρ_0 be the density of the atmosphere at the earth's surface. Then with these introduced into Eqs. (6–191) and (6–192), we have

$$\Delta\left(\frac{a}{a_e}\right) = -4b\rho_0 a_e \left(\frac{a}{a_e}\right)^2 \int_0^\pi \frac{\rho}{\rho_0} \frac{(1 + e \cos E)^{3/2}}{(1 - e \cos E)^{1/2}} \, dE, \tag{6–193}$$

$$\Delta e = -4b\rho_0 a_e \left(\frac{a}{a_e}\right)(1 - e^2) \int_0^\pi \left(\frac{\rho}{\rho_0}\right)\left(\frac{1 + e \cos E}{1 - e \cos E}\right)^{1/2} \cos E \, dE. \tag{6–194}$$

These are in a form most convenient for applications. The density $\rho(r)$ must be expressed in terms of E through Eq. (6–185) and then the integrations can be carried out with sufficient accuracy by numerical methods.

The rates of change of perigee height and of apogee height per orbital revolution of the satellite can be found from Eq. (6–193). Let

$$q = a(1 - e) \qquad \text{and} \qquad q' = a(1 + e)$$

be the perigee and apogee distances, respectively, of the satellite. Then from Eq. (6–193), we find

$$\Delta\left(\frac{q}{a_e}\right) = -4b\rho_0 a_e(1 - e) \left(\frac{a}{a_e}\right)^2$$
$$\times \int_0^\pi \left(\frac{\rho}{\rho_0}\right)\left[\frac{1 + e \cos E}{1 - e \cos E}\right]^{1/2} (1 - \cos E) \, dE, \tag{6–195}$$

$$\Delta\left(\frac{q'}{a_e}\right) = -4b\rho_0 a_e(1 + e) \left(\frac{a}{a_e}\right)^2$$
$$\times \int_0^\pi \left(\frac{\rho}{\rho_0}\right)\left[\frac{1 + e \cos E}{1 - e \cos E}\right]^{1/2} (1 + \cos E) \, dE. \tag{6–196}$$

To find the time rates of change of the perigee and apogee heights, we introduce the time through Kepler's third law in the form

$$n^2 a^3 = g_0 a_e^2,$$

where g_0 is the superficial gravity of the earth. Then from Eqs. (6–195)

TABLE 6-1

ATMOSPHERIC DRAG EFFECTS ON EXPLORER III*

Date (1958)	q(km)	q'(km)
March 26	188	2800
April 15	175	2410
May 5	170	2000
May 25	155	1560
June 14	150	1000
June 24	140	550

* W. H. Stafford and R. M. Croft, "Artificial Earth
Satellites and Successful Solar Probes 1957–1960,"
NASA Technical Note D–601, March, 1961, p. 108 ff.

and (6–196), we find

$$\frac{d}{dt}\left(\frac{q}{a_e}\right) = -\frac{c}{\pi}\left(\frac{g_0}{a_e}\right)^{1/2}\left(\frac{a}{a_e}\right)^{1/2}(1-e)I_1, \qquad (6\text{--}197)$$

$$\frac{d}{dt}\left(\frac{q'}{a_e}\right) = -\frac{c}{\pi}\left(\frac{g_0}{a_e}\right)^{1/2}\left(\frac{a}{a_e}\right)^{1/2}(1+e)I_2, \qquad (6\text{--}198)$$

where $c = 2b\rho_0 a_e$ and I_1 and I_2 are the integrals occurring in Eqs. (6–195) and (6–196), respectively. These equations yield directly the time rates of change of q and q' when the latter are expressed in units of earth radii, a_e.

By constructing a model atmosphere with an assumed density function $\rho = \rho(r)$, calculating the time rates of change of q, q', a, and e, and then comparing the results with observations, one can determine that model which approximates closely the actual physical atmosphere of the earth. When the satellite moves in a highly eccentric orbit and the atmospheric density diminishes rapidly with increasing r, the integrations in Eqs. (6–197) and (6–198) need to be made only over a limited range in E near perigee. The effect of air resistance is confined to a small arc of the orbit. Under these circumstances, it can be shown from Eqs. (6–197) and (6–198) that (q'/a_e) decreases more rapidly than (q/a_e). This has the effect over a long period of time of decreasing the eccentricity of the orbit as well as the major axis. As the satellite moves in an orbit which is more nearly circular, the further effect of the air resistance causes it to spiral toward extinction in the lower and denser parts of the atmosphere. As an illustration, we exhibit here in Table 6–1 the changes in perigee and apogee distances for the satellite 1958γ (Explorer III), which was sent into orbit 26.7396 March 1958 U.T. The satellite burned up in the earth's atmosphere on June 27, 1958.

Problems

1. Suppose that the satellite is moving through a stratum of the atmosphere for which $\rho/\rho_0 = 0.1$ and this is presumed constant during the time that the satellite is near perigee. For the rest of the orbit $\rho = 0$. Let E be small so that $\cos E \sim 1 - (E^2/2)$. Calculate the changes in (q/a_e) and (q'/a_e) in one revolution. How do they compare? What is the change in the eccentricity per orbital revolution at this time?

2. A comet moves in a resisting medium which produces a tangential force per unit mass $F = -\alpha V/r^2$, where V is the orbital speed and α is a small positive constant. Calculate the changes Δa and Δe per orbital revolution. Assume that e is small so that powers of $e > 2$ can be neglected.

References

Brouwer, D., and Clemence, G. M., *Methods of Celestial Mechanics*. New York and London: Academic Press, 1961.

Brown, E. W., *An Introductory Treatise on the Lunar Theory*. New York: Dover Publications, Inc., 1960.

Danby, J. N. A., *Fundamentals of Celestial Mechanics*. New York: The Macmillan Company, 1962.

Dubyago, A. D., *The Determination of Orbits*. New York: The Macmillan Company, 1961.

Finlay-Freundlich, E., *Celestial Mechanics*. New York: Pergamon Press, 1958.

Herget, P., *The Computation of Orbits*. University of Cincinnati: privately published by the author, 1948.

Moulton, F. R., *An Introduction to Celestial Mechanics*. 2nd ed. New York: The Macmillan Company, 1914.

Plummer, H. C., *An Introductory Treatise on Dynamical Astronomy*. New York: Dover Publications, Inc., 1960.

Smart, W. M., *Celestial Mechanics*. New York: Longmans, Green and Co., Inc., 1953.

Williams, K. P., *The Calculation of Orbits of Asteroids and Comets*. Bloomington, Indiana: The Principia Press, 1934.

In addition to the above one must mention the classical treatises such as:

Poincaré, H., *Méthodes Nouvelles de Mécanique Céleste*, 3 vols. Paris: Gauthier-Villars et Fils, 1892–1899.

Tisserand, F., *Traité de Mécanique Céleste*, 4 vols. Paris: Gauthier-Villars et Fils, 1889.

Much current work in the celestial mechanics of close earth satellites appears in the *Astronomical Journal* for the years 1957 to the present.

INDEX

Aberration, 63, 70
  correction, planetary, 85
Acceleration, radial and transverse
      components, 4
  tangential and normal components,
      3
Acceleration vector, defined, 2
Angular momentum, about center of
      mass, 14
  in central force motion, 21
  conservation of, in three-body
      problem, 95
  constancy of, in central force
      motion, 21
  defined, 7
  about fixed point, 15
  rate of change of, 15
Angular momentum integral, in
      central force motion, 21
  in three-body problem, 94
Angular speed, in central force motion,
      21
Angular velocity, of earth's rotation,
      167
  vector representation of, 16
Anomaly, eccentric, defined, 46
  mean, defined, 47
  true, defined, 38
Apogee height, rate of change for close
      earth satellite, 177
Apsides, advance of, in moon's motion,
      162
Area, integrals of, in three-body
      problem, 96
Areal velocity constant, 20
Areal velocity, defined, 5
  in parabolic orbit, 54
Areal velocity integrals, in three-body
      problem, 95
Areal velocity vector, 5
Argument of perihelion, defined, 38
Ascending node, defined, 35
  longitude of, defined, 36
Asteroid, perturbation by Jupiter, 131
Astronomical unit, 36
  numerical value of, 37

Atmospheric drag, 128
  perturbation rates due to, 176

Canonical system of units, 45
Cassini division, in rings of Saturn,
      131, 135
Celestial latitude, defined, 67
Celestial longitude, defined, 67
Celestial sphere, position on, 62
Center of force, defined, 19
Center of mass, angular momentum
      about, 14
  defined, 13
  motion of, 14
    in three-body problem, 93
    in two-body problem, 32
  uniform motion of, 33
Central force motion, angular
      momentum in, 21
  angular speed in, 21
  constancy of angular momentum, 21
  defined, 19
  equation of orbit, 23
  integral of energy in, 22
  Kepler's second law for, 20
  linear speed in, 20
Classical integrals, in n-body problem,
      99
Comet Barnard, 55
Comet Comas Solá, 69
Comet Forbes, 53
Comet Schwassman-Wachman II, 50
Conic section, eccentricity of, 25
  polar equation of, 25
Conservation of energy, 8
  in central force motion, 22
  in three-body problem, 98
Constant of gravitation, Gaussian
      value of, 44
Constants of integration, n-body
      problem, 99
Coordinates, geocentric, defined, 63, 65
  equatorial, 65
  heliocentric, defined, 63
  equatorial, 64
  rectangular ecliptic, 64

Counterglow, or gegenschein, 126
Curvilinear motion, dynamics of, 6

Declination, defined, 67
Descending node, defined, 35
Disturbing function, 102
　for close-earth satellite motion, 171
　for the moon, 160
　for several masses, 102
Dynamical postulates of Newton, 1

Earth, angular velocity of rotation, 167
　eccentricity of orbit, 158
　mass of, 12, 42, 43, 51, 53, 117, 126
　radius of, 12, 42, 43, 51, 53
Earth-moon system, perturbations of,
　158
Eccentric anomaly, defined, 46
Eccentric circle, 45
Eccentricity, of conic section, 25
　of ellipse, 26
　of hyperbola, 26
　of parabola, 26
Ecliptic plane, 63
Ellipse, eccentricity of, 26
　energy in, 27
Elliptic orbit, parameters for, 25
Elliptic terms, in moon's motion, 160
Energy, conservation of, 8
　in three-body problem, 98
　in elliptical orbit, 27
　in hyperbolic orbit, 27
　integral of, in three-body problem,
　　97
　kinetic, defined, 8
　　in three-body problem, 98
　in parabolic orbit, 27
　potential, defined, 8
　　in three-body problem, 98
Equation of orbit, in central force
　motion, 23
Equilateral-triangle solution, in
　three-body problem, 105
　in restricted three-body problem, 117
Equinox, standard, 70
　vernal, 63, 67
Evection term, in moon's motion, 160
Explorer III, 178
　atmospheric drag on, 178

Force, center of, defined, 19
　inverse square, 25

moment of, 7
　perturbative, due to oblate
　　spheroid, 166
　resisting, due to air drag, 175
Force center, power of, 25
Force field, conservative, 9
Force law, determination of, 30
Forces, perturbing; radial,
　transverse, and orthogonal
　components, 144
　tangential, normal, and orthogonal
　components, 147
Functional determinant, or Jacobian,
　133

Gaussian gravitational constant, 44
Gauss's method, for orbit
　determination, 86
　triangular areas in, 87
Gegenschein, or counterglow, 126
Geocentric coordinates, defined, 63,
　65
　equatorial, 65
Gravitation, constant of, 44
　law of, 1
　Newton's law of, 10

Heliocentric coordinates, defined, 63
　equatorial, 64
　rectangular ecliptic, 64
Heliocentric latitude, defined, 63
Heliocentric longitude, defined, 63
Hyperbola, eccentricity of, 26
　energy in, 28
　Kepler's second law for, 56

Inclination of orbit, defined, 36
Inequalities, long-period, defined, 156
　short-period, defined, 156
Inertia, moments of, defined, 17
　products of, 17
Infinitesimal body, in restricted
　three-body problem, 109
Integral of angular momentum, 21
Integral of areas, in two-body
　problem, 35
Integrals of area, in three-body
　problem, 96
Integral of energy, in central force
　motion, 22
　in three-body problem, 97
Invariable line, 96

Invariable plane, 96
  for solar system, 97
Inverse square force, 25

Jacobian, evaluation of, 139, 140, 141
  or functional determinant, 133
Jupiter, 38, 96, 118, 122, 126, 131, 158
  mass of, 118, 126

Kepler's equation, 73, 75
  defined, 47
  graphical solution of, 47
  series solution of, 48
Kepler's laws, 1
  second law, for central force motion, 20
    for hyperbola, 56
  third law, in two-body problem, 43
Kinetic energy, defined, 8
  in three-body problem, 98
Kirkwood gaps, 131

Lagrange's brackets, cartesian
    components of, 133
  classification of, 138
  defined, 132
  evaluation of, 137
  properties of, 135
  time independence of, 136
  values of, 141
Lagrangian points, collinear, 115
  in restricted three-body problem, 113
  stability of motion, 118
  in three-body problem, 108
Laplace's method, for orbit
    determination, 76
Latitude, celestial, defined, 67
  heliocentric, defined, 63
Law, gravitation, 1
Law of areas, central force motion, 20
Laws, Kepler's, 1
Legendre coefficients, 151, 159
Legendre polynomials, 150, 164
Librations, short and long period, 127
Light time, correction for, 91
Line of apsides, advance of, in moon's
    motion, 162
Line of nodes, defined, 35
Linear momentum, defined, 6
Linear speed, in central force motion, 20

Longitude, celestial, defined, 67
  heliocentric, defined, 63
Long-period inequalities, defined, 156

Mars, 1, 29, 30, 53, 131
Mass, center of, defined, 13
Mass of the earth, 12, 42, 43, 51, 53, 117, 126
  of Jupiter, 118, 126
  of the moon, 117
  of the sun, 45, 117
Mass, potential due to, 10
Mean anomaly, defined, 47
Mean daily motion, defined, 44
"Mean distance" of a planet, 44
Mercury, 50
Meteoroid, 55
Mimas, 131, 135
Moment of a force, 7
Moments of inertia, defined, 17
Momentum, angular, defined, 7
  time rate of change, 15
  linear, defined, 6
Moon, disturbing function for, 160
  mass of, 117
  orbital inclination of, 158
  orbital perturbation by sun, 158
Motion, central force, defined, 19
  curvilinear, dynamics of, 6
  equations of, in three-body problem, 93
  in two-body problem, 33
  mean daily, defined, 44
  Newton's laws of, 1
  relative, in three-body problem, 100
  in two-body problem, 33
  rotational, Newton's second law of, 7

n-body problem, classical integrals in, 99
  properties of, 98
Newton's laws of motion, 1
  second law, for rotational motion, 7, 15
Node, ascending, defined, 35
  longitude of, defined, 36
  average rate of regression, for close
    earth satellite, 170
  descending, defined, 35
  motion of, for close earth satellite, 169
  regression of, in moon's motion, 162

Nodes, line of, defined, 35
Nutation, 63, 70

Oblate planet, perturbations due to, 167
Oblate spheroid, moments of inertia of, 165
  perturbative force due to, 166
  potential due to, 163
Oblateness, of a planet, 128
Orbit, eccentricity of, defined, 38
  elements of, 38
  elliptic, parameters for, 25
    position in, 51
  equation of, in central force motion, 23
  in heliocentric reference frame, 63
  hyperbolic, position in, 55
  inclination of, defined, 36
  mean distance in, 44
  near-parabolic, position in, 57
  osculating, defined, 129
  parabolic, areal velocity in, 54
    parameters in, 55
    position in, 54
  polar equation of, in central force motion, 24
    under inverse square force, 25
  semimajor axis of, defined, 38
Orbit determination, Gauss's method, 86
  from known radius vector, 70
  Laplace's method, 76
Orbital elements, time derivatives of, 143
Osculating orbit, defined, 129

Parabola, eccentricity of, 26
  energy in, 27
Parameters, method of variation of, 128
  in parabolic orbit, 55
Particles, systems of, 12
Perigee, 38
  advance, for close earth satellite, 170
  height, rate of change for close earth satellite, 177
Perihelion, argument of, defined, 38
Perihelion passage, time of, 38
Peri-Jove, 38

Perturbation, in moon's longitude due to evection term, 162
  periodic, 156
  secular, 156
  for close earth satellite, 173
Perturbation equations, solution of, 142
Perturbation function, expansion of, 149
  trigonometric expansion of, 154
Perturbation rates, due to atmospheric drag, 176
  due to evection term, in moon's motion, 161
  for radial, transverse, and orthogonal components, 147
Perturbations, from air drag, 175
  defined, 92
  due to oblate planet, 167
  earth-moon system, 158
  short-period, for close earth satellite, 173, 174
  theory of, 128
Perturbative force, due to oblate spheroid, 166
Perturbative function, 102
Perturbing forces, radial, transverse, and orthogonal components, 144
  tangential, normal, and orthogonal components, 147
Planetary aberration correction, 85
Planetary system, stability of, 157
Position, on celestial sphere, 62
  in elliptical orbit, 51
  in hyperbolic orbit, 55
  in near-parabolic orbit, 57
  in parabolic orbit, 54
Position vector, defined, 2
Potential, defined, 10
  difference, 10
  due to oblate spheroid, 163
  due to point mass, 10
  due to solid sphere, 12
  due to a sphere, 9
  due to spherical shell, 11
Potential energy, defined, 8
  in three-body problem, 98
Potential function, for oblate spheroid, 166
  at surface of the earth, 167
Power of force center, 25

Precession, 63, 70
Primary inertial system, 6
Products of inertia, 17

Relative motion, in three-body
    problem, 100
  in two-body problem, 33
Resisting force, due to air drag, 175
Restricted three-body problem, 109
  collinear Lagrangian points in, 115
  infinitesimal body in, 109
  Lagrangian points in, 113
  triangular points in, 116
  zero velocity contours in, 112
Right ascension, defined, 67

Saturn, 96, 131, 135, 158
Sector-triangle ratios, 88
Secular perturbation, 156
  for close earth satellite, 173
Short-period inequalities, defined, 156
Short-period perturbations, for close
    earth satellite, 173, 174
Stability of motion, near Lagrangian
    points, 118
  near L_1 point, 122
  near L_4 point, 120
  of Trojan asteroid, 126
Stationary solutions, defined, 103
  in three-body problem, 102
Straight-line solution, in three-body
    problem, 106
Sun, geocentric equatorial coordinates
    of, 65
  mass of, 45, 117
  radius of, 117
Systems of particles, 12

Three-body problem, angular
    momentum integral, 94
  areal velocity integrals, 95
  center of mass motion, 93
  conservation of angular momentum,
    95
  conservation of energy in, 98
  equations of motion, 93
  equilateral-triangle solution, 105
  integral of energy, 97
  integrals of area, 96
  kinetic energy in, 98

Lagrangian points in, 108
  potential energy in, 98
  relative motion in, 100
  restricted, 109
  stationary solutions in, 102
  straight-line solution, 106
  vector relations in, 92
Torque of a force, 7
Triangular points, in restricted
    three-body problem, 116
Trojan asteroid, 118, 122, 126
  stability of motion, 126
True anomaly, defined, 38
  in two-body problem, 51
Two-body problem, acceleration in,
    34
  cartesian equations in, 34
  center of mass motion, 32
  integral of areas, 35
  Kepler's third law in, 43
  relative acceleration in, 34
  relative motion in, 33

Units, canonical system of, 45

Vanguard I, 174
Variation term, in moon's motion, 160
Vector, acceleration, 2
  areal velocity, 5
  position, defined, 2
  velocity, defined, 2
Vector relations, in three-body
    problem, 92
Velocity, angular, vector
    representation of, 16
  areal, defined, 5
    in parabolic orbit, 54
  in circular orbit, 43
  in elliptical orbit, 28, 42
  in hyperbolic orbit, 29
  in parabolic orbit, 27, 42
  radial and transverse components, 4
Velocity contours, in restricted
    three-body problem, 112
Velocity of escape, 27
Velocity vector, defined, 2
Venus, 135
Vernal equinox, 63, 67

Zonal harmonics, 164